Welcome to

HOW IT WORKS

BOOK OF

SPACE

Mankind has always questioned its place in the universe, and sought to understand the celestial mysteries through a combination of observation and sheer intuitive thinking. Nowadays, with the cutting edge technology being developed daily by the world's space agencies, we're starting to understand space in unprecedented detail. This new revised edition of the **How It Works Book of Space** has been brought right up to date with the latest discoveries, the latest missions – including the infamous Curiosity landing on Mars – and some absolutely stunning space photography from the most advanced telescopes on the planet. Taking you from the heart of our solar system through to the edge of the Oort Cloud, and then beyond into deep space itself, we show you solar storms and supernovas, meteor showers and black holes – even a sombrero shaped galaxy. Get ready for lift off.

HOW IT WORKS
BOOK OF
SPACE

Imagine Publishing Ltd
Richmond House
33 Richmond Hill
Bournemouth
Dorset BH2 6EZ
☎ +44 (0) 1202 586200
Website: www.imagine-publishing.co.uk
Twitter: @Books_Imagine
Facebook: www.facebook.com/ImagineBookazines

Head of Publishing
Aaron Asadi

Head of Design
Ross Andrews

Production Editor
Gavin Thomas

Senior Art Editor
Danielle Dixon

Design
Newton Ribeiro de Oliveira

Cover and contents images
DK Images, NASA and SpaceX

Printed by
William Gibbons, 26 Planetary Road, Willenhall, West Midlands, WV13 3XT

Distributed in the UK & Eire by
Imagine Publishing Ltd, www.imagineshop.co.uk. Tel 01202 586200

Distributed in Australia by
Gordon & Gotch, Equinox Centre, 18 Rodborough Road, Frenchs Forest,
NSW 2086. Tel + 61 2 9972 8800

Distributed in the Rest of the World by
Marketforce, Blue Fin Building, 110 Southwark Street, London, SE1 0SU

How It Works Book of Space Volume 1 Second Revised Edition © 2012 Imagine Publishing Ltd

ISBN 978-1908955647

Part of the

HOW IT
WORKS
bookazine series

IMAGINE PUBLISHING

HOW IT WORKS BOOK OF SPACE
CONTENTS

All images © NASA

© NASA and ESA

133
Mega rockets

049

060

066

030

090

163

018
Exploring the Sun

047
Solar eclipse

046
Our amazing Sun

All Images © NASA

188
Planets

024
Venus

232
Telescopes

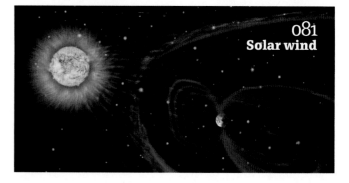

081
Solar wind

026
Earth

Astronomy

034
Saturn

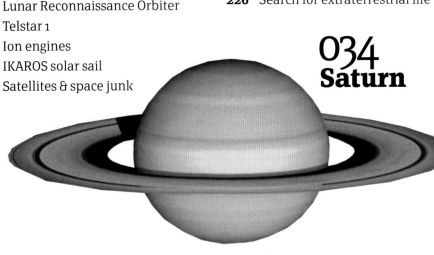

SOLAR SYSTEM

All Images © NASA

Journey through the
Solar system

Bound to the immense mass of the Sun by gravity, the contents of our solar system are numerous and spectacular

The solar system formed about 4.6 billion years ago, when part of a giant molecular cloud had a gravitational collapse. The centre became the Sun, which comprises more than 99 per cent of the solar system's total mass. The rest became a dense, flat rotating disk of gas from which planets formed, called a protoplanetary disk. In our solar system, most of that disk became the eight planets, each of which orbits the Sun.

There are two different categories of planets: gas giants and terrestrials. The gas giants are the four outer planets: Jupiter, Saturn, Uranus and Neptune. They are much bigger than the terrestrial planets and are mostly made of helium and hydrogen, although Uranus and Neptune also contain ice. All of the outer planets have ring systems made of cosmic dust. These planets comprise more than 90 per cent of the rest of the solar system's mass.

The four inner planets are very close to the Sun. To grant perspective, for example, the distance between Jupiter and Saturn is larger than the radius of all the inner planets put together. These terrestrials are made up from rocks and metals, have no ring systems and have a low number of satellites (moons). They include Mercury, Venus, Earth and Mars. Except for Mercury, the inner planets also have recognisable weather systems operating in their atmospheres.

In addition to the eight main planets, there are also dwarf planets such as Pluto. The five dwarf planets are Ceres, Pluto, Haumea, Makemake and Eris. In addition, the solar system is home to numerous small solar system bodies, which include all minor planets, asteroids and comets. ✿

Earth to Saturn in a Mini Metro!

How long would it take to reach the planets in a moderately priced car?

Can't afford that ticket on the next spaceship out of town? Well, fear not, for if you are the patient type and hold an interplanetary driving licence then you can drive to that Earth colony orbiting Saturn in next to no time… well, relatively speaking. In our souped-up Mini Metro, travelling at an average speed of 120mph, any traveller can reach Saturn in only 842 years. Better stock up on travel sweets then…

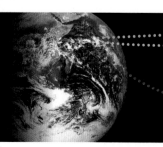

Head to Head
LARGEST PLANETS

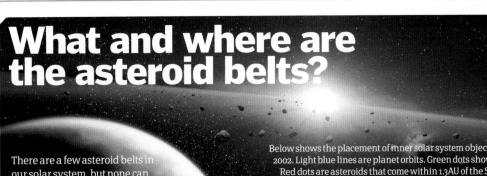

BIG **1. Uranus**
Diameter at equator: 25,559km
Average distance from Sun:
2.88 billion km (19 AU)
Orbital period: 84.02 years
Mass (Earth=1): 14.37
Earth masses

BIGGER **2. Saturn**
Diameter at equator:
60,260km
Average distance from Sun:
1.4 billion km (9.4 AU)
Orbital period: 29.5 years
Mass (Earth=1): 95 Earth masses

BIGGEST **3. Jupiter**
Diameter at equator:
142,985km
Average distance from Sun:
778 million km (5.2 AU)
Orbital period: 11.86 years
Mass (Earth=1): 318 Earth masses

DID YOU KNOW? Astronomers estimate there may be billions of solar systems in our galaxy. About 70 have been discovered

What and where are the asteroid belts?

There are a few asteroid belts in our solar system, but none can compare to the main belt, a massive ring between the orbits of Mars and Jupiter. Here the dwarf planet Ceres, the large asteroids 2 Pallas, 10 Hygiea and 4 Vesta, and millions of small asteroids and dust particles orbit the Sun. Most of the larger asteroids have elliptical orbits and an orbital period of a few years. Some astronomers believe that the main belt's contents are left over from a planetary collision or from a planet that never formed due to the strong gravitational pull of Jupiter.

Image courtesy of NASA

Below shows the placement of inner solar system objects on 20 July 2002. Light blue lines are planet orbits. Green dots show asteroids. Red dots are asteroids that come within 1.3AU of the Sun. Comets are dark blue squares, and dark blue points are Jupiter Trojans

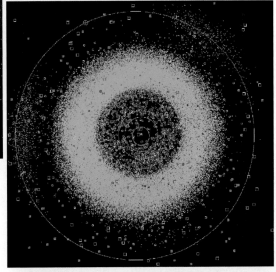

Bound together by gravity

When the International Astronomical Union (IAU) defined planets in 2006, part of that definition included the requirement that a planet has enough mass that its self-gravity causes it to reach hydrostatic equilibrium. The planet is able to resist compressive forces in space to hold together and stay rounded in shape.

Planets also "clear the neighbourhood" around their orbits. This means that there are no other bodies of the same size in its orbit. The Sun has a strong enough pull to keep the planets and other bodies orbiting around it.

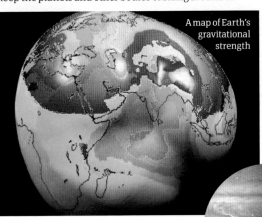

A map of Earth's gravitational strength

Measuring our solar system
Understanding the size of planets and where they are

Before the development of radar, astronomers measured the distance between planets through trigonometry, a process where distance to an object is derived from the measurements of angles and distances taken between two known positions. Today, radar is the predominant method of measuring distance and allows for more accurate measurements to be attained. This process works by astronomers timing how long it takes the radar beam, which is travelling at the speed of light, to travel the distance to an object and back. By multiplying the speed of light by time taken, then dividing that in two, scientists can derive the distance to the object.

Once distance has been derived, the mass of the object can be ascertained by monitoring the orbital periods of circling satellites. To do this astronomers measure the angular separation between the satellite and the object and then use trigonometry to convert that angular separation into distance. Astronomers can then use Kepler's third law to determine total mass.

1 AU (astronomical unit) = 92,960,000 miles, the mean distance between the Sun and the Earth

THE SOLAR SYSTEM IN AU

MERCURY	VENUS	EARTH	MARS	JUPITER	SATURN	URANUS	NEPTUNE	PLUTO
0.39AU	0.72AU	1AU	1.52AU	5.20AU	9.54AU	19.2AU	30.1AU	39.5AU

Pluto the dwarf

Since its discovery in 1930, Pluto had been considered the ninth planet in our solar system. However, more recent discoveries of dwarf planets larger in size and mass than Pluto have made some astronomers question its status. In 2006, the International Astronomical Union (IAU) decided upon a conclusive definition of what constituted a planet. Pluto's low mass – not even a fifth the mass of the Moon – excluded it from that definition. Now Pluto is considered a dwarf planet,

Size compared to Earth
Pluto is a dwarf-planet, smaller than our own moon

Jupiter – 459 years
Mars a little too dusty? Then why not visit Jupiter, only 459 years of 120mph driving away.

Neptune – 2,497 years
One for colder climates? Then Neptune should be top of your list. At 2,497 years distance, though, it is a long drive, so make sure you take regular breaks and keep at 120mph!

Mars – 134 years
At 120mph you could drive to the planet named after the Roman god of war in only 134 years.

"Saturn is so light that if it could be hypothetically placed in a galactic-sized ocean of water it would float"

8. Neptune

Neptune was imaged for the first time in 1989, discovering an encircling set of rings and six of its 13 moons. Neptune's structure is very similar to that of Uranus, with no solid surface and central layers of water, methane and ammonia ices as well as a possible rock/ice-based core.

The Statistics

Neptune

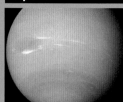

Type: Gas giant
Rotation (Equatorial): 60,179 days
Rotation (Polar): 16.11 hours
Volume: (Earth = 1) 57.74
Average distance from Sun: 2.8 billion miles
Number of moons: 13
Speed: 5.43km/s
Surface temp: -220°C

5. Jupiter

The largest and most massive of all planets in the solar system, Jupiter has almost 2.5 times the mass of the other eight planets combined and over 1,300 Earths could fit inside it. Jupiter is also the first of the gas giants and is largely not solid in composition, consisting of an outer layer of gaseous hydrogen and helium, an outer layer of liquid hydrogen and helium and an inner layer of metallic hydrogen. However, deep in its body (roughly 37,000 miles in) there is a solid core made up of rock, metal and hydrogen compounds.

7. Uranus

The first planet to be discovered by telescope, Uranus appears to the eye as a pale blue, characterless disk, encircled by a thin system of 11 rings and 27 tiny moons. Its blue colour is a result of the absorption of the sunlight's red wavelengths by methane-ice clouds within the planet's cold atmosphere – a process which also renders its atmosphere calm and inert thanks to the creation of haze particles. In reality, however, Uranus's atmosphere is active and consistently changing with huge winds driving systems of ammonia and water over its surface.

The Statistics

Uranus

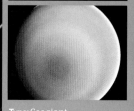

Type: Gas giant
Rotation (Equatorial): 30,799 days
Rotation (Polar): 17.24 hours
Volume: (Earth = 1) 63.1
Average distance from Sun: 1.78 billion miles
Number of moons: 27
Speed: 6.81km/s
Surface temp: -214°C

6. Saturn

A massive ball of gas and liquid, Saturn is the least dense of all the planets in the solar system. Circled by a spectacular system of rings, which are composed of stellar dust, boulders and gases, Saturn has a hazy appearance and due to its rapid spin is a massive ten per cent larger at its equator than at its pole. Interestingly, Saturn is so light – thanks to its composition from the lightest elements – that if it could be hypothetically placed in a galactic-sized ocean of water it would float. As with Jupiter, Saturn is a gas giant with a tiny solid core composed of rock and ice.

The Statistics

Saturn

Type: Gas giant
Rotation (Equatorial): 10,759 days
Rotation (Polar): 10.66 hours
Volume: (Earth = 1) 763.59
Average distance from Sun: 888 million miles
Number of moons: 34
Speed: 9.69km/s
Surface temp: -140°C

Comets

Comets are small, fragile, irregularly shaped bodies composed of a mixture of non-volatile grains and frozen gases

9. Pluto

Often mistaken as the last planet in our solar system, Pluto is actually not one but instead a dwarf planet. Dwarf planets are bodies that orbit the Sun and have enough mass and gravity to be spherical, but ones that have not cleared the region around its orbit. Pluto is such a dwarf planet and is one of the furthest circling bodies of our solar system. Pluto's atmosphere is 99.97 per cent nitrogen and it is astronomically cold, with an average temperature of -230 degrees Celsius.

The Statistics

Pluto

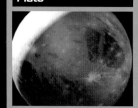

Type: Dwarf
Rotation (Equatorial): 90,613 days
Rotation (Polar): N/A
Volume: (Earth = 1) 0.0059
Average distance from Sun: 3.7 billion miles
Number of moons: 3
Speed: 4.666km/s
Surface temp: -230°C

The Sun

4.6 billions years old and currently in its main-sequence stage, our Sun is a huge sphere of exceedingly hot plasma containing 750 times the mass of all the solar system's planets put together. Deep in its core nuclear fusion of hydrogen produces massive energy that is gradually carried outwards through convection before escaping into space.

The Statistics

The Sun

Type: Star
Rotation (Equatorial): 25 days
Rotation (Polar): 34 days
Mass: (Earth = 1) 333,000
Surface temperature: 5,500°C
Core temperature: 15 million °C
Diameter (Equatorial): 864,900 miles

Main belt

Often referred to as the asteroid belt, the Main belt is an encircling ring of meteors, asteroids, dwarf planets and dust particles that sits between the terrestrial planets and the gas giants.

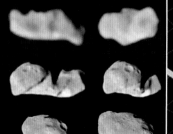

Lightweight
1 Hypothetically speaking, Saturn is so light that if it were placed in a galactic sized swimming pool it would float. Hard experiment to carry out though!

Binary
2 Due to the size and short orbital distance between Pluto and its largest moon Charon, it is often treated as a binary system as its centre of mass lies with neither.

Dust bowl
3 Mars, often referred to as the 'red planet', is actually red thanks to its coating of iron dust, which prevails in its carbon dioxide-rich atmosphere.

Big boy
4 Jupiter is so large that over 1,300 Earths could fit inside it and it has a mass which is 2.5 times larger than the total of all other eight planets combined.

Tantastic
5 During the day on Mercury, the closest planet to our Sun in the solar system, the temperature reaches up to a positively scorching 430 degrees Celsius.

DID YOU KNOW? Our solar system is nearly five billion years old and is made up of eight planets and 170 moons

The Statistics
Jupiter

Type: Gas giant
Rotation (Equatorial): 4,331 days
Rotation (Polar): 9.93 hours
Volume: (Earth = 1) 1,321
Average distance from Sun: 483.6 million miles
Number of moons: 63
Speed: 13.07km/s
Surface temp: -110°C

The Statistics
Earth

Type: Terrestrial
Rotation (Equatorial): 365.26 days
Rotation (Polar): 23.93 hours
Mass: (Earth = 1) 1
Average distance from Sun: 93 million miles
Number of moons: 1
Speed: 29.783km/s
Surface temp: 15°C

3. Earth

While similar in internal composition to its neighbouring planets – composed of three distinct layers made up mainly of iron, magnesium and silicates respectively – Earth differs on its surface thanks to an abundance of liquid water and an oxygen-rich atmosphere. Due to Earth's rotation the planet bulges at its equator by 13 miles when compared to both its poles and its spin axis is tilted at an angle of 23.5 degrees, one of the factors that gives rise to its seasons.

4. Mars

Known as the red planet thanks to its rust-red colouring, and named after the Roman god of war, Mars is home to the highest volcanoes (albeit dry and inactive) of any planet in the solar system. Current research and evidence suggests that while Mars is an inert planet now, in the past it was very much active, with volcanic activity and water existing over large parts of it. Mars is the outermost of the four terrestrial 'rocky' planets and its internal structure is rich in sulphur, iron sulphide and silicate rock.

The Statistics
Mars

Type: Terrestrial
Rotation (Equatorial): 687 days
Rotation (Polar): 24.63 days
Mass: (Earth = 1) 0.15
Average distance from Sun: 141.6 million miles
Number of moons: 2
Speed: 24.007km/s
Surface temp: -125°C – 25°C

Map of the solar system
Discover the star, planets and space phenomena that make up our solar system

The Statistics
Mercury

Type: Terrestrial
Rotation (Equatorial): 88 days
Rotation (Polar): 59 days
Mass: (Earth = 1) 0.056
Average distance from Sun: 36 million miles
Number of moons: 0
Speed: 47.87km/s
Surface temp: -187°C – 427°C

1. Mercury

Iron-rich Mercury is the second smallest planet in the solar system and the closest to the Sun. There is almost no protective atmosphere surrounding Mercury and, because of this, temperatures on the planet fluctuate massively from 427 degrees Celsius during the day to -187 degrees Celsius during the night. Worryingly, if an observer were able to stand on the planet they would experience a period of 176 Earth days between one sunrise and the next. Better stock up on suntan lotion and woolly socks then…

2. Venus

The hottest of all planets, Venus – thanks to its permanent atmospheric blanket of dense gaseous clouds – has an average temperature of 464 degrees Celsius. The surface is dry, lifeless, scorching hot and littered with volcanoes and dust storms. Named after the Roman goddess of love and beauty due to its beautiful, sun-reflecting, cloud-based atmosphere, in reality Venus holds one of the most hostile environments of any planet. Interestingly, Venus spins in the opposite direction from most other planets.

The Statistics
Venus

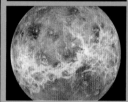

Type: Terrestrial
Rotation (Equatorial): 224.7 days
Rotation (Polar): 243 days
Mass: (Earth = 1) 0.86
Average distance from Sun: 67.2 million miles
Number of moons: 0
Speed: 35.02km/s
Surface temp: 464°C

Inside the Sun
The giant star that keeps us all alive...

A celestial wonder, the Sun is a huge star formed from a massive gravitational collapse when space dust and gas from a nebula collided, It became an orb 100 times bigger and weighing over 300,000 times that of Earth. Made up of 70 per cent hydrogen and about 28 per cent helium (plus other gases), the Sun is the centre of our solar system and the largest celestial body anywhere near us.

"The surface of the Sun is a dense layer of plasma at a temperature of 5,800 degrees kelvin that is continually moving due to the action of convective motions driven by heating from below," says David Alexander, a professor of physics and astronomy at Rice University. "These convective motions show up as a distribution of what are called granulation cells about 1,000 kilometers across and which appear across the whole solar surface."

At its core, the Sun's temperature and pressure are so high and the hydrogen atoms are moving so fast that it causes fusion, turning hydrogen atoms into helium. Electromagetic radiation travels out from the Sun's core to its surface, escaping into space as electromagnetic radiation, a blinding light, and incredible levels of solar heat. In fact, the core of the Sun is actually hotter than the surface, but when heat escapes from the surface, the temperature rises to over 1-2 million degrees. Alexander explained that astronomers do not fully understand why the Sun's atmosphere is so hot, but think it has something to do with magnetic fields. ✿

Radiative zone
The first 500,000k of the Sun is a radioactive layer that transfers energy from the core, mostly toward the outer layers, passed from atom to atom.

Sun's core
The core of a Sun is a dense, extremely hot region – about 15 million degrees – that produces a nuclear fusion and emits heat through the layers of the Sun to the surface.

Beneath the surface of the Sun
What is the Sun made of?

Convective zone
The top 30 per cent of the Sun is a layer of hot plasma that is constantly in motion, heated from below.

Right conditions
The core of the Sun, which acts like a nuclear reactor, is just the right size and temperature to product light.

Engine room
The centre of a star is like an engine room that produces the nuclear fusion required for radiation and light.

The Statistics
The Sun

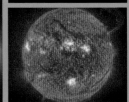

Diameter: 100 times Earth
Mass: 300,000 times Earth
Average surface temp: 1-2 million degrees
Core temp: 15 million degrees

All images courtesy of NASA

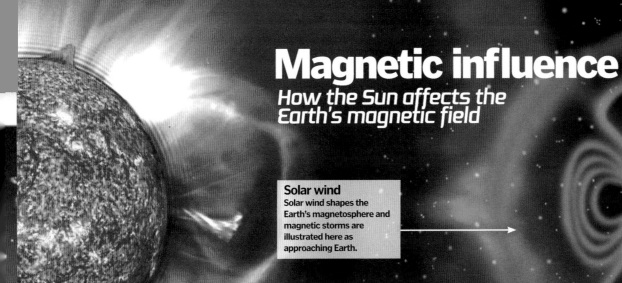

Magnetic influence
How the Sun affects the Earth's magnetic field

Solar wind
Solar wind shapes the Earth's magnetosphere and magnetic storms are illustrated here as approaching Earth.

Plasma release
The Sun's magnetic field and plasma releases directly affect Earth and the rest of the solar system.

Bow shock line
The purple line is the bow shock line and the blue lines surrounding the Earth represent its protective magnetosphere.

What is a solar flare?

A massive explosion, but one that happens to be several million degrees in temperature...

"A solar flare is a rapid release of energy in the solar atmosphere (mostly the chromosphere and corona) resulting in localised heating of plasma to tens of millions of degrees, acceleration of electrons and protons to high energies, some to near the speed of light, and expulsion of material into space," says Alexander. "These electromagnetic disturbances here on Earth pose potential dangers for Earth-orbiting satellites, space-walking astronauts, crews on high-altitude spacecraft, and power grids on Earth."

Solar flares can cause geomagnetic storms on the Sun, including shock waves and plasma expulsions

Solar eclipses
When the Moon blocks out the Sun

A solar eclipse is a unique phenomena where the Moon passes directly into a line between the Earth and the Sun, partially or completely blocking our view of the Sun. The Sun is blocked according to the relative orbits of each celestial body. There are two kinds of eclipses: one where the Moon orbit shows the outer edge of the Sun, or where the Moon lines up perfectly and the Sun is blocked completely from view.

Sometimes, the orbits of the Earth and Sun line up perfectly so that the Sun is blocked (eclipsed) by the Moon, shown here with a shadow cast from the eclipse, taken from the ISS

How big is the Sun?
Our Sun has a diameter of 1.4 million km and Earth a diameter of almost 13,000km

What is a sunspot?

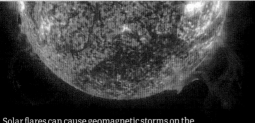

Signifying cooler areas, sunspots show up as dark dots on the photosphere (the visible layer of plasma across the Sun's surface). These 'cool' regions – about 1,000 degrees cooler than the surface temperature – are associated with strong magnetic fields. Criss-crossing magnetic-field lines can disturb the flow of heat from the core, creating pockets of intense activity. The build up of heat around a sunspot can be released as a solar flare or coronal mass ejection, which is separate to but often accompanies larger flares. Plasma from a CME ejects from the Sun at over 1 million miles per hour.

If the Sun were the size of a basketball, Earth would be a little dot no more than 3.3 mm

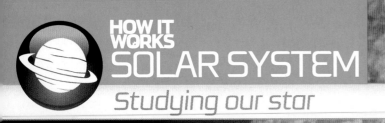

Exploring the Sun

Discover how space agencies both on Earth and out in orbit are bringing us spectacular imagery and awe-inspiring information about our star

We tend to take the Sun for granted, but it's much more than just our source of light and energy. Once we figured out that the Earth was revolving around the Sun instead of the other way around, we've been striving to learn more about this amazing star.

After hundreds of years of observation via the naked eye and telescope, we were finally able to get a closer look when NASA launched the Pioneer space program in the late-Fifties. Pioneer probes 6 through 9 were all designed to orbit the Sun and take measurements about cosmic rays, the magnetic field, the bursts of charged particles known as solar wind, and solar storms. These first probes showed how these phenomena affected Earth's communications and power.

The Helios probes were the next to visit the Sun. Helios I was launched in 1974 and Helios II just over a year later. Unlike the Pioneer program, which was designed overall to explore various regions of the solar system, the Helios program focused solely on the Sun. In this co-operative mission between NASA and the Federal Republic of Germany, both Helios probes expanded on the data provided by the Pioneer probes, and also performed experiments on magnetic fields and electrical fields.

NASA had initially planned an Apollo mission to observe the Sun, which would use elements from the Apollo Lunar program. The Apollo Telescope Mount (ATM) was a solar observatory that attached to NASA's first space station, Skylab, when it launched in 1973. The ATM had windmill-like solar panels, which provided power for Skylab as well as its eight telescopes. During Skylab's tenure in the sky, UV and x-ray telescopes provided the first hi-res photographs of the Sun.

The success of Skylab and the ATM spurred NASA to launch another mission in 1980. The Solar Maximum Mission, or SolarMax, specifically studied solar flares using seven different instruments. These instruments measured ultraviolet, gamma and x-ray radiation emitted by the flares. They also measured the electromagnetic radiation emitted by the Sun overall, known as the solar constant. SolarMax revealed that during the

DID YOU KNOW? *The Ulysses probe crossed the path of two comet tails, in 1996 and 1999*

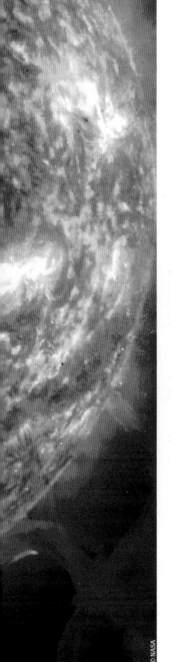

SDO – living with a star

The SDO (Solar Dynamics Observatory) is part of NASA's Living With a Star program, which studies the relationship between the Sun and the Earth. Its mission is to provide information on the solar atmosphere. It comprises three instruments. The Helioseismic and Magnetic Imager (HMI) studies changes in magnetic solar activity and measures the magnetic field. The Extreme Ultraviolet Variability Experiment (EVE) measures the Sun's extreme ultraviolet radiation, which heats the Earth's atmosphere. The Atmospheric Imaging Assembly (AIA) provides the most highly detailed, highest-resolution images of the Sun of any other satellite.

High gain antenna
The SDO's high gain antenna rotates one time per the spacecraft's orbit so it is always facing the Earth. The antenna beams 150 million bits of data per second.

AIA
The Atmospheric Imaging Assembly (AIA) takes images of the Sun in ten different electromagnetic wavelengths. These images will help scientists make connections between the changes on the Sun's surface with changes in its interior.

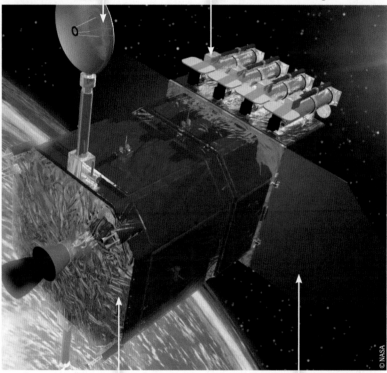

Propulsion module
The SDO manoeuvres using a bi-propellant system using monomethyl hydrazine (MMH) fuel and nitrogen tetroxide (NTO) oxidiser.

Solar arrays
These two solar panels produce 1450 watts of power for the spacecraft. Their shape prevents them from blocking the antenna.

greatest concentration of sunspots, the rest of the Sun actually gets brighter.

Meanwhile, the ESA partnered with NASA to create a reusable research laboratory for use in space. Spacelab was used in more than two dozen missions. Spacelab 2, launched in July 1985, measured the magnetic fields in the photosphere (the visible surface of the Sun). Most importantly, Spacelab 2 took detailed images of the granulation on the Sun's surface. These small cells on the surface form when the hot liquid inside rises, spreads, cools, and then sinks back into the Sun.

In 1990, NASA launched another probe, Ulysses, which focused on measuring the speed of solar wind and size of magnetic waves around the Sun's polar regions. The Japanese Space Agency also got into Sun exploration in 1991 when it launched the Yohkoh satellite. Using a different type of x-ray telescope, Yohkoh sent back information about different types of solar flares and

dynamic coronal activity. Hinode, the follow-up to Yokoh, launched in 2006 and is observing magnetic fields.

There are numerous on-going observations of the Sun via spacecraft, satellites and telescopes. In 1995, NASA and the ESA launched another spacecraft, the Solar and Heliospheric Observatory (SOHO). While SOHO was designed to further explore the outer layer of the Sun and solar wind, it also probes the Sun's inner structure. From 1998 to 2010, NASA's TRACE (Transition Region and Coronal Explorer) satellite provided detailed solar images.

In 2006, NASA launched STEREO (Solar Terrestrial Relations Observatory). Two probes will study how energy and matter flow between the Sun and the Earth and give 3D images of coronal mass ejections. In 2010, NASA launched the Solar Dynamics Observatory (SDO). This craft is studying how the Sun impacts the Earth, through an observation of the solar atmosphere, and how the Sun's energy is created, stored, and released. ✻

AMAZING SUN DISCOVERIES
What have we found out about the Sun?

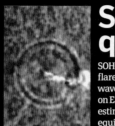

Solar quakes
SOHO revealed that solar flares create seismic waves similar to quakes on Earth. One was estimated to be equivalent to an 11.3 magnitude earthquake.

Sunspots
The observation of sunspots reveals changes in the Sun's life cycle and shows it is brightening overall by about 0.1 per cent each year.

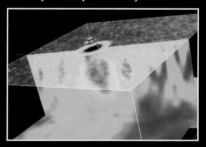

Space weather
Surface activity creates space weather such as solar wind, which result in bursts of radiation that can affect communications on Earth.

Solar cycle
Continuous observation has revealed a nearly 11-year cycle, which has predictable variations of radiation, weather, and seismic activity too.

Coronal mass ejections
Skylab revealed coronal mass ejections – massive bursts of plasma and solar wind that rise in loops above the surface of the Sun.

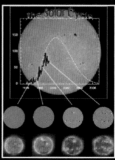

All images © NASA

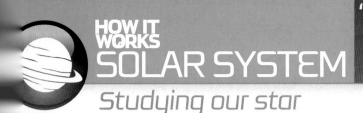
SOHO – observing the Sun

SOHO, NASA's two-ton spacecraft launched in December 1995, carries 12 different instruments that work separately or together to observe the Sun. These instruments measure and explore the Sun's three-layered atmosphere (corona, transition region, and chromosphere) as well as weather activity such as solar wind. Helioseismology, a study of the Sun's interior activity, is also observed.

Payload module
SOHO's payload module houses all 12 of its different scientific instruments.

© NASA/ESA

High gain antenna
SOHO's high gain antenna suffered an equipment failure in 2003, which causes a reduction in the flow of data every few months.

Service module
The lower part of SOHO comprises all of the equipment necessary for power, telecommunications, orientation, and thermal control. SOHO sends a stream of data at 200 kilobits per second to the NASA Deep Space Network.

Solar panels
When deployed, its solar panels make SOHO 9.5 metres long. They provide 1,500 watts of power and are supported by 20 batteries.

SOHO's Sun images

Images of the Sun from SOHO come from different instruments on the spacecraft. The EIT (Extreme ultraviolet Imaging Telescope) takes hi-res images of the Sun's corona in the ultraviolet spectrum, on four different wavelengths. EIT ceased taking images for the most part in July 2010, as the AIA on SDO can take better images. LASCO (Large Angle and Spectrometric Coronagraph Experiment) takes images only of the Sun's corona by blocking the solar disc, essentially creating an artificial solar eclipse. It features coronal streamers, beams of light extending from areas of high magnetic activity and elongated by solar wind The goal is to learn more about the evolution and activity of the Sun's corona. MDI (Michelson Doppler Imager) creates images from acoustic data using the Doppler effect. It produces two different types of images: magnetograms are visual representations of changes in the Sun's magnetic field, while continuums look more like how the Sun appears to us and focus mainly on sunspots.

EIT
Hot
This image was taken at 171 Angstrom (one Angstrom is 0.1 nanometre). At this wavelength, the brightest areas are 1 million degrees Kelvin.

MDI
Magnetic fields
Dark areas represent magnetic fields moving inward, light areas are the opposite, and the grey areas have no magnetic field.

EIT
Hotter
In this image the brightest areas are at 195 Angstrom and 1.5 million degrees Kelvin.

STEREO-B took this image of the transit of the Moon across the Sun on 25 Feb 2007

LASCO
Inner solar corona
C2 images show the inner part of the Sun's extended outer atmosphere, or corona. It extends about 8 million kilometres from the Sun's surface

The Sun's song

SOHO contains the Michelson Doppler Imager (MDI), which records waves that travel across the Sun's surface by observing their Doppler effect – where each wave changes in frequency. It then translates them into sounds and images. Scientists hope to learn about the Sun's core, its active outer shell, and its life cycle.

Instruments on board SOHO

EIT
This telescope's filters record specific ultraviolet light so the images aren't obscured by the Sun's brightness.

MDI
This measures magnetic fields in the photosphere for images most like the Sun at sunrise/set.

LASCO
Creates an artificial solar eclipse to block out the light from the Sun to study the solar corona.

LASCO
Long range corona
C3 images encompass a diameter of 45 million kilometres, which is half the diameter of Mercury's orbit.

This illustration shows a coronal mass ejection particle cloud blasted from the Sun impacting Earth and creating aurora

EIT
Cooler
Here the brightest areas are at about 80,000 degrees Kelvin and 304 Angstrom.

MDI
Sunspots
Continuum images show sunspots, dark areas where the magnetic fields are disrupted and cut off heat, light and energy flowing from the Sun's interior.

EIT
Hottest
At 284 Angstrom, the brightest areas of the Sun in this image are 2 million degrees Kelvin.

The Sun's magnetic field reverses direction approximately every 11 years

© NASA and ESA

© NASA

Coronal holes

Skylab also showed areas of lower-density plasma, which are darker and colder than the surrounding area, called coronal holes.

The Sun is multilayered

The Sun comprises six different layers: the core, the radiative layer, the convective layer, the photosphere, the chromosphere, and the corona.

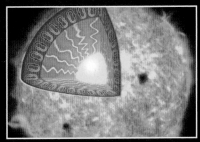

Solar tornadoes

Data from SOHO and SDO has revealed massive gaseous tornadoes at the Sun's poles, with speeds up to 50,000kph.

The Sun's heartbeat

Ground observation and SOHO data shows that the Sun has a pulse; internal gases speed and slow down every 16 months.

Sungrazing comets

SOHO has discovered nearly 2,000 small comets called sungrazers, some of which pass within just a few thousand kilometres of the Sun.

All Images © NASA

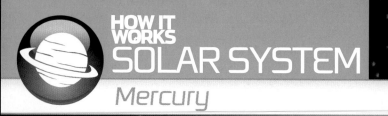
Mercury

Compared to the other planets, we know relatively little about the smallest planet in our solar system

Although we've been observing Mercury from Earth for thousands of years, its close proximity to the Sun – about 58 million kilometres, on average – has made it difficult for astronomers to learn much about the planet. The Hubble Space Telescope cannot observe it, because turning that close towards the Sun would damage the telescope's instruments. Most of what we know came from the 1975 Mariner 10 space probe's fly-by.

With the naked eye, Mercury can only be seen at dawn or dusk, depending on the time of year (unless there is a solar eclipse). This is due to the Sun's glare. Mercury can also be seen as a small black spot moving across the Sun at intervals of seven, 13 and 33 years. This is known as a transit of Mercury across the Sun and occurs when the planet comes between the Earth and the Sun.

Mercury has the shortest year of any planet at 88 Earth days. It also orbits around the Sun faster than any other planet, which is why it was named after the speedy Roman messenger god. Conversely, Mercury has the longest day of any planet due to its slow rotation. Because it revolves so quickly around the Sun, yet only rotates on its axis once every 59 Earth days, the time between sunrises on Mercury lasts 176 Earth days. Mercury also has the most eccentric, or stretched-out, elliptical orbit. Like our moon, Mercury can be observed going through apparent changes in its shape and size called phases. ✿

Atmosphere

Mercury has a very thin, almost airless atmosphere. At one time it was believed that the planet didn't have an atmosphere at all, but it does contain small concentrations of the gases helium, hydrogen and oxygen as well as calcium, potassium and sodium. Because of Mercury's size, it does not have a strong enough gravitational pull to keep a stable atmosphere. It is constantly being lost and replenished via solar wind, impacts and radioactive decay of elements in the crust.

Surface
Mercury's surface is covered in tiny minerals called silicates

Outer core
It's hypothesised that Mercury has a liquid iron outer core

Inside Mercury

A cross-section of the smallest planet in our solar system

5 TOP FACTS
MERCURY

Heavily cratered surface
1 Although telescopes had revealed that Mercury looked much like our moon, the nearly 10,000 images recorded by Mariner 10 confirmed that it had a heavily cratered surface.

Lobate scarps
2 Mariner 10's images showed that Mercury was also covered in curved cliffs called lobate scarps, which formed when the planet's core cooled and shrank.

Ultraviolet radiation
3 Mariner 10 recorded large amounts of ultraviolet radiation near Mercury. It was eventually determined to come from a nearby star called 31 Crateris.

Magnetic field
4 The Mariner 10 space probe's instruments picked up a magnetic field on Mercury, which is rather similar to Earth's own magnetic field.

Exosphere
5 Mercury has an atmosphere like the exosphere on Earth – the upper layer of our planet's atmosphere. Its lightness and low density allows molecules to escape into space.

DID YOU KNOW? *Ancient Greeks believed that Mercury was two planets: one called Hermes and one called Apollo*

Terrestrial planet

Like Earth, Mercury is a rocky planet. It comprises about 70 per cent metal and 30 per cent silicate materials. Because Mercury is so dense – almost as dense as Earth, although it's much smaller – it probably has a very large, iron-rich core. Scientists believe that Mercury's core makes up almost half of the planet's total volume and three-fourths of its total radius. It also contains more molten iron than any other major planet in the solar system. The core is estimated to have a radius of about 1,800 kilometres, with a mantle about 600 kilometres thick and a crust about 300 kilometres thick. There are a few potential explanations for this large core. Mercury may have had a more substantial crust and mantle that were stripped away by high temperatures and solar wind from the Sun, or it could have been hit by a still-forming planet called a planetesimal.

© Science Photo Library

The Statistics
Mercury

Diameter: 4,879 kilometres
Mass: 3.3022×10^{23} kilograms
Density: 5.427 grams per cubic centimetre
Average surface temperature: 179°C
Average distance from the Sun: 57,910,000 kilometres
Surface gravity: 0.38 g

Mantle
A rocky mantle, much like Earth's

Core
A huge iron core sits at the heart of the planet

Calori Montes
Mercury has several mountains known as montes, the tallest and largest of which are the Caloris Montes. This is a series of circular mountain ranges up to three kilometres in height located on the rim of the huge Caloris Basin. The Caloris Montes are massifs, formed when Mercury's crust flexed and fractured due to impact.

Temperature extremes
While Mercury has an average surface temperature of around 179°C, temperatures on the planet fluctuate wildly depending on the location on the planet, the time of day and how close it is to the Sun in its orbit. At night, surface temperatures can go down to -170°C. During the day, they can reach 450°C. Some scientists believe that ice may exist under the surface of deep craters at Mercury's poles. Here temperatures are below average because sunlight cannot penetrate.

Moon-like surface

The surface of Mercury looks much like the surface of our moon. The largest crater on Mercury is the Caloris Basin at 1,300 kilometres across. The impact caused lava eruptions and shockwaves that formed hills and furrows around the basin. Mercury also has two different types of plains. The smooth plains were likely formed by lava flows, while inter-crater plains may have been formed by lava or by impacts. The most unusual features are the wrinkles and folds across its plains and craters, caused by the cooling and contraction of the planet's core.

4. Shockwaves
Impacts with large meteorites actually send shockwaves through the core of the planet and around its perimeter

1. Meteorite impact
Mercury has been continually hit with comets and meteorites. The largest of these impacts have effects across the planet

2. Crater
Some craters are relatively shallow and narrow, but impacts with meteorites leave large craters

5. Uplifted crust
The shockwaves force the rocky mantle to buckle upwards through the crust, forming mountains

3. Ejecta
Impacts force debris high into the air on Mercury. Falling debris settles around the crater, creating an ejecta blanket

Sizes...
Mercury's diameter is two-fifths that of the Earth, and its mass is slightly less than Earth's.

4,879km   12,756.3km

The transit of Mercury
Every seven, 13 and 33 years, Mercury can be seen as a black spot moving across the Sun

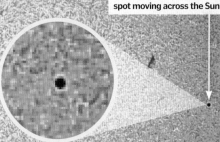

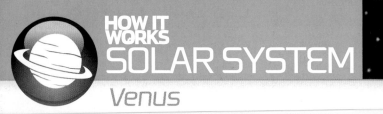
Venus

Discovering just how similar this planet actually is to Earth…

Venus has often been called Earth's sister planet because of their similarities. Both planets are terrestrial (meaning that they are made up of silicate rocks) and close in size, mass and gravity. Venus probably has a similar structure to Earth, with a crust, mantle and core. It has a diameter of around 12,000 kilometres, 650 kilometres smaller than Earth. Its mass is about 80 per cent of Earth's mass, and its gravity 90 per cent of Earth's gravity.

However, there are also many differences between Venus and Earth. Venus is about 108 million kilometres from the Sun and has an almost perfectly circular orbit, while all of the other planets have elliptical orbits. Venus completes one orbit every 225 days and has one of the slowest rotations of any planet, with one every 243 days. Venus's consistently high temperature means that it has no surface water.

The planet also has more than 1,500 volcanoes, many of which are more than 100 kilometres across. Most of the volcanoes are extinct, but some believe that there has been recent volcanic activity. Because Venus doesn't have rainfall, lightning could have been caused by ashy fallout from a volcanic eruption. These eruptions have created a rocky, barren surface of plains, mountains and valleys.

Venus is also covered with more than 1,000 impact craters. While Earth and other planets also have craters, Venus's are unusual because most of them are in perfect condition. They haven't degraded from erosion or other impacts. Venus may have experienced a massive event as much as 500 million years ago that resurfaced the planet and changed its atmosphere completely. Now bodies entering its atmosphere either burn up or are slowed down enough to avoid making a crater.

It has proven difficult to learn more about Venus, in part due to its dense atmosphere. Although probes first visited the planet in the early Sixties, it was not fully mapped by radar until the 1989 NASA Magellan probe. The Venus Express, launched by the European Space Agency in 2005, is a long-term exploration probe currently orbiting the planet and sending back data about its atmosphere. ✿

False colour view of Venus

Photographic view of Venus

5 TOP FACTS
VENUS

Venus has phases like a moon
1 When closest to the Earth, Venus appears bright and crescent-shaped. When it is further away, the planet is dim and round.

Venus rotates backwards
2 Venus has a retrograde, or west to east, rotation. This is actually the opposite direction of its revolution around the Sun.

Venus was the first 'probed' planet
3 NASA's Mariner 2 probe was launched in 1962. It passed within 30,000 kilometres of Venus and took microwave and infrared readings.

Venus has no moons
4 Venus probably had a moon billions of years ago, but it was destroyed when the planet's rotation direction was reversed.

Venus is brighter than the stars
5 Venus is brighter than any star and can be easily seen in the middle of the day, especially when the Sun is low in the horizon.

DID YOU KNOW? *Because Venus shines so brightly, it has often been misreported as a UFO*

Venus' atmosphere
Immense pressure of the atmosphere

Venus's atmospheric pressure is greater than that of any other planet – more than 90 times that of Earth's. This pressure is equivalent to being almost one kilometre below the surface of Earth's oceans. The atmosphere is also very dense and mostly carbon dioxide, with tiny amounts of water vapour and nitrogen. It has lots of sulphur dioxide on the surface. This creates a Greenhouse Effect and makes Venus the hottest planet in the solar system. Its surface temperature is 461 degrees Celsius across the entire planet, while Mercury (the closest planet to the Sun) heats up to 426 Celsius only on the side facing the Sun.

The NASA Magellan spacecraft

Beneath the surface of Venus
What lies at the core of Earth's sister planet?

Mantle
Venus's mantle is probably about 3,000 kilometres thick and made of silicate rock

Crust
Venus likely has a highly basaltic, rocky crust about 100 kilometres thick

© DK Images

Core
Scientists believe that Venus's core is a nickel-iron alloy and partially liquid, with a diameter of 6,000 kilometres

Mapping Venus
Red indicates highland areas and blue indicates lower elevations in the false-colour view of Venus

1. Ishtar Terra
One of two 'continents', or major highland areas, on Venus, Ishtar Terra is located at the planet's North Pole. It is a little smaller than the continental United States

2. Maxwell Montes
Located on the north edge of Ishtar Terra, Maxwell Montes is the largest mountain range on Venus at nearly 11 kilometres high

3. Lakshmi Planum
This plateau in western Ishtar Terra rises about 3.5 kilometres above the surface of Venus. It is covered with lava flows

4. Guinevere Planitia
Venus is covered with regions of lowland plains such as Guinevere Planitia, which contains several volcanoes, impact craters and fissures

5. Beta Regio
Beta Regio is one of several volcanic rises on Venus's surface, more than 1,000 kilometres wide

The surface of Venus
Venus is covered in broad plains and elevated regions dotted by volcanoes

This computer-generated image shows a 7,500-kilometre-long region on the northern hemisphere of Venus known as Eistla Regio. It contains two volcanoes, Gula Mons on the right and Sif Mons on the left. Gula Mons is about three kilometres high and Sif Mons stands at two kilometres.

Earth   Venus

Sizes...
Venus and Earth are very similar in size. Venus's diameter is only 650km less than that of Earth, and the mass is 81.5 per cent of Earth's.

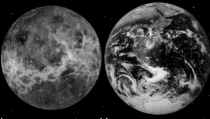

Images courtesy of NASA

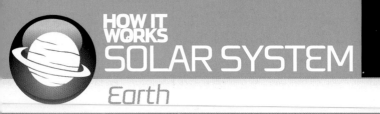

Earth

From astronaut snaps taken with handheld cameras to advanced satellite imagery that enables us to predict natural disasters, discover the planet as you've never seen it before

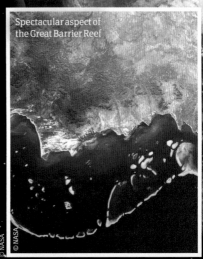

Spectacular aspect of the Great Barrier Reef

© NASA

© NASA

On Christmas Eve 1968, the crew of Apollo 8 captured this unique view of Earth. Known as 'Earthrise', this photo of Earth rising over the lunar horizon was humankind's first glimpse of the Earth from deep space

© NASA

5 TOP FACTS
EARTH OBSERVATION

First
1 Explorer VII was the first Earth observation satellite. It was launched on 13 October 1959 and measured thermal energy that was reflected by the Earth.

Largest
2 The ESA's environmental satellite Envisat is the world's largest operational non-military Earth observation satellite. It is the size of a double-decker bus.

Worldwide terrain map
3 1.3 million images from the Terra satellite's telescopes, covering 99% of the Earth's surface, have created the most complete terrain map of our planet.

Accuracy
4 The Landsat satellites discovered that maps of small islands in the Pacific Ocean were indicated as much as 16km (10 miles) from their true position.

Polar
5 Most Earth observation satellites travel in polar orbits that go over the North and South Poles, and are able to view the whole of the globe as it turns beneath it.

DID YOU KNOW? ISS astronauts spend ten mins each day taking photos of Earth with digital and 35mm and 70mm film cameras

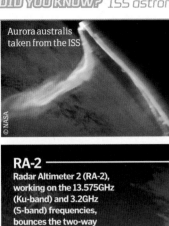
Aurora australis taken from the ISS
© NASA

ESA's Envisat

The European Space Agency's environmental satellite (Envisat) was launched into a polar orbit on 1 March 2002. Its instruments are used to study the ocean, agriculture, ice formations and atmospheric conditions of Earth.

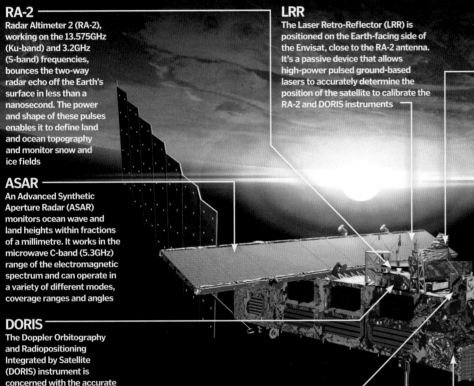
© ESA

RA-2
Radar Altimeter 2 (RA-2), working on the 13.575GHz (Ku-band) and 3.2GHz (S-band) frequencies, bounces the two-way radar echo off the Earth's surface in less than a nanosecond. The power and shape of these pulses enables it to define land and ocean topography and monitor snow and ice fields

LRR
The Laser Retro-Reflector (LRR) is positioned on the Earth-facing side of the Envisat, close to the RA-2 antenna. It's a passive device that allows high-power pulsed ground-based lasers to accurately determine the position of the satellite to calibrate the RA-2 and DORIS instruments

GOMOS
The Global Ozone Monitoring by Occultation of Stars (GOMOS) is the first instrument to use the occultation of stars to measure trace gases and aerosols from 15-100km (9-62mi) above the Earth. In each orbit, it can check 40 stars and determine the presence of atmospheric chemistry by the depletion of their light

ASAR
An Advanced Synthetic Aperture Radar (ASAR) monitors ocean wave and land heights within fractions of a millimetre. It works in the microwave C-band (5.3GHz) range of the electromagnetic spectrum and can operate in a variety of different modes, coverage ranges and angles

MERIS
The MEdium Resolution Imaging Spectrometer (MERIS) consists of five cameras that are each linked to spectrometers to measure the reflectance levels emitted from the Earth. These determine the amount of chlorophyll and sediments in oceans and coastal waters, and can examine the effectiveness of plant photosynthesis

DORIS
The Doppler Orbitography and Radiopositioning Integrated by Satellite (DORIS) instrument is concerned with the accurate tracking of Envisat, which it achieves by measuring microwave radio signals transmitted by 50 ground beacons that cover 75% of its orbit. By determining its orbit within ten centimetres (four inches), with an error of one centimetre, it is used for navigating the satellite and calibrating its on-board instruments

MIPAS
The Michelson Interferometer for Passive Atmospheric Sounding (MIPAS) spectrometer works in the near- to mid-infrared wavelengths to measure nitrogen dioxide (NO_2), nitrous oxide (N_2O), ammonia (NH_3), nitric acid (HNO_3), ozone (O_3) and water (H_2O) in the stratosphere

MWR
The MicroWave Radiometer operates at frequencies of 23.8GHz and 36.5GHz. It's a nadir-pointing instrument (faces down at the Earth) that can measure vapour content of clouds and the atmosphere, as well as moisture levels of landscapes

SCIAMACHY
Scanning Imaging Absorption spectroMeter for Atmospheric CartograpHY measures solar radiation primarily transmitted, backscattered and reflected in the stratosphere and troposphere. By examining UV, visible and near-infrared wavelengths, it detects low concentrations of gases and aerosols

AATSR
The Advanced Along Track Scanning Radiometer (AATSR) is a passive radiometer with a wide-angle lens that measures visible and infrared emissions from land and ocean surfaces. Its measurements of thermal brightness are accurate to at least 0.05°C

The crew of Apollo 8 were the first people to see and photograph our planet as a globe in its entirety. During the fourth orbit around the Moon, Lunar module commander William Anders took a series of photographs of the Earth that became known as 'Earthrise'. They revealed the true splendour of our planet suspended in stark contrast with the barren lunar surface, and became an icon for showing that our home is a fertile and fragile dot of life in an immense and deadly universe.

From the Sixties onwards an enormous number of Earth observation satellites have been launched to look at the hard facts about the state of our global environment, as it is assaulted by extremes of natural events and the impact of human activities.

Observations from space can study large patterns of change throughout the Earth's surface and in the atmosphere, and can be used to supplement information gained by ground or ocean-going instruments. The additional benefit of satellites is they can transmit data continuously, and cover areas of the Earth that are inaccessible or too hostile for any other methods of gaining information.

At first, Earth observation satellites simply used visible light and infrared sensors to monitor the position of clouds for weather forecasting. Later, microwave sensors were introduced to improve these forecasts by obtaining measurements of the temperature, pressure and humidity in different layers of the atmosphere.

The success of such satellites led NASA to launch the Landsat series of observation satellites in July 1972. Using multi-spectral scanner instrumentation, Landsats were able to produce images of the Earth's surface gained from up to eight different wavelengths, showing the distribution of snow and ice cover, vegetation, landscapes, coastal regions and human settlements, which proved to be a rich source of new data for cartography, geology, regional planning, forestry, agriculture, climate studies and educational purposes.

In the Seventies, Landsat data about the worldwide state of wheat crop growth was used to forecast yield rates and stabilise the market for this crop, which led to more stable prices for consumers. Using data from Landsat images, researchers recently discovered 650 previously unknown barrier islands, including a chain of 54 islands that stretch 563km (350mi) from the mouth of the Amazon River.

Satellites save lives and reduce property damage by tracking and

"Satellites provided an early warning of the approach of Hurricane Katrina"

warning of the arrival of hurricanes, tornadoes, floods and other extremes of weather or natural disaster. For example, in August 2005 satellites provided an accurate early warning of the approach of Hurricane Katrina and, a month later, Hurricane Rita. Unfortunately, responses to these warnings were slow, resulting in extensive damage and loss of life. Afterwards, satellites (NASA's TRMM and NOAA's GOES and POES) provided imagery of the damaged areas to help in the reconstruction of the areas affected. This helped bring about the pledge by nations that operate satellites to provide imagery to any nation affected by a major disaster under the terms of the International Disaster Charter.

The sensing technologies used by satellites consist of optical sensors that can detect the strength of reflections from the Earth in the visible/near infrared spectrum and thermal infrared rays that are radiated from the surface. Microwave sensors can detect radiation in this longer wavelength of the spectrum coming from the Earth's surface, or active microwave sensors can send microwaves to the Earth and observe their reflections.

Civilian Earth observation satellite surveillance is co-ordinated by the committee on Earth observation satellites (CEOS), which is currently affiliated to agencies that are operating 116 active satellites. These broadly study the long-term and changing global environment from the atmosphere, land, ice and snow, oceans, gravity and magnetic fields to the oceans. In the next 15 years, CEOS agencies are planning 260 satellites, which will carry 400 instruments to develop better weather forecasting and knowledge of climate changes.

Since the Nineties, NASA has run the Earth observing system (EOS) program that co-ordinates the activities of its polar-orbiting satellites to study "radiation, clouds, water vapour and precipitation; the oceans; greenhouse gases; land-surface hydrology and ecosystem processes; glaciers, sea ice and ice sheets; ozone and stratospheric chemistry and natural and anthropogenic aerosols." To further this research, it plans to launch 15 Earth observation satellites by 2020. The European Space Agency also plans several 'Earth explorer' missions, which includes the launch of three satellites in 2013 to study the Earth's magnetic field ('Swarm') and one to profile global winds (ADM-Aeolus). ✿

NASA Earth Observatories

NASA's range of satellites in their Earth observing system (EOS) program includes Terra and a planned launch of Aquarius in June 2011, to measure the salt levels of our oceans. Overall, they cover every aspect of surface and atmospheric environmental conditions

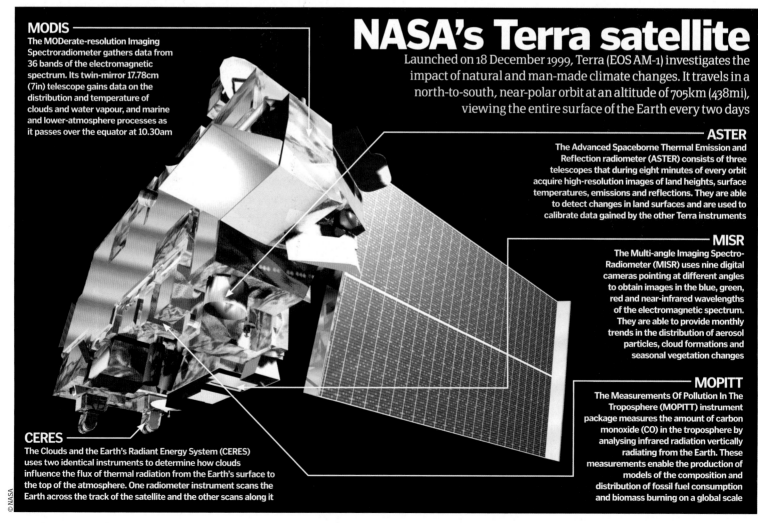

NASA's Terra satellite

Launched on 18 December 1999, Terra (EOS AM-1) investigates the impact of natural and man-made climate changes. It travels in a north-to-south, near-polar orbit at an altitude of 705km (438mi), viewing the entire surface of the Earth every two days

MODIS
The MODerate-resolution Imaging Spectroradiometer gathers data from 36 bands of the electromagnetic spectrum. Its twin-mirror 17.78cm (7in) telescope gains data on the distribution and temperature of clouds and water vapour, and marine and lower-atmosphere processes as it passes over the equator at 10.30am

ASTER
The Advanced Spaceborne Thermal Emission and Reflection radiometer (ASTER) consists of three telescopes that during eight minutes of every orbit acquire high-resolution images of land heights, surface temperatures, emissions and reflections. They are able to detect changes in land surfaces and are used to calibrate data gained by the other Terra instruments

MISR
The Multi-angle Imaging Spectro-Radiometer (MISR) uses nine digital cameras pointing at different angles to obtain images in the blue, green, red and near-infrared wavelengths of the electromagnetic spectrum. They are able to provide monthly trends in the distribution of aerosol particles, cloud formations and seasonal vegetation changes

MOPITT
The Measurements Of Pollution In The Troposphere (MOPITT) instrument package measures the amount of carbon monoxide (CO) in the troposphere by analysing infrared radiation vertically radiating from the Earth. These measurements enable the production of models of the composition and distribution of fossil fuel consumption and biomass burning on a global scale

CERES
The Clouds and the Earth's Radiant Energy System (CERES) uses two identical instruments to determine how clouds influence the flux of thermal radiation from the Earth's surface to the top of the atmosphere. One radiometer instrument scans the Earth across the track of the satellite and the other scans along it

NATURAL DISASTER

STARTLING IMAGES

ASHES

1. Japanese earthquake
Within hours of the Japanese earthquake and tsunami on 11 March 2011, Terra and Aqua satellites transmitted images.

2. Natural and man-made
AATSR instruments recorded images of the Buncefield oil depot fire in 2005 and the decline of Arctic sea ice during 2007.

3. Icelandic volcanic eruption
When Iceland's Eyjafjallajökull volcano erupted in April 2010, MERIS on Envisat recorded composition and distribution of the volcanic ash.

DID YOU KNOW? Only 24 astronauts have seen the entire Earth from space while on their Apollo missions to the Moon

Which aspects of Earth are the satellites observing?

Atmosphere

NASA launched eight Nimbus Earth observation satellites between 1964 and 1978. They pioneered the use of 'sounders' that measure the humidity and temperature of the atmosphere. They obtain temperature measurements by analysing infrared radiation (IR) on wavelengths linked with oxygen or carbon dioxide. IR or microwave sounders identify water vapour in the atmosphere to measure humidity. Microwave sounders have a lower resolution, but can be used in all weather conditions as they can sound through clouds.

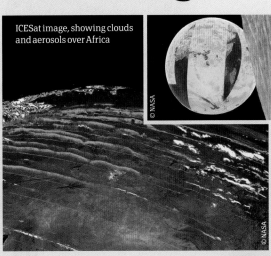

ICESat image, showing clouds and aerosols over Africa

Gulf oil spill creeps towards the Mississippi Delta

Oceans

In the Seventies the USA and USSR ran ocean observation satellite programmes, which carried synthetic aperture radar (SAR) equipment. A number of radar images are taken by SARs and combined to produce a single detailed image. This is able to determine the height of sea levels, waves, currents and their distribution and can detect oil slicks and shipping movements. The Jason 1 and 2 spacecraft currently use these techniques to study the topography and characteristics of the oceans, to give a better warning of floods or climate changes.

Land

The Shuttle Radar Topography Mission (SRTM) by the Endeavour space shuttle in February 2000 used two radar antennas to produce the most comprehensive hi-res digital topographical map of the Earth's terrain. The data is used by Google Earth to create maps that can be viewed in 2D or 3D.

Earth observation satellites are important in monitoring the seasonal variation of vegetation. Besides studying long-term changes, they are also used to observe and issue warnings of natural disasters such as volcanic eruptions, forest fires and earthquakes.

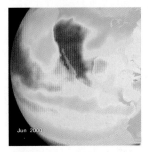

The red portion of this view of the US reveals the highest ground levels of ultraviolet radiation

Radiation

Visible blue, green and red light only provides a limited amount of information about the Earth's surface, so satellites use spectrometers to study the invisible near-infrared and infrared parts of the electromagnetic spectrum.

They can identify and track the growth of plant species, as they all reflect infrared light. The infrared 'fingerprint' of plants can also indicate the amount of water present and can warn of potential droughts. Likewise, exposed rocks radiate their own infrared fingerprint that allows geologists to identify valuable mineral/oil deposits.

Infrared data from satellites is 'false coloured', so invisible light from up to three wavelengths is rendered into a combination of visible red, green and blue.

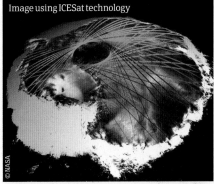

Image using ICESat technology

Ice

Carrying on from the work of Envisat, which discovered that every decade since 1978 the Arctic ice fields have shrunk by 2.7%, the European Space Agency launched CryoSat-2 on 8 April 2010. It uses radar altimeters with SAR technology, specifically designed for its mission to study the thickness and distribution of ice in the polar oceans. NASA's ICESat (2004) carried a Geoscience Laser Altimeter System (GLAS), which used pulses of laser light to measure the height and characteristics of Greenland and Antarctic ice fields. These satellites have indicated the role of greenhouse gases in the polar atmosphere and that the ozone layer has shown signs of recovery.

Perspective view of Santa Barbara, generated using data from the shuttle radar topography mission

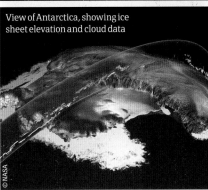

View of Antarctica, showing ice sheet elevation and cloud data

Gravity

The European gravity field and steady-state ocean circulation explorer (GOCE), launched in March 2009, carries an Electrostatic Gravity Gradiometer (EGG) to measure the gravity field of Earth. By measuring the minute variations in the tug of gravity, it enables the production of Geoid maps of the globe that can indicate ocean circulation and changes, the movement and composition of polar ice sheets and the physics of the Earth's interior.

In March 2002, NASA launched two Gravity Recovery And Climate Experiment (GRACE) spacecraft. They use a microwave system that accurately measures any minute changes between their speed and distance, indicating the influence of the Earth's gravitational pull.

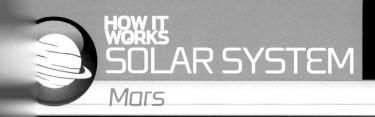
Olympus Mons

Ascraeus Mons

Valles Marineris

Claritas Rupes

Mars

Other than the fact that it's a planet in our solar system, what do we really know about Mars?

To date there have been 42 missions to Mars, with exactly half of them being complete failures. Other than the Earth it is the most studied planet in the solar system, and for centuries it has been at the heart of wild speculation and groundbreaking scientific discoveries. Observations of Mars have not only revealed otherwise unknown secrets but also posed new and exciting questions, and it is for these reasons that it has become the most intriguing planetary body of our time.

Named after the Roman god of war, Mars has fascinated astronomers since Nicolaus Copernicus first realised Mars was another planet orbiting the Sun in 1543. Its notable features such as huge impact craters, gullies and dormant volcanoes suggest it was once more geologically active than it is now, leading scientists to speculate on whether it supported water and life in the past, or indeed if it still does today. Astronomers in the 19th Century falsely believed they could see large oceans, and there were several reports of people receiving 'communications' from Martians in the form of bursts of light when they observed the planet through a telescope. Of course, we now have a better understanding of the planet, but we are still yet to unlock some of its most puzzling mysteries.

Mars sits 141 million miles (227 million km) from the Sun and takes 687 Earth days to orbit. As its orbital path is not in sync with Earth's it goes through a 26-month cycle of being closest (known as 'opposition') and furthest ('conjunction') from us, located at a distance of 35 million miles (56 million km) and 249 million miles (401 million km) respectively. This change in distance means spacecraft destined for Mars are sent in a launch window every 26 months, when Mars is closest to Earth. The next will be in November 2011, when NASA plans to launch its new Mars rover, named 'Curiosity'. The journey time is upwards of six months, so Mars will actually be closest on

Like all the planets in our solar system, it is believed Mars formed about 4.5 billion years ago inside a solar nebula, when dust particles clumped together to form the planet. At just under half the size of Earth it's quite a small planet, which is accredited to Jupiter forming first. The gravitational forces of this gas giant consumed available material that would have otherwise contributed to Mars's growth, while Jupiter's gravity prevented another planet forming between Mars and Jupiter and instead left the asteroid belt. The northern hemisphere of Mars is significantly younger and lower in elevation than the southern hemisphere, suggesting the planet was struck by a Pluto-sized object early in its lifetime.

Mars is often referred to as something of a 'dead' planet. Indeed, its lack of folded mountains like those on Earth show that it has no currently active plate tectonics, meaning carbon dioxide cannot be recycled into the atmosphere to create a

5 TOP FACTS
DISCOVERY OF MARS

1,500BC
1 Egyptians refer to Mars as 'Horus of the Hawk', a god with the head of a hawk. They note its retrograde motion, when it moves backwards in its orbit relative to Earth.

350BC
2 Aristotle first proposes that Mars orbits at a further distance than the Moon when he notes that the Moon passes in front of Mars in his observations.

1609
3 Galileo Galilei uses a telescope to become the first person to observe Mars, but is later vilified by the Vatican for asserting that the planets orbit the Sun and not Earth.

1666
4 Astronomer Giovanni Cassini calculates the length of a Martian day, notes the polar ice caps and even calculates its distance from Earth in his telescopic observations.

1840
5 Astronomers Wilhelm Beer and Johann Heinrich Mädler study Mars through a 3.75-inch telescope and produce the first sketched map of its surface.

DID YOU KNOW? Of the nine 21st Century missions to Mars only Beagle 2 has failed

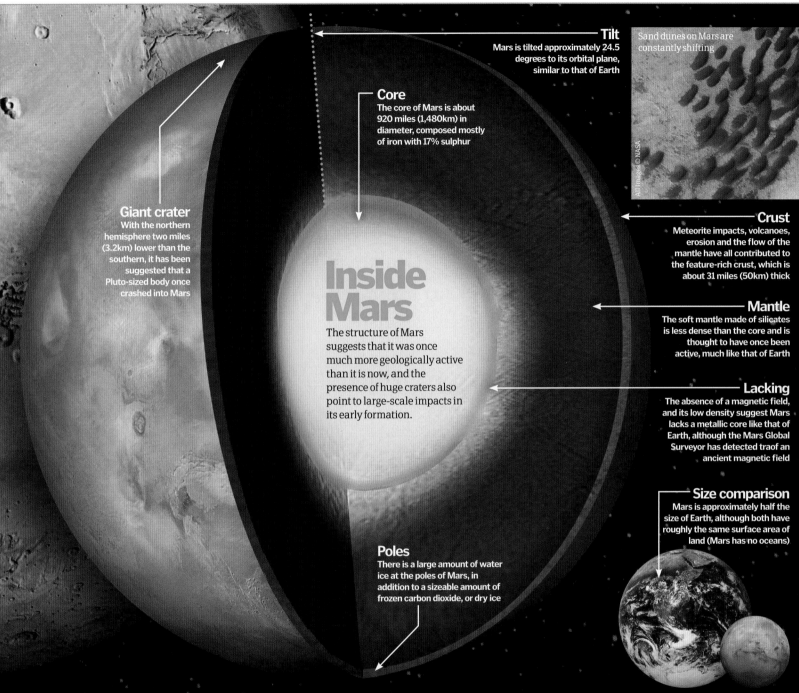

Tilt
Mars is tilted approximately 24.5 degrees to its orbital plane, similar to that of Earth

Sand dunes on Mars are constantly shifting

All Images © NASA

Core
The core of Mars is about 920 miles (1,480km) in diameter, composed mostly of iron with 17% sulphur

Giant crater
With the northern hemisphere two miles (3.2km) lower than the southern, it has been suggested that a Pluto-sized body once crashed into Mars

Inside Mars

The structure of Mars suggests that it was once much more geologically active than it is now, and the presence of huge craters also point to large-scale impacts in its early formation.

Crust
Meteorite impacts, volcanoes, erosion and the flow of the mantle have all contributed to the feature-rich crust, which is about 31 miles (50km) thick

Mantle
The soft mantle made of silicates is less dense than the core and is thought to have once been active, much like that of Earth

Lacking
The absence of a magnetic field, and its low density suggest Mars lacks a metallic core like that of Earth, although the Mars Global Surveyor has detected traof an ancient magnetic field

Size comparison
Mars is approximately half the size of Earth, although both have roughly the same surface area of land (Mars has no oceans)

Poles
There is a large amount of water ice at the poles of Mars, in addition to a sizeable amount of frozen carbon dioxide, or dry ice

much heat, with a surface temperature as low as -133°C at the poles in the winter, rising to 27°C on the day side of the planet during the summer.

Despite this, the atmosphere of Mars offers conclusive evidence that it was once geographically active. The outer planets in the solar system have atmospheres composed of predominantly hydrogen and helium, but that of Mars contains 95.3% carbon dioxide, 2.7% nitrogen and 1.6% argon, with minimal traces of oxygen and water. This strongly suggests that volcanoes once erupted across its surface and spewed out carbon dioxide, further evidenced by giant mountains such as Olympus Mons that appear to be dormant volcanoes.

It might not be geologically active, but Mars does play host to some extreme weather conditions, most notably the appearance of dust devils. These

tornadoes, ten times larger than anything similar on Earth, can be several miles high and hundreds of metres wide, creating miniature lightning bolts as the dust and sand within become electrically charged. The wind inside one of these, though, is almost unnoticeable, as the atmospheric pressure on Mars is so low. Interestingly, one of the reasons for the long survival rate of NASA's Mars rovers is that these dust devils have been cleaning their solar panels, allowing them to absorb more sunlight.

Mars's gravity is about 38% that of Earth, with just 10% of the mass. The surface pressure is just over 100 times weaker than ours at sea level, meaning that a human standing on the surface would see their blood instantly boil. The red colour on Mars's surface is the result of rusting, due to iron present in the rocks and soil reacting with oxygen to produce an iron oxide

In 1877 the American astronomer Asaph Hall, urged on by his wife, discovered that Mars had two moons orbiting so close that they were within the glare of the planet. They were named Phobos and Deimos, after the attendants of Ares in the Iliad. Interestingly, the moons are not spherical like most other moons; they are almost potato-shaped and only about ten miles wide at their longest axis, indicating that they are the fragments of the collision of larger objects near Mars billions of years ago. Phobos orbits Mars more than three times a day, while Deimos takes 30 hours. Phobos is gradually moving closer to Mars and will crash into the planet within 50 million years, a blink of an eye in astronomical terms. The moons have both been touted as a possible base, from which humans could observe and travel to Mars.

Jupiter

We take a look inside the most massive planet in our solar system

When Galileo Galilei discovered Jupiter in 1610, it is doubtful that he was aware of the impact this giant planet had on the surrounding solar system. From altering the evolution of Mars to preventing the formation of a ninth planet, the size and mass of Jupiter has seen it exert an influence on its neighbours second only to the Sun.

Jupiter's mass and composition almost more closely resemble a star than a planet, and in fact if it was 80 times more massive it would be classified as the former. It can virtually be regarded as being the centre of its own miniature solar system; 50 moons to date are known to orbit the gas giant, with the four largest (Io, Europa, Ganymede and Callisto, the Galilean satellites) each surpassing Pluto in size.

The comparison of Jupiter to a star owes a lot to the fact that it is composed almost entirely of gas. It has a large number of ammonia-based clouds floating above water vapour, with strong east-west winds in the upper atmosphere pulling these climate features into dark and light stripes. The majority of its atmosphere, however, is made up of hydrogen and helium.

The strength of Jupiter's gravity is such that it is held responsible for much of the development of nearby celestial bodies. The gravitational force of the gas giant is believed to have stunted the growth of Mars, consuming material that would have contributed to its size. It also prevented a new planet forming between these two and instead gave rise to the asteroid belt.

Much of our knowledge of Jupiter comes from seven spacecraft missions to visit the planet, starting with NASA's Pioneer 10 in 1973. The only man-made object to orbit the planet is the Galileo spacecraft, which studied the planet from 1995 until 2003, when it was sent crashing into Jupiter so as not to contaminate its moons with the debris. ⚙

NASA's Jupiter orbiter Juno launched on its five-year journey in 2011

All Images © NASA

Jupiter's diameter is 11 times that of Earth, and 318 times the mass

DID YOU KNOW? *The Greeks and later the Romans named the gas giant after their most important deities – Zeus and Jupiter*

Jupiter's anatomy

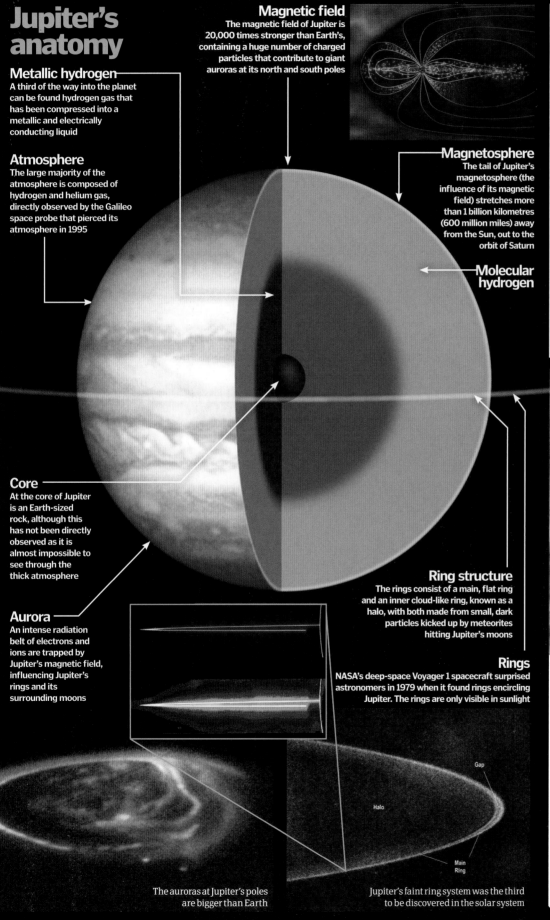

Metallic hydrogen
A third of the way into the planet can be found hydrogen gas that has been compressed into a metallic and electrically conducting liquid

Atmosphere
The large majority of the atmosphere is composed of hydrogen and helium gas, directly observed by the Galileo space probe that pierced its atmosphere in 1995

Magnetic field
The magnetic field of Jupiter is 20,000 times stronger than Earth's, containing a huge number of charged particles that contribute to giant auroras at its north and south poles

Magnetosphere
The tail of Jupiter's magnetosphere (the influence of its magnetic field) stretches more than 1 billion kilometres (600 million miles) away from the Sun, out to the orbit of Saturn

Molecular hydrogen

Core
At the core of Jupiter is an Earth-sized rock, although this has not been directly observed as it is almost impossible to see through the thick atmosphere

Aurora
An intense radiation belt of electrons and ions are trapped by Jupiter's magnetic field, influencing Jupiter's rings and its surrounding moons

Ring structure
The rings consist of a main, flat ring and an inner cloud-like ring, known as a halo, with both made from small, dark particles kicked up by meteorites hitting Jupiter's moons

Rings
NASA's deep-space Voyager 1 spacecraft surprised astronomers in 1979 when it found rings encircling Jupiter. The rings are only visible in sunlight

The auroras at Jupiter's poles are bigger than Earth

Gap
Halo
Main Ring

Jupiter's faint ring system was the third to be discovered in the solar system

Moons of Jupiter

Jupiter's four largest moons are known as the Galilean satellites, named after their discoverer Galileo Galilei

Io
Europa
Ganymede
Callisto

This photograph of Jupiter, with the Red Spot visible at the centre, was taken by NASA's Voyager 2 on 29 June 1979, as it flew past at a distance of almost 9 million kilometres (6 million miles)

The Great Red Spot

One of Jupiter's most iconic features is the Great Red Spot, a storm more than twice the size of Earth that has been raging for hundreds of years. The redness is believed to be the result of compounds being brought up from deeper inside Jupiter, which turn brown and red upon exposure to the Sun. Although once highly elliptical in shape, it has become squashed in recent years for unknown reasons and is expected to become circular other the next few decades, although this anti-cyclonic storm shows no sign of dying out any time soon.

Inside Saturn

Saturn is believed to have a small rocky core, with a temperature of more than 11,000°C. It is surrounded by a layer of gases and water, followed by a metallic liquid hydrogen and a viscous layer of liquid helium and hydrogen. Near the surface, the hydrogen and helium become gaseous. Saturn has no solid surface.

Inner layer
This thickest layer surrounding the core is liquid hydrogen and helium

Wave-like structures in the clouds can be seen in Saturn's atmosphere

Saturn

Only Jupiter is larger than this gas giant, best known for its ring system

We've been viewing Saturn with the naked eye since prehistoric times, but the planet's most unique feature – its ring system – wasn't discovered until 1610. Each ring contains billions of chunks of dust and water-ice. Saturn has about 14 major ring divisions, but there are also satellites and other structures within some of the rings and gaps. Saturn's rings are believed to have come from the remains of moons, comets or other bodies that broke up in the planet's atmosphere.

The rings aren't the only fascinating thing about Saturn, however. This gas giant is less dense than any other planet in our solar system and has a mostly fluid structure. It radiates a massive amount of energy, thought to be the result of slow gravitational compression. Saturn takes about 29.5 years to revolve around the Sun, and its rotation is a bit more complex – different probes have estimated different times, the latest estimate is ten hours, 32 minutes and 35 seconds. The variations probably have something to do with irregularities in the planet's radio waves, due to the similarities between its magnetic axis and its rotational axis.

Saturn has a cold atmosphere comprising layered clouds of both water-ice and ammonia-ice. It also has winds of up to 1,800 kilometres per second. Occasionally Saturn has storms on its surface, similar to those of Jupiter. One such storm is the Great White Spot, a massive storm in the planet's northern hemisphere that has been observed about once every Saturnian year since 1876. ✿

Outer layer
The outer layer is gaseous hydrogen and helium, blending with its atmosphere

Rings in view

Saturn takes 29.5 years to orbit the Sun, and it has an elliptical orbit like most planets. The closest Saturn comes to the Sun is 1.35 billion kilometres, while at its furthest, Saturn is 1.5 billion kilometres away. Saturn has a tilt of 26.7 degrees relative to the orbital plane. During half of its orbital period, the northern hemisphere is facing the Sun, while the southern hemisphere faces the Sun during the other half. When viewing Saturn from Earth, this impacts whether we can see the rings full-on or as a thin line.

North pole tilt
The northern hemisphere is visible with the rings appearing below

Both hemispheres
Both hemispheres are visible with the rings appearing as a thin line

Orbit
Saturn has an elliptical orbit of 29½ years

South pole tilt
The southern hemisphere is visible from Earth with the rings above

DID YOU KNOW?

Discovering the rings
Galileo thought that he was seeing moons orbiting Saturn instead of rings because his telescope was not powerful enough. Astronomer Christiaan Huygens observed the rings in 1655, but thought they were a single ring.

DID YOU KNOW? Images from the Cassini probe show that Saturn has a bright blue northern atmosphere

The Statistics
Saturn

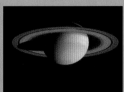

Diameter: 120,535 km
Mass: 5.6851 x 10^{26} kg
Density: 0.687 grams per cm^3
Average surface temperature: -139°C
Core temperature: 11,000°C
Moons: 62
Average distance from the Sun: 1,426,725,400km
Surface gravity: 10.44 metres per second squared

Extreme bulge
Saturn is an extreme example of an oblate spheroid – the difference between the radius of the planet at its poles and at its circumference is about ten per cent. This is due to its very short rotational period of just over ten hours.

Inner core
The inner core is likely very small and contains silicate rock, much like Jupiter's core

Cassini probe
The first spacecraft to ever orbit Saturn, the Cassini probe has provided incredible images of the planet and its ring system

Float that planet
If we had a big enough pond, we could float Saturn on its surface. Although Saturn is the second-largest planet as well as the second-most massive, it's the least-dense planet in our solar system. Its density is just 0.687 grams per cubic centimetre, about one-tenth as dense as our planet and two-thirds as dense as water.

Outer core
Saturn's outer core is much thicker than its inner core, containing metallic liquid hydrogen

Saturn's southern storm
In 2004, the Cassini space probe discovered a massive, oddly shaped convective thunderstorm in Saturn's southern atmosphere. Dubbed the Dragon Storm, this weather feature emitted strong radio waves. Like storms on Earth, the Dragon Storm emits flashes of lightning that appear as white plumes. Scientists believe it exists deep in the atmosphere and can occasionally flare up.

An artist's impression of Saturn's ring particles

Rings
Saturn's rings comprise particles of ice and dust that range from microscopic to several thousand kilometres in diameter

© DK Images

All Images © NASA

> "Uranus has a complex ring system and a total of 27 moons"

Uranus

Seventh planet from the Sun, third-largest and fourth most massive in the solar system. Uranus was the first planet to be discovered by telescope

Four times the size of Earth and capable of containing 63 Earths inside it (it is only 14.5 times as dense however, as it is a gas giant), Uranus is the third largest and forth most massive planet in our solar system. Appearing calm and pale blue when imaged, Uranus has a complex ring system and a total of 27 moons orbiting its gaseous, cloudy main body. Due to its distance from the Sun the temperature at the cloud-top layer of the planet drops to -214°C and because of its massive distance from Earth it appears incredibly dim when viewed, a factor that led to it not being recognised as a planet until 1781 by astronomer William Herschel. ✿

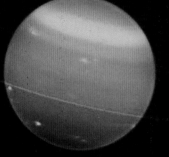

Upper atmosphere, cloud tops

Core
Made up of rock and ice

1. Atmosphere
Uranus's blue colour is caused by the absorption of the incoming sunlight's red wavelengths by methane-ice clouds. The action of the ultraviolet sunlight on the methane produces haze particles, and these hide the lower atmosphere, giving the planet its calm appearance. However, beneath this calm façade the planet is constantly changing with huge ammonia and water clouds carried around the planet by its high winds (up to 560mph) and the planet's rotation. Uranus radiates what little heat it absorbs from the Sun and has an unusually cold core

2. Rings
Uranus's 11 rings are tilted on their side, as viewed from Earth, and extend from 12,500 to 25,600km from the planet. They are widely separated and incredibly narrow too, meaning that the system has more gap than ring. All but the inner and outer rings are between 1km and 13km wide, and all are less than 15km in height. The rings consist of a mixture of dust particles, rocks and charcoal-dark pieces of carbon-rich material. The Kuiper Airborne Observatory discovered the first five of these rings in 1977

Oberon
The first Uranian moon to be discovered

Umbriel
The darkest of the major moons, reflecting only 16 per cent of light

Titania
Uranus' largest moon appears grey with an icy surface

Inside Uranus
A cross-section of the blue planet

Ariel
The brightest and with the youngest surface of the major moons

Miranda
Features a scarred, piecemeal structure

5 TOP FACTS
URANUS

Old man
1 Uranus is named after the Greek deity of the same name who, in Greek mythology, was Zeus's grandfather and the father of Cronus.

Passing wind
2 Uranus is one of the solar system's most windy planets, with speeds that can reach up to a monumental 250 metres per second.

Bonus
3 Upon discovering Uranus, William Herschel was gifted an annual stipend of £200 by King George III, on the condition he moved to Windsor.

Elementary
4 The element uranium was named in dedication to the discovery of Uranus eight years prior to the element's discovery in 1789.

Lone ranger
5 The only space probe to examine Uranus to date w the Voyager 2 in 1986, wh passed with 82,000km o planet's cloud-tops.

DID YOU KNOW? *Many of Uranus's moons are named after characters from the plays of Shakespeare*

Miranda is littered with impact craters and is heavily scarred with faults

Miranda
The smallest and innermost of Uranus's five major moons, Miranda is like no other moon in our solar system

When the Voyager 2 passed by Uranus in 1986 it not only observed the planet but also many of its moons, coming close to its innermost Miranda at a distance of 32,000km. However, the images it recorded were not what were expected as on closer inspection it showed the satellite's surface consisted of a series of incongruous surface features that seemed to have been crushed together and butted up unnaturally. Miranda was an ancient terrain that seemed to have been constructed from various smaller segments from different time periods, instead of forming as one distinct whole at one time. Scientists have theorised that this was probably caused by a catastrophic collision in the moon's past that caused it to shatter into various pieces before then being reassembled in this disjointed way.

Verona Rupes
Found on Uranus' moon Miranda, this cliff face is estimated to be ten kilometres deep, almost ten times the depth of the Grand Canyon. This makes it the tallest known cliff in the entire solar system

Atmosphere
Consists of hydrogen, helium and other gasses

Mantle
A large layer of water, methane and ammonia ices

4. Orbi
Uranus takes 84 Earth years to complete a single orbit around the Sun, through which it is permanently tilted on its side by 98° – a factor probably caused by a planetary-sized collision while it was still young. Due to its sideways tilt, each o the planet's poles points to the Sun for 21 years at a time, meaning that while one pole receives continuous sunlight, the other receives continuous darkness. The strength of the sunlight that Uranus receives on its orbit is 0.25 per cent of that which is received o Earth. There is a difference of 186 million kilometres between Uranus's aphelion (furthest point on an orbit from the Sun and perihelion (closest point on an orbit

3. Structure
Uranus consists of three distinct sections an atmosphere of hydrogen, helium and other gases, an inner layer of water methane and ammonia ices, and a smal core consisting of rock and ice. Electri currents within its icy layer are postulated by astronomers to generate Uranus's magnetic field, which is offset by 58.6° from the planet's spin axis. Its large layers o gaseous hydrogen and constantly shifting methane and ammonia ices account for the planet's low mass compared to its volume

Sizes...
Uranus' diameter is nearly five times that of Earth, with a mass that's equivalent to 14 and a half Earths.

12 756.3km   51 118km

Neptune

The smallest and coldest of the four gas giants, as well as the most distant from the Sun, Neptune is the windiest planet in our solar system

Over 4.5 billion kilometres from Earth and with an average temperature of -220°C, Neptune is the furthest planet from the Sun and the coldest in our solar system, excluding the dwarf planet Pluto. It is a massive (49,532km in diameter) sphere of hydrogen, helium and methane gas, formed around a small but mass-heavy core of rock and ice that, despite its similar size and structure to its inner neighbour Uranus, differs in appearance dramatically, presenting its turbulent, violently windy atmosphere on its surface. Find out what makes Neptune so unique and volatile right here. ✿

A gigantic storm the size of Earth

Inside Neptune
A cross-section of the smallest gas giant

Dark spot

5 TOP FACTS
NEPTUNE

True blue
1 Neptune's eye-catching deep blue colouring is caused by the methane gas in its atmosphere, absorbing red light and reflecting blue.

Gale force
2 Around its equatorial region Neptune is privy to winds in excess of 1,340 miles per hour as well as extremely violent storms.

Belt buster
3 Due to the fast nature of Neptune's spin around its axis, its equatorial region is 527 miles larger in diameter than at its poles.

Son of god
4 Neptune's one major moon is actually named, funnily enough, after his Greek counterpart Poseidon's son, Triton.

The four seasons
5 Neptune undergoes seasons just like here on Earth. However, they last 40 years each instead of just the three months we're used to.

DID YOU KNOW? Neptune is not visible to the naked eye, with a small telescope necessary to discern it as a star-like point of light

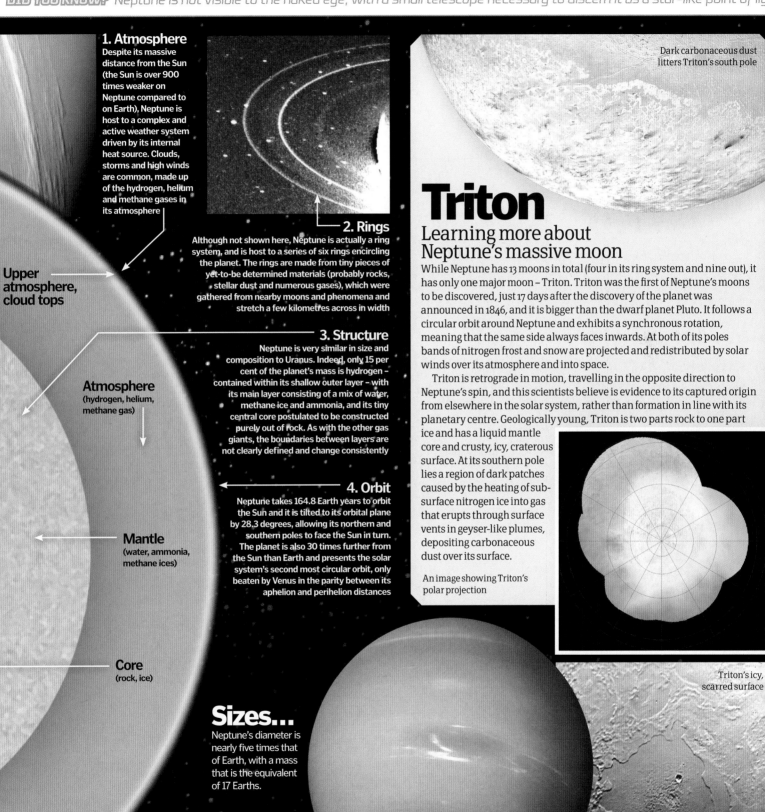

1. Atmosphere
Despite its massive distance from the Sun (the Sun is over 900 times weaker on Neptune compared to on Earth), Neptune is host to a complex and active weather system driven by its internal heat source. Clouds, storms and high winds are common, made up of the hydrogen, helium and methane gases in its atmosphere

Upper atmosphere, cloud tops

Atmosphere
(hydrogen, helium, methane gas)

Mantle
(water, ammonia, methane ices)

Core
(rock, ice)

2. Rings
Although not shown here, Neptune is actually a ring system, and is host to a series of six rings encircling the planet. The rings are made from tiny pieces of yet-to-be determined materials (probably rocks, stellar dust and numerous gases), which were gathered from nearby moons and phenomena and stretch a few kilometres across in width

3. Structure
Neptune is very similar in size and composition to Uranus. Indeed, only 15 per cent of the planet's mass is hydrogen – contained within its shallow outer layer – with its main layer consisting of a mix of water, methane ice and ammonia, and its tiny central core postulated to be constructed purely out of rock. As with the other gas giants, the boundaries between layers are not clearly defined and change consistently

4. Orbit
Neptune takes 164.8 Earth years to orbit the Sun and it is tilted to its orbital plane by 28.3 degrees, allowing its northern and southern poles to face the Sun in turn. The planet is also 30 times further from the Sun than Earth and presents the solar system's second most circular orbit, only beaten by Venus in the parity between its aphelion and perihelion distances

Sizes...
Neptune's diameter is nearly five times that of Earth, with a mass that is the equivalent of 17 Earths.

Dark carbonaceous dust litters Triton's south pole

Triton
Learning more about Neptune's massive moon

While Neptune has 13 moons in total (four in its ring system and nine out), it has only one major moon – Triton. Triton was the first of Neptune's moons to be discovered, just 17 days after the discovery of the planet was announced in 1846, and it is bigger than the dwarf planet Pluto. It follows a circular orbit around Neptune and exhibits a synchronous rotation, meaning that the same side always faces inwards. At both of its poles bands of nitrogen frost and snow are projected and redistributed by solar winds over its atmosphere and into space.

Triton is retrograde in motion, travelling in the opposite direction to Neptune's spin, and this scientists believe is evidence to its captured origin from elsewhere in the solar system, rather than formation in line with its planetary centre. Geologically young, Triton is two parts rock to one part ice and has a liquid mantle core and crusty, icy, craterous surface. At its southern pole lies a region of dark patches caused by the heating of sub-surface nitrogen ice into gas that erupts through surface vents in geyser-like plumes, depositing carbonaceous dust over its surface.

An image showing Triton's polar projection

Triton's icy, scarred surface

12,756.3km

49,532km

Images courtesy of NASA

"With the arrival of the New Horizons spacecraft in 2015 we should know more about this very distant body"

Pluto

The elusive Planet X that became an ex-planet and still has many X factors

The astronomer Percival Lowell predicted the existence of a ninth planet in our solar system, beyond the orbit of Neptune. Lowell failed to find Planet X in his lifetime, but Clyde Tombaugh – using the Lowell Observatory in Arizona – confirmed his calculations. Shortly after Planet X's discovery back in January 1930 it was named Pluto. In 1978, however, it was determined that Lowell's theory based on the mass of Pluto and its effects on Uranus and Neptune were incorrect. Tombaugh's discovery was just a very lucky coincidence.

The dwarf planet Pluto takes a leisurely 248 years to orbit the Sun. Its highly elliptical orbit takes it to a maximum of 7.4 billion kilometres from the sun (at aphelion, or farthest from the Sun) to as close as 4.5 billion kilometres (at perihelion, or closest to the Sun). Twice in this orbit it is actually closer to the Sun than Neptune, as was the case from January 1979 to February 1999.

All the other planets orbit on the plane of the ecliptic, but Pluto's orbit is at an inclination of 17 degrees to this plane. Pluto is also unusual because it rotates at an angle of 122 degrees to its own axis, in a clockwise direction. This retrograde motion means it is spinning in an opposite direction to its counter-clockwise orbit around the Sun.

So far, even the Hubble Space Telescope has only obtained grainy pictures of its surface, and it is not until the arrival of the New Horizons spacecraft in 2015 that we should know more about this small, distant and very cold body. ✿

Surface details

Using observations by the Hubble Space Telescope, and maps produced since the Eighties, it has been found that the surface of Pluto undergoes many large variations in brightness and colour.

From 1994 to 2003, the southern hemisphere darkened, while the northern hemisphere got brighter. It has a slightly less red colour than Mars, with an orange cast similar to Jupiter's moon Io. It got redder from 2000 to 2002, and other colour variations of dark orange, charcoal black and white have been observed. These seasonal variations are regarded as being due to the orbital eccentricity and axial tilt of Pluto that are reflecting topographic features and the flux of the frozen surface of the planet with its rarefied atmosphere.

Core
This is about 1,700 kilometres in diameter. It is mainly composed of iron-nickel alloy and rock. At its centre might be hot radioactive material or ice

Mantel 1
Composed of rock and water ice

Surface
A rocky surface covered by frozen nitrogen, methane and carbon monoxide

Mantel 2
If Pluto has a hot radioactive core, then there could be a 180-kilometre thick liquid water ocean between the core and the outer mantel

Inside Pluto
So far, we know little about the composition of Pluto. Ice beneath Pluto's surface might cause movement and changes on the surface, in the same way glaciers do on Earth

© DK Images

5 TOP FACTS
PLUTO

Finding Pluto
1 Clyde Tombaugh systematically photographed the sky and checked 1.5 million stars recorded by his photographic plates before he found Pluto.

Naming Pluto
2 Venetia Burney, an 11-year-old schoolgirl in Oxford, put forward the name Pluto. She picked it after the Roman god of the underworld. Her reward was a £5 note.

Nix and Hydra
3 The Hubble Space Telescope discovered these moons of Pluto in 2005. Nix orbits Pluto at a distance of 48,000 kilometres and Hydra, 65,000 kilometres.

Kuiper Belt
4 Pluto is part of a cluster of Kuiper Belt Objects (KBOs) that orbit beyond Neptune. It consists of icy and rocky objects that failed to form into planets.

Triton
5 It was thought that Pluto was a satellite of Neptune. This is no longer regarded as possible, but Pluto does have many characteristics similar to Neptune's moon, Triton.

DID YOU KNOW? Out of 1,000 names suggested for Planet X, three were shortlisted: Minerva, Cronus and Pluto

The Statistics

134340 Pluto

Diameter: 2,320 kilometres
Mass: 1.3×10^{22} kilograms
Density: 2 grams per cubic centimetre
Average surface temperature: -230°C or -382°F (44K)
Core temperature: Unknown
Average distance from the Sun: 5,913,520,000 kilometres (39.5 AU)
Surface gravity: 0.067g
Moons: 3

Atmosphere

When Pluto's elongated orbit takes it relatively close to the Sun, the frozen nitrogen, methane and carbon monoxide on its surface sublimates into a tenuous gaseous form. This creates winds and clouds, but the weak gravitational force of Pluto means that it can escape into space and interact with its moon, Charon.

In the process of sublimation an anti-greenhouse effect is created, which lowers the temperature of Pluto to -230°C against the expected -220°C, which is the temperature of Charon. In the lower atmosphere, a concentration of methane creates a temperature inversion that makes the upper atmosphere warmer by three to 15 degrees every kilometre upwards. On average, the upper atmosphere is 50°C warmer than the surface of Pluto.

When Pluto's orbit takes it away from the Sun, the gaseous atmosphere freezes and falls to the surface.

An example of the anti-greenhouse effect visible on Titan, Saturn's largest moon

Charon

Pluto's closest moon is Charon, which was discovered in 1978. It is 19,640 kilometres from Pluto, so from Earth they look like one planet. Charon has the same 6.4 day rate of rotation as Pluto so they always present the same face to each other. On Pluto, the surface facing Charon has more methane ice than the opposite face, which has more carbon monoxide and nitrogen ice.

Charon has a diameter of 1,210 kilometres, and has a grey surface with a bluer hue than Pluto. This indicates the surface could be covered in water ice rather than nitrogen ice. It is also speculated that methane has leaked from the grasp of its weak gravity to Pluto.

An artist's impression of the New Horizons craft

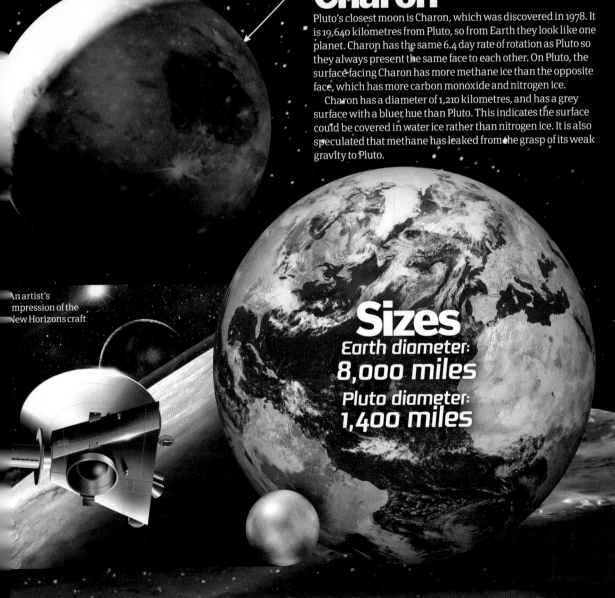

Sizes
Earth diameter:
8,000 miles
Pluto diameter:
1,400 miles

What is a planet?

Pluto's status as a planet was safe until the Nineties. This was when huge 'hot Jupiter' extra-solar planets were discovered, and objects were observed beyond the orbit of Neptune that rivalled the size of Pluto. Faced with the dilemma of defining a planet the International Astronomical Union (IAU) decided that it must be spherical, that it orbits the Sun and is clear of any planetary neighbours. Consequently, the IAU reclassified Pluto as a dwarf planet on the 24 August 2006.

An image of Pluto, with Charon visible to the bottom-left

Plutoids

Plutoids, as defined by the IAU, are dwarf planets that orbit the Sun beyond Neptune, are round, have not cleared the neighbourhood of other similar bodies, and are not satellites of another planetary body. There could be at least 70 trans-Neptunian objects (TNOs) that might be plutoids.

So far only a few have been found and named. Besides Pluto, Makemake, Haumea and Eris have been classified as plutoids. Mike Brown and his Caltech team at the Palomar Observatory discovered them all in 2005. Eris is virtually the same size as Pluto and might have been regarded as a planet before the new classification system came into effect.

DEADLY SOLAR STORMS

Discover why huge explosions from the Sun can cause major problems on Earth

Weather isn't just a phenomenon for Earth's atmosphere; there's an entirely different type of weather occurring out in the space between Earth and the Sun, thanks to changes in the latter's magnetic activity cycle. Among other things, this cycle modulates powerful outbursts from the Sun's surface that can have a direct impact on our lives. These are known as geomagnetic, or solar, storms.

Solar storms can also include a wide range of related phenomena, including auroras and electromagnetic emissions as well as solar energetic particle events, solar flares, and coronal mass ejections. Some of these have little effect on Earth.

TOP
CTS
RD SOLAR
VITY

Black hole sun
1 The Sun gets holes in its corona. These areas are darker and colder than the surrounding area and have open magnetic field lines, allowing for solar wind to develop.

Solar tsunamis
2 Solar flares generate massive, fast-moving shock waves on the corona known as Moreton waves. They can move as fast as 1,500 kilometres (932 miles) per second.

Loop the loop
3 Cooled plasma can loop 700,000km (435,000 mi) from the Sun's surface in a formation known as a solar prominence. They can break off and form coronal mass ejections.

Parker spiral
4 Thanks to the influence of solar wind, the Sun's magnetic field takes on the shape of an arithmetic spiral as it rotates and extends throughout the solar system.

Somersaulting Sun
5 During the solar maximur the Sun's poles switch – t north pole points south a vice versa – as increased sunspot activity causes it magnetic field to change.

DID YOU KNOW? Some estimate that a super solar storm could cause $2 trillion USD in damage

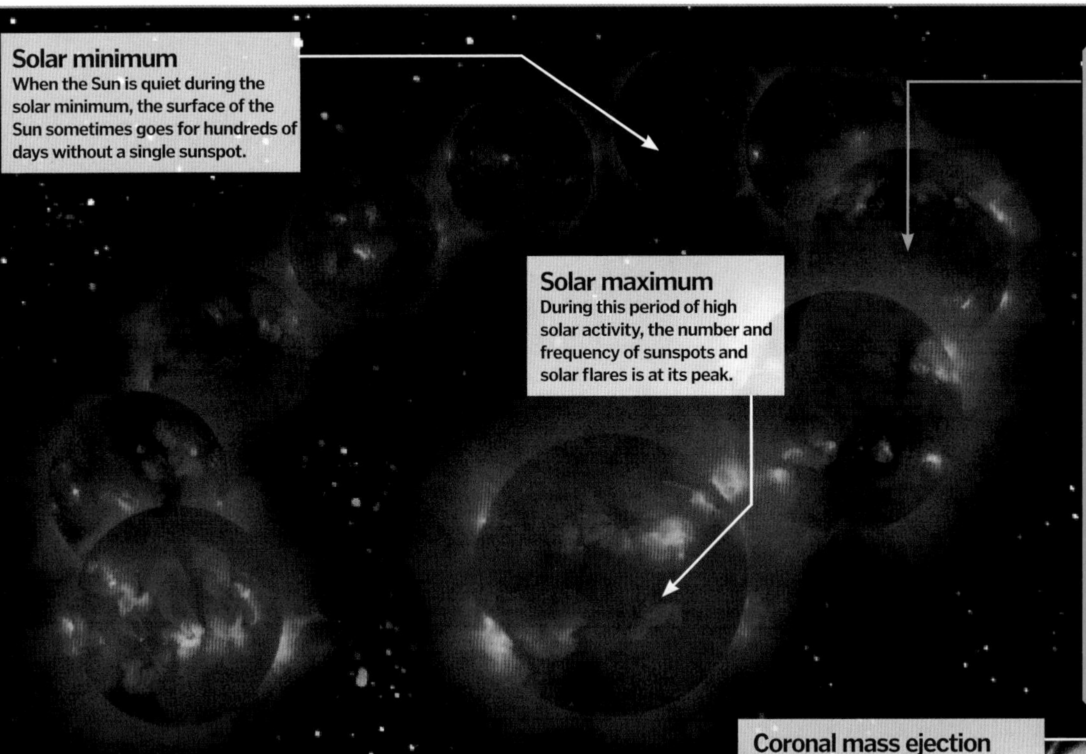

Solar minimum
When the Sun is quiet during the solar minimum, the surface of the Sun sometimes goes for hundreds of days without a single sunspot.

Solar maximum
During this period of high solar activity, the number and frequency of sunspots and solar flares is at its peak.

The solar cycle

Sunspots are temporary dark spots of intense magnetic activity on the Sun's surface. They change according to a cycle that lasts roughly 11 years. Clustered into two bands around the Sun's mid-latitudes, they move closer to the equator over the course of the cycle. During the cycle, the period of fewest sunspots is the solar minimum, while the time of greatest activity is the solar maximum. This cycle has been a quiet one, with 50 per cent less activity than predicted. However, astronomers believe we are now approaching solar maximum, with the apex occurring in 2013, and wonder if the Sun might make up for lost time with more intense solar storms.

"Large solar storms have the potential to cause serious damage"

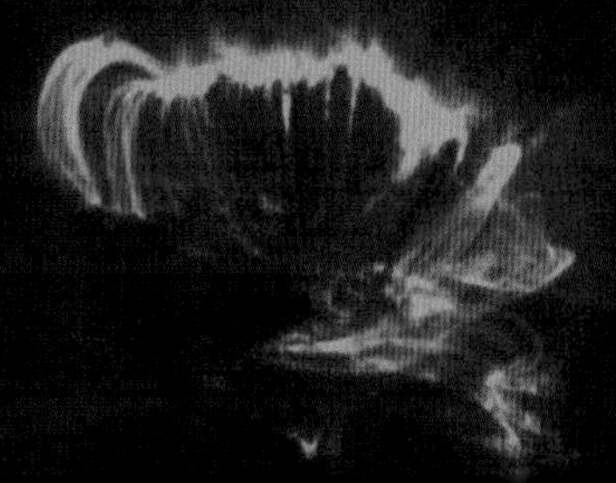

Not all solar storms affect Earth

Solar Flare

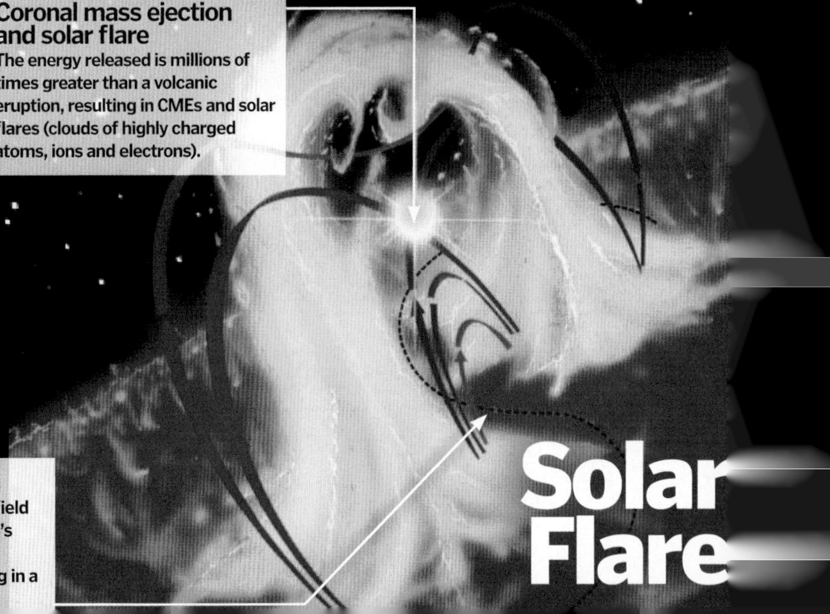

Coronal mass ejection and solar flare
The energy released is millions of times greater than a volcanic eruption, resulting in CMEs and solar flares (clouds of highly charged atoms, ions and electrons).

Magnetic field lines
North and south magnetic field lines break through the Sun's surface near sunspots and reconnect in loops, resulting in a massive burst of energy.

"A storm like the Carrington Event would have a much greater effect on our society"

Geomagnetic superstorms

Solar flares and coronal mass ejections
These two of the most powerful solar phenomena can release the same energy as millions of 100-megaton hydrogen bombs.

Solar wind
This continuous stream of charged particles from the Sun pushes matter to Earth, approximately 150 million kilometres (93 million miles).

Sun
Solar storms occur when magnetically active areas of the Sun located around sunspots are super-heated, ejecting masses of plasma, gas and charged particles.

"CMEs can release 100 billion kilograms of highly charged particles"

Super-strong

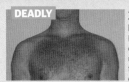

1. Ultraviolet radiation
Exposure to UV rays can cause skin cancer, including melanoma, which accounts for 75 per cent of skin cancer deaths.

2. Electromagnetic radiation
The loss of power and communications from a severe solar storm has the potential to cause numerous deaths around the world.

© Jen, 2009

3. X-Class solar flare
An astronaut standing on the Moon during these strongest of solar flares could die instantly from radiation poisoning.

DID YOU KNOW? During the Carrington Event, some telegraph operators could still send messages due to the storm's currents

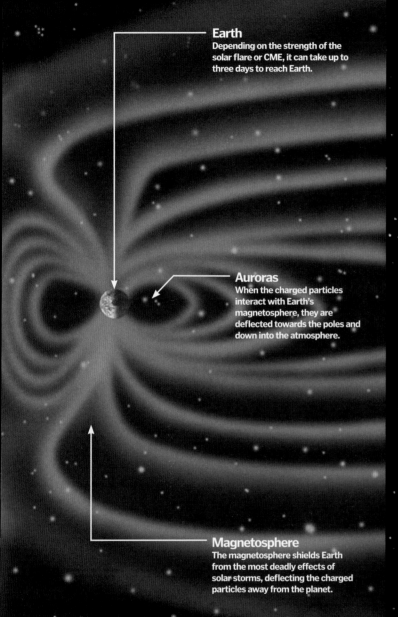

Earth
Depending on the strength of the solar flare or CME, it can take up to three days to reach Earth.

Auroras
When the charged particles interact with Earth's magnetosphere, they are deflected towards the poles and down into the atmosphere.

Magnetosphere
The magnetosphere shields Earth from the most deadly effects of solar storms, deflecting the charged particles away from the planet.

Super solar storm effects

The Carrington Event, the most severe solar storm ever recorded, wreaked havoc from 28 August to 2 September 1859. Telegraph systems in North America and Europe were disrupted by the powerful electrical currents. They electrocuted telegraph operators, while snapped wires sent out sparks and set fires. Intense red and green auroras were reported in places they'd never been seen before, including the Rocky Mountains and the Caribbean.

A storm like the Carrington Event would have a much greater effect on our society. Radios, for example, rely on reflections of waves off the ionised gas in the Earth's ionosphere. Intense radiation disrupts the gas and prevents reflection, rendering radios useless. Air heated by intense ultraviolet emissions would rise and increase the density of the gasses in low-Earth orbit, putting drag on satellites stationed there and causing them to slow down or even fall out of orbit entirely. The flood of charged ions and electrons would also cause electronic overloads, either damaging or disabling the satellites entirely. Electronic currents entering power lines could overload transformers and generators and blow them out. Travel would come to a standstill as planes would be unable to navigate and power grid failures could leave people in the dark for weeks or even months.

"Auroras were seen in places they had never been before"

The main effects of a solar superstorm
- Auroras
- Radio and TV blackouts
- Mobile phone tower failures
- Astronauts and satellites at risk
- Power grid failure
- Networks offline
- Phantom currents in power lines
- Hardware damaged
- Air travel crippled
- Banking systems down
- Exploding gas lines

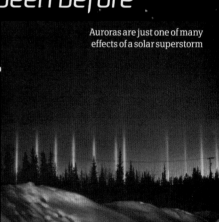

Auroras are just one of many effects of a solar superstorm

Space weather forecasts

NASA has several different spacecraft and satellites in place to report on space weather. These include two spacecraft orbiting on opposite sides of the Sun, known as STEREO (Solar Terrestrial Relations Observatory), that can provide stereoscopic images of 90 per cent of Sun's surface to catch the first signs of activity such as CMEs and solar flares.

The Solar Dynamics Observatory (SDO) gives readings of the Sun's magnetic activity, UV output and images from near Earth. Finally, the satellite known as ACE monitors solar wind and radiation, with the ability to give a 30-minute warning before a storm hits the Earth. Accurate space weather forecasts can give us the time to do things like divert planes, put satellites and communications hubs into 'safe' mode, and even identify and disable power transformers that are most at risk from solar storms.

STEREO (2)

RHESSI

Cluster–ESA (4)

SOHO–ESA

ACE

SDO CINDI AIM

WIND

Hinode–JAXA

TIMED

THEMIS (5)

TWINS (2)

Voyager (2)

Geotail–JA

IBEX

Between NASA, the US Air Force, the ESA and JAXA, there are 16 different heliophysics missions currently in operation

Image © NASA

It's the Sun, but not as we know it

■ These amazing images of the Sun are the first taken by NASA's Solar Dynamics Observatory (SDO). Taken on 30 March 2010, this false colour image traces the different gas temperatures with reds relatively cool (about 60,000 Kelvin or 107,540 F), while blues and greens are hotter (1 million Kelvin or 1,799,540 F). The SDO provides images with clarity ten times better than high-definition TV.

5 TOP FACTS
SOLAR ECLIPSES

Larger than it appears
1 In a total eclipse the Sun and the Moon appear to be the same size, due to their respective diameters and distances. The size difference is actually monumental.

Don't stare directly
2 Our retinas cannot sense any pain, so permanent vision loss caused by staring at an eclipse may not become evident until hours later, so be sensible when viewing.

'Tis the season
3 Eclipse season happens twice a year (approximately every 173 days), when the Moon crosses the orbital plane of the Earth. Each season lasts between 24 and 37 days.

A brief observation
4 Total eclipses generally take a couple of hours from start to finish, with the period of totality lasting for a few minutes and plunging an area into complete darkness.

An indirect view
5 The best and safest way to view any kind of eclipse is through a special solar filter (such as eclipse sunglasses) or possibly a pinhole camera.

DID YOU KNOW? *Ancient cultures were often frightened by solar eclipses and attributed them to supernatural beings*

This is an image of the Moon's transit across the Sun, taken from NASA's STEREO-B spacecraft

Solar eclipse

Solar eclipses occur when the Moon passes between the Earth and the Sun

During a solar eclipse, the Moon casts shadows on the Earth known as umbra or penumbra. The umbra is the darkest part of the shadow, while the penumbra is the area where part of the Moon is blocking the Sun. Partial eclipses happen when the Sun and Moon are not in perfect alignment – only the penumbra of the Moon's shadow passes over the surface of the Earth. In a total eclipse, the umbra touches the Earth's surface.

There are also annular eclipses, in which both the Sun and the Moon are in alignment but the Moon appears to be slightly smaller than the Sun. The Sun appears as a bright ring, or annulus, around the Moon's profile. The umbra is still in line with a region on the Earth's surface, but the distance is too great to actually touch the surface of the Earth.

Depending on your location, an eclipse may appear to be any of the three possible types. For example, if your region lies in the path of totality, you will experience a total eclipse, while people in other regions may only see a partial eclipse. Solar eclipses occur between two and five times per year, with most of these being partial or annual eclipses.

Total eclipses have four phases. First contact occurs when you first notice the shadow of the Moon on the Sun's surface. During second contact, you will observe a phenomenon called Baily's beads, when sunlight shines jaggedly through the rugged peaks and valleys of the Moon's surface. When one bead of light is left, it appears as a single dot in the ring, known as the diamond ring effect. Next, the Moon completely covers the Sun's surface with only a corona of light showing. The final stage is third contact, when the Moon's shadow moves away from the Sun.

The solar eclipse is a truly breathtaking sight

The view of the shadow cast by the Moon during a solar eclipse in 1999, taken by the Mir space station

When the Moon blocks out the Sun
The relationship between the Sun, Moon and Earth during an eclipse is geometric

1. Sun
The Sun and the Moon often appear to be the same size, because the ratio between their diameters is about the same as the ratio between their respective distances from Earth.

2. Moon
The magnitude of an eclipse is the ratio between the angular diameters of the Moon and Sun. During a total eclipse this ratio is one or greater.

3. Umbra
The umbra is the central area of the shadow of the Moon. If this area passes over you, you'll see a total eclipse. The sky will be completely dark.

4. Penumbra
The penumbra is the outer part of the Moon's shadow. You will see a partial eclipse if this part passes over you and the sky will only be partially dark.

5. Earth
In an annular solar eclipse, the umbra never touches the Earth because the Moon is too far away in its orbit. The Sun appears as a bright ring around the Moon's profile.

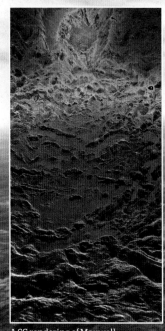

A CG rendering of Maxwell Montes's eastern slope

A re-creation of Maxwell Montes based on data from the Magellan radar-mapping spacecraft

Cleopatra crater

This impact crater on Venus is found on the Ishtar Terra mountain range on Maxwell Montes. It stretches 100 kilometres (62 miles) in diameter and has two discernible rings inside. At first it was thought to be the remains of a volcano, but new research (and the discovery of the rings) indicate it was formed from a meteorite impact. Its dark centre is covered in a fine dust, while the outer ring is made of the ejected debris from the initial impact. It's thought to have formed in the last few centuries.

Maxwell Montes

We take a closer look at the highest peaks on Venus

Maxwell Montes is a giant mountain range located on Ishtar Terra, which is the most northern of the two major highlands on Venus. It is a part of the Lakshmi Planum, a large plain that likely resulted from smooth lava flows on the surface of the planet. Maxwell Montes rises to an elevation of 11 kilometres (6.8 miles) at the highest point and is 797 kilometres (495 miles) in diameter. It has very steep slopes, particularly on the chain's western side, likely a result of how the lava flowed in the past.

Venus is the hottest planet in the solar system. Its incredibly high surface temperature can be accounted for by its dense atmosphere, which retains almost all of the sunlight that passes through it. However, the presence of dormant volcanoes like Maxwell Montes suggests that Venus was once a volcanically active planet, and indeed these volcanoes may have been major contributors to the thick atmosphere that currently surrounds our closest neighbour. Precisely when Venus was volcanically active in its 4.7 billion year lifetime is currently a matter of debate.

Volcanic
The terrain of Venus is littered with signs of dormant volcanoes like Maxwell Montes

Impacts
Despite its thick atmosphere, many meteorites have hit the surface and created craters

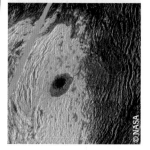

Halley's Comet

What is this fiery ball and why does it return to the night sky?

Comets are dirty snowballs made of dust and ice left behind when our solar system formed. Halley's Comet is the best-known short period comet – a comet that has orbited around the Sun more than once in recorded history.

Comets' orbits can be tilted at a large angle relative to the orbits of the planets. Halley's Comet's orbit is so tilted it looks to orbit backwards compared to the planets. Its orbit is also very elongated so the distance between Halley's Comet and the Sun changes dramatically as it travels.

When the comet is far from the Sun, it's a frozen ball called a nucleus. As it comes closer, it heats up and spews out dust and gas to form a glowing cloud – the coma – and long tail. Each time Halley's Comet returns towards the Sun, it loses more ice until, eventually, there will be too little to form a tail.

We'll have to wait until 2061 to see this sight again

DID YOU KNOW? Over the centuries, Halley's Comet has been blamed for earthquakes, the births of two-headed animals and even the Black Death.

5 TOP FACTS
COMETS

1 Dinosaur extinction
A comet hitting the Earth 200 million years ago could have cleared the way for dinosaurs to rule the world until another comet wiped them out 135 million years later.

2 Lightweight
A person weighing 45kg on Earth would weigh 0.005kg on a comet and could jump off into space. A comet's small size gives it little gravity to hold objects down.

3 Gushing gas
Comet Hale-Bopp could have lost 250 tons of dust and gas every second as it swung by the Sun in early 1997 – more than 50 times greater than most comets.

4 Time capsule
Comets could hold a deep-frozen record of the early solar system. Scientists think they formed 5 billion years ago and have remained almost perpetually frozen since.

5 Seeding life
Dust collected from comet Wild 2 in 2004 contained a chemical, glycine, used by living organisms. Scientists think some building blocks for life could have arrived from space on comets.

What is the Kármán line?

Want to turn from an aeronaut into an astronaut? Just cross the Kármán line

The Kármán line is an official boundary between the Earth's atmosphere and space, lying 100km (62 miles) above sea level. Fédération Aéronautique Internationale (FAI), the governing body for air sports and aeronautical world records, recognises it as the line where aeronautics ends and astronautics begins.

The line is named after aeronautical scientist Theodore von Kármán. He calculated that approximately 100km above sea level it was more efficient for vehicles to orbit than fly. The air thins with increasing altitude and aircraft rely on air flowing over their wings to keep them aloft, so must move faster. Above 100km they'd have to move faster than the velocity satellites orbit around the Earth. Thin air also explains why the Earth's sky looks blue and space is black. Atmospheric gases scatter blue light more than other colours, turning the sky blue. At higher altitudes, less air exists to scatter light.

The layers in Earth's atmosphere

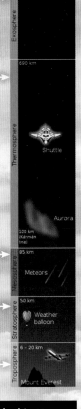

Exosphere
Many satellites orbit in the exosphere – the highest atmospheric layer. It extends to 10,000km above sea level and gets thinner and thinner until it becomes outer space

Thermosphere
'Thermos' means hot. Air molecules in this layer can be heated to over 1,000°C by the Sun's incoming energy, but we would feel cold because there is so little air

Mesosphere
Meteorites entering the Earth's atmosphere normally burn up in the mesosphere, the coldest layer in the atmosphere that lies 50 to 80km above sea level

Stratosphere
The stratosphere stretches from around 12km to 50km above sea level. This layer contains the ozone layer, which shields us from the Sun's potentially harmful ultraviolet radiation

Troposphere
The atmosphere's lowest layer contains 75 per cent of its mass and almost all its weather. It varies from around 8km high at the poles to 20km over the equator

10,000 km — Exosphere
690 km — Thermosphere
Shuttle
Aurora
100 km (Kármán line)
85 km — Mesosphere
Meteors
50 km — Stratosphere
Weather balloon
6 – 20 km — Troposphere
Mount Everest

DID YOU KNOW? The first man-made object to cross the Kármán line was a German V-2 rocket during a 1944 test flight.

"There are five different instruments on board Suomi NPP, but by far the most important is the VIIRS"

Imaging Earth

How are iconic pictures of our planet like the Blue Marble photographed?

Taking an image of Earth is no easy feat. Since NASA's Explorer 6 satellite first took a blurry photo of our world back in 1959, methods and techniques to snap that perfect picture of our home have come on leaps and bounds, and the images often become very famous. In fact, 2002's Blue Marble image was so popular that it eventually ended up as the default background on Apple's iPhone.

The first Blue Marble image of the entire Earth – coined for apparently portraying our planet as a marble-like object – was taken by Apollo 17 astronauts in 1972 as they made their way back from a mission. The image they took 40 years ago was just a single snapshot, but today image-editing software such as Photoshop is used to enhance the picture, though great pains are gone to not to detract from the reality of the shot.

NASA's most recent Earth portrait, dubbed 'Blue Marble 2012', was taken by an Earth observation satellite called Suomi NPP. For the satellite to shoot this image technicians on the ground had to take a picture of Earth six times as the satellite passed over one point, allowing them to combine several layers into one image.

There are five different instruments on board Suomi NPP, but by far the most important for this task is the Visible/Infrared Imager Radiometer Suite (VIIRS). This scanning radiometer can collect visible and infrared imagery of Earth in addition to measurements of the planet's atmosphere, land mass and oceans.

The image was taken in January 2012 and compiled by NASA scientist Norman Kuring. The satellite flies in a polar orbit at a height of 824 kilometres (512 miles). However, the perspective of the image is from an altitude of 12,743 kilometres (7,918 miles) at a point ten degrees south latitude and 45 degrees east longitude, owing to the nature of the composite image.

For a scale representation of how far Suomi NPP is from the surface, imagine our planet as a basketball. The Earth has a diameter of about 12,756 kilometres (7,926 miles), while a basketball has a diameter of 25 centimetres (ten inches). If you hold the basketball 1.5 centimetres (half an inch) from your face, that's how close Suomi NPP is to Earth. The width of each section of Earth the VIIRS images as it flies over is about 3,001 kilometres (1,865 miles). In comparison, the Apollo 17 astronauts who captured the first Blue Marble were about 76 centimetres (30 inches) away from the basketball (45,000 kilometres/28,000 miles from Earth).

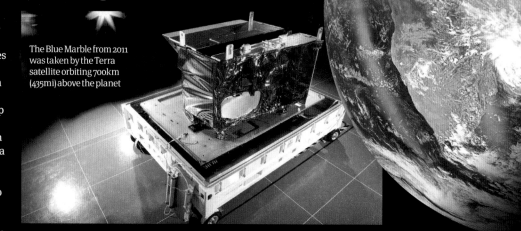

The Blue Marble from 2011 was taken by the Terra satellite orbiting 700km (435mi) above the planet

Red
671 nanometre band

Green
551 nanometre band

Blue
443 nanometre band

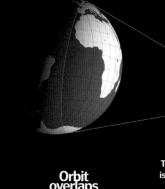

Orbit overlaps

Bands
Images in red, blue and green bands are combined to produce an image of a strip of the Earth

Perspective
The perspective of the image is from a distance of 2,743km (7,918mi), although Suomi orbits at a height of only 824km (512mi)

Sunlight
The four vertical hazy lines are the reflection of sunlight off the oceans from each single image

Clouds
Each part of the composition, such as clouds and the oceans, was added in layers to produce the best image possible

Compile
By overlapping each strip with one another, a complete image of

MOST-VIEWED IMAGE

3.1m

The Blue Marble 2012 image of Earth's western hemisphere racked up 3.1 million views on Flickr in just a week upon its release in January 2012, making it one of the most-viewed images of all time.

DID YOU KNOW? In 2004's Next Generation mission to image Earth's surface each hi-res pixel represented 500m on the ground

NASA claims that this is the most high-resolution image of Earth ever taken

Images through the ages

1959
Explorer 6
This is the first-ever image of Earth taken from space. It was captured by the Explorer 6 satellite on 14 August 1959, from a height of about 27,000 kilometres (17,000 miles). Our capability to image Earth has come a long way since.

1972
Apollo 17
The first 'Blue Marble' image of Earth was taken by astronauts on the Apollo 17 mission. They snapped the image in one take as they were on their way back to the surface.

1990
Pale Blue Dot
This famous image of Earth was captured by the Voyager 1 spacecraft from Saturn at the behest of the late astronomer Carl Sagan, who coined it the 'Pale Blue Dot'.

2011
Messenger
NASA's Messenger spacecraft took this image of the Earth and Moon from Mercury. The two are so close that they look a little like a binary star.

2011
Juno
This picture of the Earth and Moon was taken by the solar-powered Juno spacecraft en route to Jupiter. It is expected to reach the gas giant by 2016, where it will be taking many more images.

"True solar time is based on the apparent motion of the Sun as we observe it"

Day and night, night and day

This seemingly simple phenomenon that we call night and day is anything but simple

© NASA

What we term 'night and day' is a phenomenon known as rotation. The Earth rotates around its axis, an imaginary line that extends from its North Pole to its South Pole, once every 24 hours. This axis of our planet is tipped at an angle of about 23.5 degrees from the vertical.

As the Earth rotates, the part of it illuminated by the Sun experiences daytime, while the dark part experiences night. When the Sun appears above the horizon in the east and sinks below it in west, we call this sunrise and sunset. But this is an illusion created by the Earth's counter-clockwise rotation – because of course the Sun isn't actually rising or sinking at all.

True solar time is based on the apparent motion of the Sun as we observe it, as with a sundial. This measurement varies from day to day because of the Earth's elliptical orbit – it rotates faster when closer to the Sun and slower when further away from it. The tilt of Earth's axis also means that true solar days are shorter at some times of the year and longer at others. A mean solar day is an average so that all of our days are of equal length. This is the time we use to set our clocks. Sidereal time takes into account how long it takes the Earth to rotate with respect to the apparent movement of the stars instead of the Sun. A sidereal day is about four minutes shorter than a mean solar day. Astronomers use sidereal time to determine the placement of the stars in the sky at any given time.

Although a rotation of the Earth takes 24 hours, that doesn't mean that daytime and nighttime are each 12 hours long. On average, nights are shorter than days. This is due to the Sun's apparent size in our sky as well as the way that our atmosphere refracts sunlight. The lengths of our days and nights depend on our location on the Earth's surface as well as the time of year.

Days and nights around the world

Depending on the time of year and where you live, the length of days and nights can vary. These shifts occur during specific moments of the year known as equinoxes and solstices. The equinoxes occur around 20 March and again around 22 September. This is when the Earth's axis is tilted neither towards nor away from the Sun. Solstices occur around 21 June and 21 December, when the Earth's axis is most inclined either toward (in June) or away (in December) from the Sun.

Locations around the equator experience the most even night and day lengths, with increases in variation spreading outwards to the tropic of Cancer at the northernmost point and the tropic of Capricorn at the southernmost point. The differences are the most extreme at the poles. Once a year, the North Pole is tilted towards the Sun and experiences a day of 24 hours of sunlight. During this time, the South Pole has 24 hours of darkness. The reverse happens six months later.

The North Pole experiences days of complete darkness, and days of complete daylight

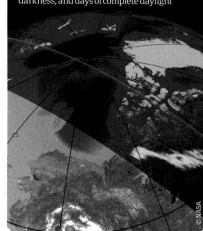

© NASA

Day and night explained

This image shows the Earth's axis is tilted towards the Sun during the summer, or northern solstice. This occurs around 21 June and changes the lengths of nights and days depending on where you live. The five major circles of latitude mark the shifts in length.

Rotation axis

N

Sun never sets

NIGHT

Long days

DAY

SUNLIGHT

Equal days and nights

Sun never rises

Short days

S

1. Arctic Circle
Above the Arctic Circle, the region around the North Pole experiences a 24-hour day of sunlight during the summer solstice

2. Tropic of Cancer
During summer solstice, the area around the tropic of Cancer experiences much longer days than nights due to the extreme tilt of the Earth's axis towards the Sun

3. Equator
The region around the equator is the only place on Earth where days and nights are generally the same length of time regardless of the time of year

4. Tropic of Capricorn
Below the tropic of Capricorn, the region has much shorter days than nights

5. Antarctic Circle
The Antarctic Circle marks a region that experiences a 24-hour period, or "day", of darkness due to the summer solstice

In the event of reversal: finding your bearings

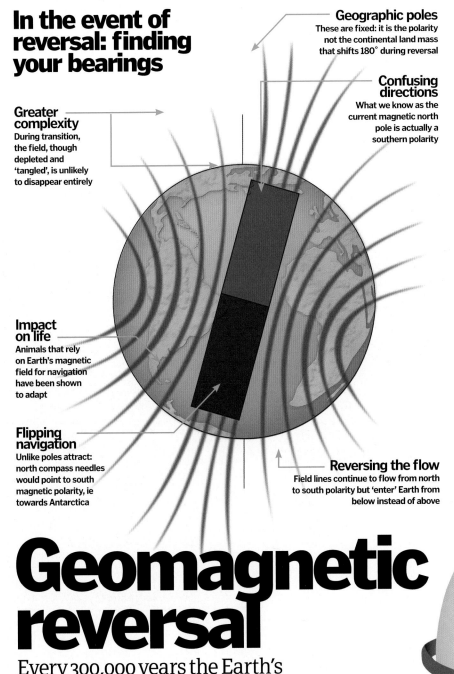

Geographic poles
These are fixed: it is the polarity not the continental land mass that shifts 180° during reversal

Greater complexity
During transition, the field, though depleted and 'tangled', is unlikely to disappear entirely

Confusing directions
What we know as the current magnetic north pole is actually a southern polarity

Impact on life
Animals that rely on Earth's magnetic field for navigation have been shown to adapt

Flipping navigation
Unlike poles attract: north compass needles would point to south magnetic polarity, ie towards Antarctica

Reversing the flow
Field lines continue to flow from north to south polarity but 'enter' Earth from below instead of above

Geomagnetic reversal

Every 300,000 years the Earth's magnetic poles switch places and we're overdue a change! So just what causes this to happen...

A geomagnetic reversal is a change in the orientation of Earth's magnetic field where magnetic north and south become interchanged. This occurs as Earth's magnetic field derives from the fluid motion in its outer-core, with heat from the inner-core causing this 'fluid' to rise. It is the currents that flow in this electrically conductive iron-rich fluid that generate the magnetic field, so when these change, so does the field's direction.

On average, every 300,000 years Earth's magnetic poles switch places; a process

historically described and dated by the orientation of magnetite crystals set in place by cooling volcanic rocks. It is thought, though, that every few thousand years or so the fluid outer-core attempts to reverse, but that the solid inner-core can only change by diffusion and, because of this, acts as a braking mechanism. When it does actually occur, lengthy falls in field intensity tend to precede a reversal.

Interestingly, while current field strength is relatively high, it has continued to fall for approximately the past 2,000 years.

What is the Coriolis effect?

How our windy atmosphere gets left behind thanks to this deceptive force

It's actually all an illusion. The winds blowing in Earth's atmosphere are affected by the Coriolis effect, though that's somewhat hard to see. You may be wondering what the Coriolis effect is? It's a visual effect seen, for example, when a ball rolls forward on a rotating platform, and you're on the receiving end. The ball appears to curve on the platform, when actually it's rolling in a straight line.

The Earth's atmosphere has continual rising layers of hot air, predominately from the equator. The hot air later cools and settles back down to Earth, moving away from the equator to both the North and South poles. This huge travelling flow of air moves in a straight path, but as the Earth rotates easterly, the air, as it moves from hot to cold, is left behind and falls somewhere further west. If the atmosphere was visual, the winds would most likely appear to be bending. ✿

On the move
The intended path (dotted arrow) is not where the winds end up (curved arrows)

Rotating Earth
As Earth spins to the east, the rising hot air in the atmosphere lands somewhere unexpected

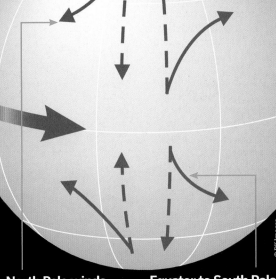

North Pole winds
As winds travel from the North Pole to the equator, their path looks curved but they move straight

Equator to South Pole
From the equator to the South Pole the winds actually end up ahead of themselves as the Earth moves

© DK Images

053

How the seas

Get out your flashlight and a beach ball, it's time to talk about tilt

The Earth is a wonky planet. Every year we make a complete near-circular revolution around the Sun, but every day our planet spins around a lopsided axis. This imaginary line that runs through the centre of the planet from the North Pole to the South Pole is tilted at a 23.5° angle, and this wonky tilt is the reason for the seasons.

During June and July in the northern hemisphere, the North Pole is tilted toward the Sun and South Pole tilted away. This means that solar radiation hits the northern hemisphere "head on" and is absorbed in a more concentrated area. Because the southern hemisphere is angled away from the Sun, the same amount of solar radiation is spread across a much larger surface area.

But differences in solar intensity aren't enough to create summer and winter. The tilt of the axis also creates radical differences in the length of solar exposure, what we define as daylight. If we go back to our June and July example, the northern hemisphere is directly facing the Sun, which means the Sun carves a high path across the sky, creating longer daylight hours. In the southern hemisphere, the Sun travels much closer to the horizon, which limits daylight hours significantly.

The combination of longer days and concentrated sunlight gives us summer. Shorter days and dispersed solar energy gives us winter. Autumn and spring mark the transitional periods when days are getting longer or shorter and temperature variations tend to be less extreme. ✿

3. Summer solstice
On roughly 21 June, the North Pole tilts the closest to the Sun, bathing the northern hemisphere in summer and the southern hemisphere in winter

2. Tilted axis
The seasons are powered by the angle of the Earth's axis, which tilts 23.5 degrees away from being perfectly perpendicular with its orbital plane

1. Revolution
The Earth travels in an elliptical orbit around the Sun, but the path is nearly circular, meaning our distance from the Sun is relatively constant year-round

1. The tropics
All year long, the region within the tropics of Cancer and Capricorn receives the most direct and intense sunlight

2. Concentrated surface area
Since the Sun's rays strike the region around the equator at nearly a 90° angle, the intensity of the radiation is concentrated on a relatively small surface area

3. Scattered surface area
Near the poles, the Sun's angle of incidence is much lower, meaning solar radiation scatters across a much larger surface area, losing its intensity

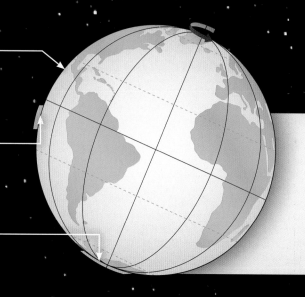

5 TOP FACTS
SEASONS ON OTHER PLANETS

Long summer
1 Because Neptune is so far away from the Sun, it takes over 164 Earth years to complete a revolution. That makes its summer around 40 years long.

"Tropical" Venus
2 Since Venus' axis only tilts at a 3° angle, all of its seasons are roughly the same, which results in a rather steamy 750K all year round.

Serious tilt
3 Uranus spins on an axis tilted at 98°, and much of the planet is bathed in continuous darkness or continuous light for 20 years at a time.

Springtime on Uranus
4 There are no April showers on Uranus. When spring arrives after 20 years of darkness, the warming atmosphere generates violent storms.

Long days
5 Due to its slow rotation on its axis and rapid movement around the Sun, a day on Mercury is the equivalent of 176 Earth days.

DID YOU KNOW? *Contrary to common sense, the Earth is closest to the Sun (147,300,000km) on or around 3 January*

ons work

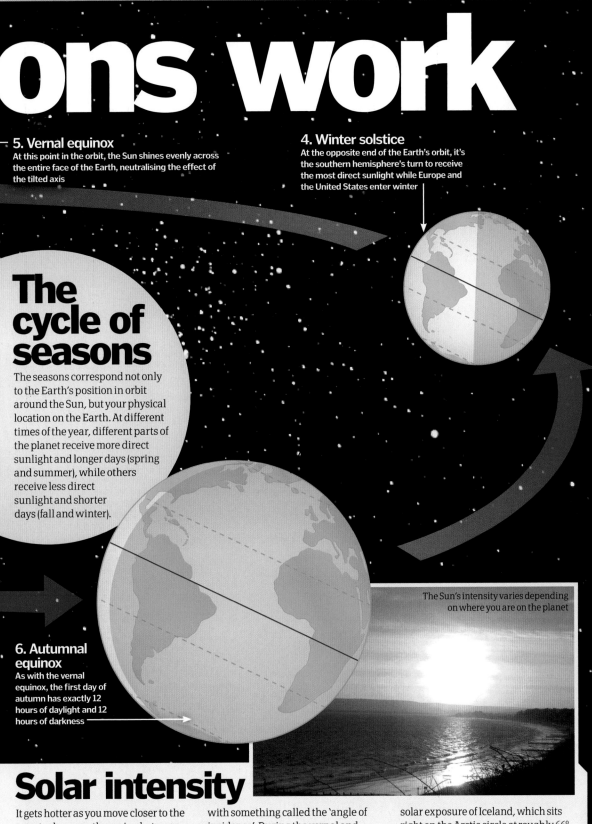

5. Vernal equinox
At this point in the orbit, the Sun shines evenly across the entire face of the Earth, neutralising the effect of the tilted axis

4. Winter solstice
At the opposite end of the Earth's orbit, it's the southern hemisphere's turn to receive the most direct sunlight while Europe and the United States enter winter

The cycle of seasons
The seasons correspond not only to the Earth's position in orbit around the Sun, but your physical location on the Earth. At different times of the year, different parts of the planet receive more direct sunlight and longer days (spring and summer), while others receive less direct sunlight and shorter days (fall and winter).

6. Autumnal equinox
As with the vernal equinox, the first day of autumn has exactly 12 hours of daylight and 12 hours of darkness

The Sun's intensity varies depending on where you are on the planet

Solar intensity
It gets hotter as you move closer to the equator because the region between the tropic of Cancer and the tropic of Capricorn receives more direct and concentrated solar radiation.

The reason for this is not because the tropics are 'closer' to the Sun than other parts of the planet. It has to do with something called the 'angle of incidence'. During the vernal and autumnal equinoxes, the Sun's rays strike the equator at a precise 90° angle. Since the solar radiation rains down on the Earth so directly, its intensity is concentrated in a relatively small area. Compare this with the solar exposure of Iceland, which sits right on the Arctic circle at roughly 66° north of the equator. During the autumnal equinox, the Sun's rays hit Iceland on a much shallower angle of 70°, spreading their radiation across a much larger surface area, thereby decreasing their intensity.

Solstice vs equinox
The winter solstice is commonly referred to as the "shortest day of the year". Although 21 December is still 24 hours long, it has the fewest hours of sunlight. On this day, the North Pole is tilted the furthest from the Sun, causing the Sun to trace a low path in the sky. As the months pass, the Sun's course drifts upward until we reach the vernal equinox, a day with exactly 12 hours of light and 12 hours of darkness. Around 21 June, the North Pole tilts closest to the Sun, the Sun rides high in the sky and we have the summer solstice, the longest day of the year. As the Sun's path sinks back toward the horizon, we reach the autumnal equinox, the second time all year when day and night are perfectly equal.

Here comes the Sun... flower

Seasons at the top of the world
For people living at the equator, seasons are virtually meaningless. The closer you are to the equator, the less your weather is affected by the tilt of the Earth. If you tilt a globe back and forth, the top and bottom appear to move further away from you, while the middle will remain relatively central.

In high-latitude regions the differences between seasons are extreme. In the dead of winter in northern Norway, the northern hemisphere is tilted so far away from the Sun that it doesn't peak over the horizon for two months. In the middle of summer, the Sun travels directly overhead, tracing a loop through the sky that holds back the night for 2.5 months.

"Our entire solar system is entombed in an almost perfect sphere of ice"

How ocean tides work

Gravitational forces tip ocean waters like a bathtub

You're sitting on a beach, cooking a barbecue with the family. The Sun sets in the distance. You look around and – like the famous scene from *Chitty Chitty Bang Bang* – you're surrounded by water. The phenomenon of ocean tides is caused by gravitational forces as the Earth moves around the Sun, and the Moon moves around the Earth. ✿

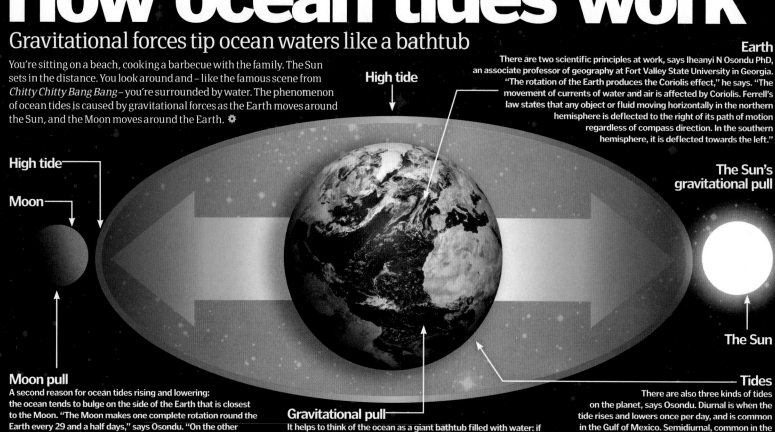

High tide

Earth
There are two scientific principles at work, says Iheanyi N Osondu PhD, an associate professor of geography at Fort Valley State University in Georgia. "The rotation of the Earth produces the Coriolis effect," he says. "The movement of currents of water and air is affected by Coriolis. Ferrell's law states that any object or fluid moving horizontally in the northern hemisphere is deflected to the right of its path of motion regardless of compass direction. In the southern hemisphere, it is deflected towards the left."

High tide

Moon

The Sun's gravitational pull

The Sun

Moon pull
A second reason for ocean tides rising and lowering: the ocean tends to bulge on the side of the Earth that is closest to the Moon. "The Moon makes one complete rotation round the Earth every 29 and a half days," says Osondu. "On the other hand, the Sun also influences the tides. It should, however, be noted that the Moon has a greater influence on tides than the Sun because it is nearer, even though the Sun is much larger."

Gravitational pull
It helps to think of the ocean as a giant bathtub filled with water: if you tipped the bathtub to one side, the water would rise. In the ocean, the water levels change when gravity pulls water to one side of the Earth, which causes the water level to lower on the other side

Tides
There are also three kinds of tides on the planet, says Osondu. Diurnal is when the tide rises and lowers once per day, and is common in the Gulf of Mexico. Semidiurnal, common in the Atlantic coasts, has two similar tides per day. Mixed tides, where there are two dissimilar tides per day, are common in the Pacific coasts

Ice haloes are fairly common in cold climates

© Doug Wilson

Ice haloes

How do these rings of light form?

Ice haloes are a fairly common sight in cold climates, where the Sun or Moon appears to be surrounded by a ring of light. The haloes are caused by millions of tiny ice crystals contained in high, thin clouds in the troposphere. Each crystal acts like a lens, and refracts (or bends) light from the Sun or Moon at 22 degrees, which corresponds to the radius of the halo, subsequently causing the circular band of light to form.

Each ice crystal has the same hexagonal shape, so they refract the incoming light at the same rate, producing an almost perfect circle. However, the reason for the formation of ice crystals in some clouds but not others remains something of a mystery. ✿

How orbits work

Why does the Moon not crash into Earth?

Orbits work because two bodies of mass are attracted to each other with force and that for every action there is an equal and opposite reaction, as explained in Newton's Third Law of Motion. In terms of orbits, this means that when one object rotates around another of a higher mass it experiences continuous free fall towards the larger body, undertaking a constant gravitational acceleration towards the greater object that deflects what would otherwise be its straight-line motion into a curved trajectory. In essence, any orbit is maintained by the direction of its motion and acceleration, both of which alter constantly, thereby producing its curved orbit.

All closed orbits are elliptical in shape, the degree of which varies from a perfect circle to a stretched egg form, and is referred to as an orbit's eccentricity. Many of our solar system's orbits – such as our moon's around Earth – are pretty circular with a low eccentricity. Here, both bodies rotate around the joint centre of mass – which in the Earth/Moon relationship is deep inside the Earth – and the lesser body remains relatively circular throughout its orbit. Others, such as Pluto's orbit around the Sun, are highly elliptical and elongated, with a large gap between its perigee (its closest point of approach) and its apogee (the point where it is farthest from the orbit's focus). In the case of Pluto and its own moon Charon, while Charon follows a largely circular orbit due to its large size and close proximity (it is roughly half Pluto's size), the mass centre of the two objects is not within Pluto but out in space between the two.

An easy way to understand orbits is to imagine a cannonball fired out of a cannon from the top of an impossibly high mountain – a visual image first used by Isaac Newton in the 18th Century. Once fired the cannonball moves sideways and falls towards the Earth (the central body), however it has so much tangential velocity that it misses the central object as it curves away beneath it due to its circular shape and continues to fall indefinitely, caught in an equilibrium sustained by its velocity and the pull of gravity. ✿

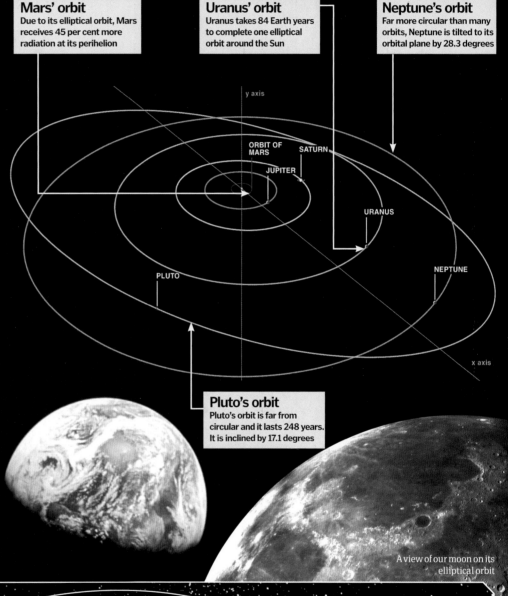

Mars' orbit
Due to its elliptical orbit, Mars receives 45 per cent more radiation at its perihelion

Uranus' orbit
Uranus takes 84 Earth years to complete one elliptical orbit around the Sun

Neptune's orbit
Far more circular than many orbits, Neptune is tilted to its orbital plane by 28.3 degrees

y axis

ORBIT OF MARS   SATURN

JUPITER

URANUS

PLUTO

NEPTUNE

x axis

Pluto's orbit
Pluto's orbit is far from circular and it lasts 248 years. It is inclined by 17.1 degrees

A view of our moon on its elliptical orbit

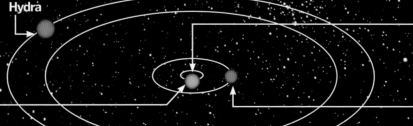

The Pluto system

The orbits around Pluto

Hydra

Nix

Pluto's orbit
Pluto orbits around its mass centre and around the Sun – the latter is highly eccentric

Barycentre
The barycentre is a system's mass centre. Pluto's is out of the planet in space

Charon's orbit
Charon is a large moon compared to Pluto and orbits it every 6.38 Earth days

1. Wax and wane
Waxing is when the Moon is growing in the first half of a lunar month. Waning is when it's shrinking away again in preparation for the next full moon. It's called a crescent when it's less than half illuminated and gibbous otherwise

2. Crescent moon
On the equator the crescent moon looks like a smile. In the southern hemisphere the Moon appears upside-down so it would be a reversed mirror image of what we see

3. Distance
The Moon is on average 250,000 miles away and it takes light 1.52 seconds to reflect from its surface to the Earth. Travelling by car, however, light would take 130 days of solid motoring

4. Revolutions
It only takes 27 days and seven hours for the Moon to make a full revolution of the Earth. Since the lunar month is longer at 29 days the various phases of the Moon can occur any time in the calendar month

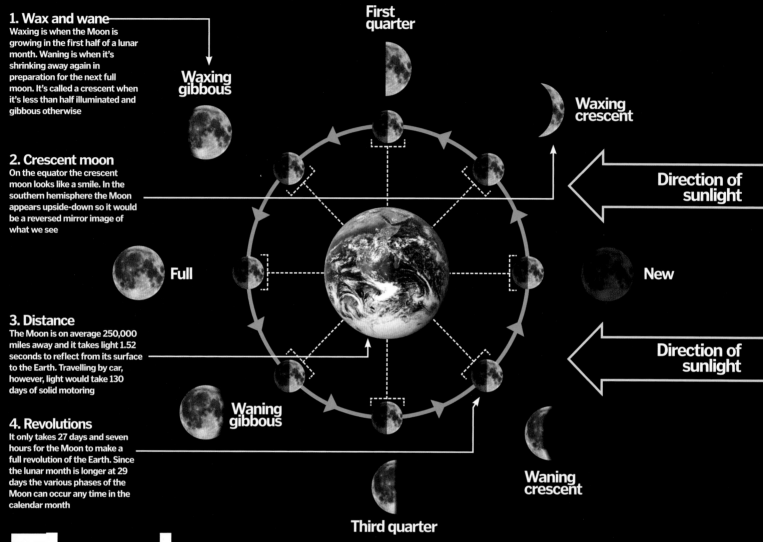

First quarter

Waxing gibbous

Waxing crescent

Direction of sunlight

Full

New

Waning gibbous

Direction of sunlight

Waning crescent

Third quarter

The phases of the Moon explained

Understanding the constantly morphing Moon is all a matter of perspective...

A full moon is a majestic sight, and one surrounded with all manner of superstition and romantic implications. The full moon is just one of eight phases during a lunar month, however. During this cycle (lasting 29.5 days) it changes constantly, moving from a fully lit disc to an invisible planetary body and back again. But what causes this cycle and how do we decipher the difference between a waxing gibbous moon from a waning crescent? It's all a matter of perspective, and understanding this geometry is helped by a simple clock analogy.

Let's pretend that the Earth is at the very centre of a massive celestial clock face. From this central

point the Moon would sit on the hour hand travelling on its lunar orbit around the Earth. Constantly shining in towards the Earth from the three o'clock position is the Sun – it's the Sun that lights the face of the Moon so we can see it, except when it's in the three o'clock position. When the Moon is right between the Sun and the Earth no sunlight touches the face of the Moon that faces us. This is called a new moon and its apparent invisibility marks the beginning and the end of a lunar cycle. As the Moon makes its way backwards – it travels anticlockwise around the Earth – from three o'clock towards half-past one a thin, waxing crescent moon grows in size as a small sliver of

sunlight reaches a part of the Moon seen from Earth. Once it reaches 12 o'clock the full right side of the Moon is illuminated – this is the first quarter moon. When the Moon reaches the half-past ten position the lit portion of the Moon face is growing further still – this is known as a waxing gibbous moon.

At nine o'clock the Moon is exactly opposite the Earth from the Sun meaning its entire face can be seen, but from this point on in the lunar month the Moon is said to be waning from a gibbous moon, to a third quarter and then to a waning crescent moon before finally disappearing again at the end of its lunar cycle. ✿

THE
STATS
THE MOON

| AVERAGE DISTANCE FROM EARTH | 384,400km | PERIGEE (CLOSEST TO EARTH) | 363,300km |
| APOGEE (FARTHEST FROM EARTH) | 405,500km | EQUATORIAL RADIUS | 1,737.4km |

DID YOU KNOW? *In ancient times, it was wrongly believed that the Moon was magnified by atmospheric phenomena*

Close enough to touch?
Not quite...

The Moon Illusion

Why does the Moon appear so unfeasibly large near the horizon?

Now, this one's trickier than it sounds. We've all seen how a rising or setting moon on the horizon appears larger than an overhead moon, and yet scientists and psychologists still can't agree on or understand why it occurs – even NASA can't fathom it.

There are two main theories behind what's been dubbed the 'Moon Illusion'. We know the size of the Moon doesn't actually change so we can safely assume that it's a trick of the mind. One idea suggests the viewer instinctively attempts to judge the distance to the rising moon (it's hard to comprehend 400,000km) based on visual objects, such as trees and houses in the distance. These objects seem near the moon, giving a distorted point of reference, making it appear bigger. However, this theory can be called into question as pilots have also seen the illusion despite no point of reference against the ground.

The second theory has to do with the fact that we tend to think of the sky as a flattened dome, rather than the hemisphere it is, and therefore perceive things overhead (birds and planes) as much lower, or nearer than the things we see on the horizon. And so although the Moon may well be the same size whether it's above your head or off on the horizon, because you believe it is farther away at the horizon you perceive the Moon to be much larger. Either way, your brain has been tricked. ⚙

The Ponzo track

The theory that the objects in the foreground affect how far away we believe the Moon to be can be comprehended by looking at Mario Ponzo's railway track diagram in which two physically identical lines appear different sizes due to the perspective created by the tracks converging in the distance. The line at the top of the diagram appears wider than the line below because it seems to span a greater distance across the railway lines, which we wrongly perceive as parallel. We're also reminded of the *Father Ted* episode when Ted explains to Dougal that the toys cows are 'small' but the real cows outside are 'far away'.

The flattened sky

The idea that we perceive the Moon differently because we've come to mentally imagine the sky around us as a flattened dome, instead of the true half sphere that it is, can be seen here. Although you can clearly see in the diagram that the actual distance between the viewer and the Moon doesn't change, our brain's perception of the extra distance to the Moon is compensated for by showing us an apparently enlarged Moon at the horizon.

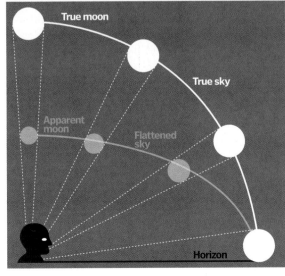

True moon
True sky
Apparent moon
Flattened sky
Horizon

Exploring the Moon

We've visited the lunar body several times but it still has many secrets to reveal…

The Moon has been shrouded in mystery since the dawn of time. For a start, where did it come from? The most popular current hypothesis is the giant impact theory. We've learned from dating lunar rocks that the Moon formed about 4.5 billion years ago, a good 30-50 million years after the Solar System. But while the Earth was just finishing its formation, it was struck by a giant celestial body about the size of Mars, which has been christened Theia. This collision blasted material out into space near the Earth, which coalesced into the body that today we call the Moon. Whether the material came from Earth or the planetoid that caused the impact (or both) is still a matter of debate.

The Moon is the second-brightest object in our sky after the Sun and it has influenced life on Earth in countless ways. The gravitational interactions with our world and the Sun give us ocean tides and lengthen our days by a tiny amount. We've also created calendars based on its phases. Until a Soviet spacecraft landed on it in 1959, we'd only been able to study the Moon from Earth. Then in 1969, humans visited the Moon – and it remains the only other body in the universe we've actually stood upon.

Thanks to decades of study, we've learned a great deal about our satellite. For example, we know that the Moon has a differentiated interior, just like Earth – it contains a core, mantle and crust. The core is rich with iron

A closer look at the surface

The Moon's two hemispheres – the one nearest to us and the one farthest away, or the 'dark side' – have very different surface features. The nearer side is dominated by maria and highlands. The maria, or 'seas' (so-named because early astronomers assumed they were full of water) are the darker areas visible from Earth. The lighter areas are the highlands. Instead of water, the maria are dark because they contain hardened lava, left over from earlier volcanism on the Moon. The far side of our satellite, in contrast, contains almost no maria at all. Both sides of our lunar neighbour are covered with impact craters, left by meteors; they can be tiny or many kilometres across. Especially strong impacts can leave rays of dust extending hundreds of metres from the crater centre. Mountains and other volcanic features emerged shortly after the Moon's formation, as the surface cooled and buckled.

Mare Orientale
A distinctive target-ring shaped feature, but it's tricky to see from Earth

Oceanus Procellarum
Aka the Ocean of Storms; site of Apollo 12 landing

Archimedes
An 83km (51.5mi)-diameter impact crater

Mare Tranquillitatis
Aka the Sea of Tranquillity; site of Apollo 11 landing

Van de Graaff
Appears to be two craters merged into a figure-of-eight

Tycho
A relatively young crater (108 million years old)

Bailly
A 311km (193mi)-wide crater and the largest found on the Moon

Mare Fecunditatis
An 840km (522mi)-wide lunar mare, aka the Sea of Fecundity, or Fertility

Tsiolkovskiy
180km (112mi) crater with a prominent central peak

Fermi
180km (112mi)-wide crater known as a walled plain; it is highly eroded

Apollo
537km (334mi) crater made up of smaller craters named after late NASA employees

The statistics...

The Moon

Average distance from Earth:
384,403km (238,857mi)

Surface temperature:
Day: 107°C (224.6°F)
Night: -153°C (-243°F)

Mean radius:
1,737km (1,079mi)

Volume (Earth=1): 0.02 Earths

Orbit period; length of lunar year: 27.32 Earth days (tidally locked)

Rotational period; length of lunar day: 29.53 Earth days

Mass (Earth=1): 0.0123 Earths

Mean density:
3.344g/cm^3 (1.94oz/in^3)

Gravity at equator (Earth=1):
0.16 Earths

solid in the centre and surrounded by a fluid outer core. The core is small in comparison to the rest of the Moon, however – roughly 350 kilometres (217 miles) thick, about 20 per cent of the Moon's total size. Surrounding the core is a 500-kilometre (311-mile), partially melted boundary layer. This is thought to have formed when a magma ocean in the mantle cooled and crystallised shortly after the Moon's formation. The mantle is the next layer, a hard and rocky area 1,000 kilometres (620 miles) thick. The Moon's crust is also rocky, and about 60-100 kilometres (37-62 miles) in thickness. Analysing rocks has shown us that most of the lunar crust comprises aluminium and titanium, with the elements pyroxferroite and tranquillityite (first

seen on the Moon and subsequently found on Earth) fairly abundant as well. The top layer is covered with dusty, broken rock that smells a bit like gunpowder and has a snowy texture, called regolith.

There's a reason why astronauts had to wear helmets on the Moon – there's very little atmosphere, and what there is doesn't contain oxygen, nitrogen or hydrogen; indeed, the atmospheric mass is less than ten metric tons. Since there's nothing to block the solar wind, it bombards the surface and causes sputtering – sprays of particles into the air. The Moon's surface also experiences outgassing, when volatile gases vent from the interior. These processes contribute sodium, potassium and

compounds of argon, radon and polonium, while solar wind contributes helium-4. All of these have been found in the atmosphere and are continually replenished. Oxygen and other neutral elements found on Earth are present in the regolith, but they don't exist in the atmosphere – probably because the solar wind quickly sweeps them out into space.

Our Moon is the second-densest to be found in the Solar System, behind Jupiter's Io. It's also the fifth largest moon in diameter, only beaten in ascending order, by Io (Jupiter), Callisto (Jupiter), Titan (Saturn) and Ganymede (Jupiter). The Moon's diameter is about one-quarter that of Earth's, but its mass is just under 0.0125 Earth masses

"Water can't exist on the Moon's surface, but might be lurking in some of the shadowy basins"

The Earth-Moon system

A closer look at the relationship between our planet and the Moon

What many people don't know is the Moon doesn't just orbit the Earth, but Earth orbits the Moon too. While the Moon is propelled around Earth in an elliptical orbit, the pull of the Moon's own gravity causes our planet to move slightly off its own centre and around in a small circle. Think of it like an Olympic hammer thrower swinging the hammer around their body while holding onto the chain: even though the hammer is many times smaller than the thrower, it's enough to pull the thrower slightly off their mark. The barycentre marks the centre of mass for this Earth-Moon relationship. The forces involved in Earth-Moon barycentre dynamics are very regular, but even so, tiny variances mean the Moon is gradually moving away from our world. When the Moon was first formed it was very close and had a powerful effect on the development of the early Earth. At first it moved away from us at a rate of ten kilometres (6.2 miles) per year, slowing down over billions of years to its current rate of just 3.8 centimetres (1.5 inches) per year.

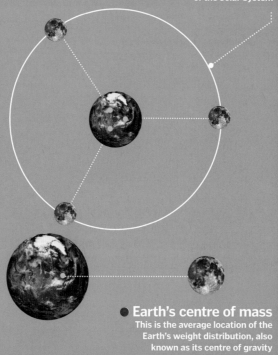

● Barycentre
This is the centre of mass at which the Earth and the Moon balance each other, located 1,710km (1,062mi) below Earth's surface

Plane of the Moon's orbit
The Moon's orbital plane is close to the ecliptic plane – the path the Earth takes as it orbits the Sun, or to be more specific, the barycentre of the Solar System

● Earth's centre of mass
This is the average location of the Earth's weight distribution, also known as its centre of gravity

The lunar body has some unique gravitational properties too. Unlike Earth, the Moon does not have a dipolar magnetic field, but it does have an external magnetic field that results in a gravity of about a sixth of that here on Earth. In addition, the Moon has 'mascons' (mass concentrations), which are large positive gravitational anomalies mostly centred around some of its largest basins. We aren't sure what causes them, although the ones in basins may come from the extremely dense lava flows filling them. We continue to search for water on the Moon, which can't exist on its surface, but might be lurking in some of the shadowy basins, deposited by comets or formed by interactions between hydrogen from the solar wind or oxygen from the regolith deposits.

The Moon is in synchronous rotation with our world. This means that its orbit and revolution periods are of equal length, so the same side of the Moon faces the Earth all of the time. We call these the near side and the far side, or the 'dark side', but the latter actually gets just as much sunlight as the former.

The phases of the Moon describe how it appears to us on the near side, which changes over the course of the Moon's orbit around our planet and Earth's orbit around the Sun. When

Apollo mission profile

We break down the key stages of a former lunar mission, from Earth to the Moon and back again

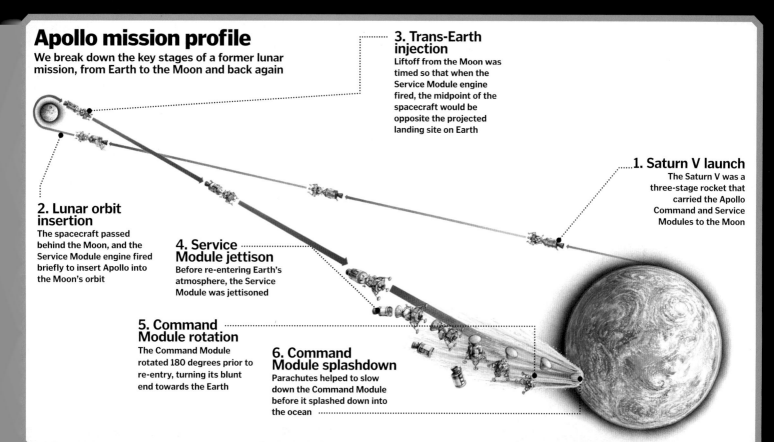

3. Trans-Earth injection
Liftoff from the Moon was timed so that when the Service Module engine fired, the midpoint of the spacecraft would be opposite the projected landing site on Earth

1. Saturn V launch
The Saturn V was a three-stage rocket that carried the Apollo Command and Service Modules to the Moon

2. Lunar orbit insertion
The spacecraft passed behind the Moon, and the Service Module engine fired briefly to insert Apollo into the Moon's orbit

4. Service Module jettison
Before re-entering Earth's atmosphere, the Service Module was jettisoned

5. Command Module rotation
The Command Module rotated 180 degrees prior to re-entry, turning its blunt end towards the Earth

6. Command Module splashdown
Parachutes helped to slow down the Command Module before it splashed down into the ocean

What a coincidence...

Many have wondered why the Moon is just the right size and distance to cover the Sun during an eclipse. The Sun is 400 times greater in diameter than the Moon; the Sun just so happens to be 400 times farther away from Earth too.

DID YOU KNOW? In 1970, two Soviet researchers theorised that the Moon was actually a hollow alien spacecraft

the Sun and Moon are on the opposite sides of the Earth, the Moon appears full. When the Sun and Moon are on the same side of the Earth, the Moon appears dark (known as a 'new moon'). The phases in between are the half and quarter-moons. Eclipses occur when the Sun, Moon and Earth all line up, also known as syzygy (pronounced siz i gee). A solar eclipse occurs when the Moon is between the Sun and Earth, while a lunar eclipse happens when the Earth is between the Sun and Moon. Variations in the orbits mean eclipses happen not with each new and full moon but according to the Saros cycle – a period of 18 years first identified by ancient Babylonian astronomers.

These astronomers created the first records of the Moon, in the 5th century BCE. Over the years astronomers in India, Greece, Persia and China theorised about everything from the source of moonlight to the tides and the Moon's phases. Astronomers in the Middle Ages

A focus on Apollo

On 25 May 1962, US President John F Kennedy proposed a goal of putting men on the Moon and returning them back to Earth by the end of the decade. It was a lofty ambition, but NASA achieved it on 21 July 1969 with Apollo 11. NASA sent astronauts to the Moon a total six times. Budgetary cuts and a shift to planning for the Skylab and Space Shuttle programmes led to the end of the Apollo programme after Apollo 17 returned to Earth in December 1972. No human has touched down on the Moon since.

thought that the Moon was a smooth sphere. Once the telescope was invented in 1608, we soon set our sights on the satellite. Near the end of the 17th century, many of the features on the Moon had been named by Italian astronomers like Francesco Maria Grimaldi.

The Space Race in the Fifties and Sixties between the USA and the Soviet Union ramped up interest in exploring the Moon, first by

orbiter and later by man. The USSR got there first, when the Luna 2 spacecraft smashed into the surface in 1959. It also completed the first soft landing and the first orbit of the Moon in 1966. However, the United States famously won the race of getting a man on the Moon with the seminal Apollo 11 mission in 1969.

It once seemed inevitable that we'd eventually establish a base on the Moon – but it hasn't happened yet, and with the future of NASA's manned space programme in flux, it may be up to another programme or even a private enterprise. But NASA, the European Space Agency, the China National Space Administration, the Indian Space Research Organisation and others continue to send orbiters and landers to the Moon. In January 2012, two spacecraft called GRAIL (Gravity Recovery and Interior Laboratory) began orbiting the Moon to better map it and learn more about its complex interior and gravity. ✿

© NASA; DK Images; Thinkstock

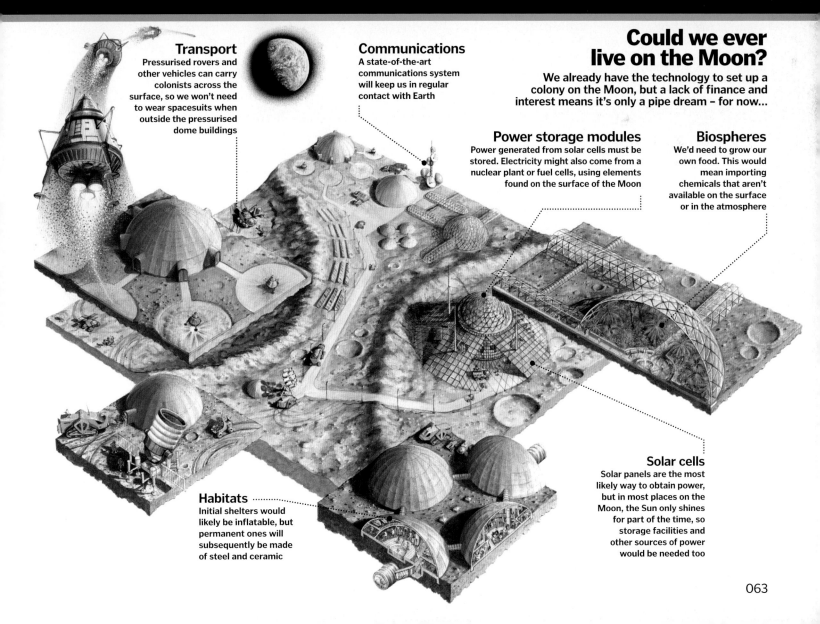

Transport
Pressurised rovers and other vehicles can carry colonists across the surface, so we won't need to wear spacesuits when outside the pressurised dome buildings

Communications
A state-of-the-art communications system will keep us in regular contact with Earth

Could we ever live on the Moon?

We already have the technology to set up a colony on the Moon, but a lack of finance and interest means it's only a pipe dream – for now...

Power storage modules
Power generated from solar cells must be stored. Electricity might also come from a nuclear plant or fuel cells, using elements found on the surface of the Moon

Biospheres
We'd need to grow our own food. This would mean importing chemicals that aren't available on the surface or in the atmosphere

Habitats
Initial shelters would likely be inflatable, but permanent ones will subsequently be made of steel and ceramic

Solar cells
Solar panels are the most likely way to obtain power, but in most places on the Moon, the Sun only shines for part of the time, so storage facilities and other sources of power would be needed too

"Recent studies of the Moon's chemistry revealed the surface is virtually identical to Earth's"

How was the Moon made?

Discover the cataclysmic events that led to the formation of Earth's only natural satellite

Between 363,570 and 405,410 kilometres (around 220,000-250,000 miles) from Earth is our only natural satellite, the Moon. It's very different from its mother planet: it has around one-eighth of the Earth's mass, a very thin, almost negligible atmosphere and it's completely devoid of life. Yet at the same time, it's very similar, with a distinct crust, mantle and solid iron core plus a mineral composition almost identical to Earth's volcanic geology. A coincidence? Scientists think not.

There are four theories of the Moon's creation, three of which have generally been discredited. One suggests the Moon is the result of dust coalescing during the formation of the Solar System, another that the Moon was an asteroid captured by Earth's gravity. Finally, 'fission theory' states that Earth was spinning so rapidly when it formed the molten mass split in two.

The generally accepted idea though is that around 4.5 billion years ago, when the Earth was forming, a Mars-sized planet – dubbed Theia – collided with it. It was such a cataclysmic event that the smaller planet was completely destroyed, sending its own iron into the Earth's core while throwing trillions of tons of debris from the surface into orbit. Eventually this coalesced to form the Moon.

This 'giant impact' theory ties into the creation of our Solar System about 50 million years before the Earth formed, during a period of intense asteroid bombardment that lasted for about 750 million years. This bombardment eventually settled, either colliding with early planets like Earth, being ejected from the Solar System or falling under the influence of the Sun's gravity and becoming part of the Asteroid Belt located between Mars and Jupiter. ✿

4.5 billion years ago (BYA)
The Earth and a smaller planetary body, Theia, form in the same orbit

4.45 BYA
Theia's orbital angle changes with its increasing mass and, after a period of many years, it collides with the Earth

4.43 BYA
Debris thrown out into orbit by Theia begins to coalesce under its own gravity to form the Moon

Scientific doubts

Recent studies of the Moon's chemistry by the University of Chicago revealed the surface is virtually identical to Earth's, which raised questions over the giant impact theory: if a Mars-sized planet struck our world, why is there no apparent trace of it? The impact is supposed to have been so colossal it nearly tore the Earth apart, causing it to warp into an oblong shape before rebounding under the force of its own gravity. Explanations include the possibility that Theia was a comet made of ice that could provide the required energy for the giant impact theory, but it subsequently evaporated. Scientists have also suggested that the Earth could have been spinning so fast at the time that Theia was thoroughly mixed into the Earth and the debris that eventually became the Moon. In either case, giant impact is still our most viable theory as to the creation of our lunar neighbour.

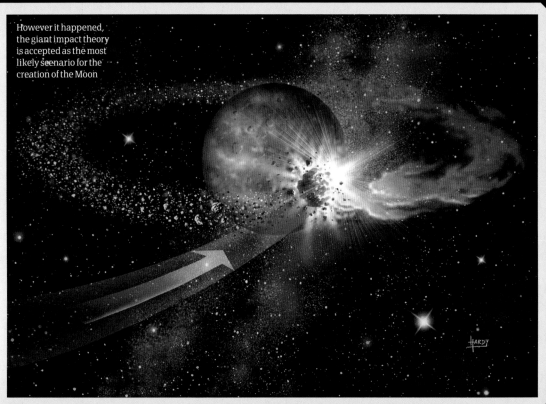

However it happened, the giant impact theory is accepted as the most likely scenario for the creation of the Moon

© NASA

DID YOU KNOW? Like a glancing shot off a snooker ball, the oblique angle Theia hit the Earth at caused our planet to spin

The giant impact theory

See, step by step, the various stages in our Moon's formation

Over time, fragments of the former planet now orbiting the Earth began to reform, eventually into the rudiments of our Moon

© Alamy

3.8 BYA
The Earth's surface cools and changes from molten to a solid crust. Asteroid bombardment on the Moon rapidly slows

2 BYA
While the building blocks of life begin to form on Earth, the Moon protects our planet from potentially deadly impactors

Today
Tectonics has seen the topography of the Earth change, but the Moon is almost exactly as it was 2 billion years ago

The Moon is too small to have created the pressure necessary for its molten iron core

What was Theia?

The Mars-sized body that hit Earth was named after the Greek Titan who gave birth to the Moon goddess Selene. One theory is that it formed in the same orbit as Earth and, over time, coalesced with the abundance of debris in our early Solar System until it was big enough to come under the influence of its own gravity. Then, like the Earth, it began to attract asteroids that added to its bulk over time. When it reached the size of the Red Planet its orbit became unstable, its orbital angle to Earth began to increase until, eventually – just over 4.5 billion years ago, it collided with our world. Originally it was thought that the Moon was mostly the remains of Theia mixed with debris from Earth, but recent research shows that the core of the Moon and the Earth have a very similar iron composition, suggesting that they both originated from the same source.

3x © SPL

THE FIRST MOON LANDING

Over 40 years ago on 21 July 1969 Neil Armstrong became the first person in history to set foot on the surface of a celestial body other than Earth, marking the culmination of a decade of work

In the Sixties the 'Space Race' between the USA and USSR was heating up. Russia had struck the initial blow by launching the first man-made satellite – Sputnik 1 – in 1957, and four years later they sent the first human – Yuri Gagarin – into space. The Americans followed suit a few weeks later but it was readily apparent they were playing catch-up to the Russians. To reassure the American people, President Kennedy issued an impassioned speech to Congress in 1961 announcing the ambitious goal of placing a human on the Moon before the end of the decade. As a result Project Apollo was born, and with it NASA was tasked with fulfilling Kennedy's lofty aim. An unprecedented technological marvel, the Apollo missions would come to define not only a generation, but also the standard by which all future manned space missions would be compared.

The crew

From left to right: Commander Neil A Armstrong; Command Module pilot Michael Collins; Lunar Module pilot Edwin 'Buzz' E Aldrin Jr. Collins remained in orbit while Armstrong and Aldrin explored the surface.

© NASA

The Eagle lander

The lander was a two-stage craft built to separate from the Command and Service Module then travel to and from the Moon's surface

Payload
At almost 47,000kg, (103,600lbs) the payload consisted of the Command, Service and Lunar Modules that travelled to the Moon

LEVA
The Lunar Extravehicular Visor Assembly (LEVA) contained gold-coated visors to protect against the Sun

PLSS
The Apollo Portable Life Support System (PLSS) contained the life-support apparatus including cooling water, oxygen tanks and electrical power

Third stage (S-IVB)
The final rocket stage contained just one J-2 engine and accelerated the spacecraft towards the Moon at about 39,400km/h (24,500mph) before

JOURNEY OF A LIFETIME

The Apollo 11 mission lasted 195 hours, 18 minutes and 35 seconds

16 July 1332 GMT
Apollo 11 launches atop a Saturn V rocket from the Kennedy Space Center and enters Earth's orbit.

19 July 1721 GMT
After a three-day journey across almost 400,000km (250,000

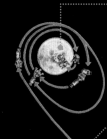

Command and Service Module remains in orbit

Lunar Module separates and lands on the Moon

Command and Service Module docks with third stage

Third-stage separation

Second-stage separation

First-stage separation

2x © DK Images

The rocket

Descent stage

Equipment for use on the Moon was stored in this lower section, which also contained a rocket and landing gear for a controlled landing. It was left behind on the Moon

Ascent stage

If the ascent stage had failed above the crew would have had no hope of rescue

This part of the Lunar Module (LM) contained the pressurised crew compartment and controls, and took the astronauts back to the Command and Service Module (CSM) in orbit

© DK Images

Size

The Saturn V rocket was as tall as a 36-storey building and, fully loaded, it weighed almost 3,000 tons

First stage (S-IC)

S-IC contained five F-1 engines that used liquid oxygen and kerosene fuel. They separated at an altitude of 61km (38 miles)

Second stage (S-II)

The five J-2 liquid hydrogen engines of S-II took Apollo 11 to an altitude of 185km (115 miles) before they were discarded

The Saturn V rocket used to take Apollo into space still retains the record of being the most powerful rocket of all time

© NASA

Spacesuits

To walk on the Moon the Apollo 11 crew required some practical 'space clobber'

Weight

The spacesuit and backpack weighed 14kg (31lb) on the Moon, but 82kg (181lb) on Earth, due to the Moon's weaker gravity

The slip-on boots reduced the transfer of heat from the Moon's surface and helped to limit surface abrasion

from the planet Earth first set foot upon the Moon, July 1969 AD. We came in peace for all mankind.'

18 11 GMT

Neil Armstrong and 'Buzz' Aldrin enter the Lunar Module (LM) and separate from the Command and Service Module (CSM).

20 July 2017 GMT

The Lunar Module lands in Mare Tranquillitatis (the Sea of Tranquillity), tracked by Collins in orbit aboard the CSM.

21 July 0256 GMT

Armstrong steps onto the lunar surface, the first human to set foot on another world. Aldrin follows 19 minutes later, and they begin deploying instruments and taking photos.

21 July 1754 GMT

Having traversed a distance of about 250m (820ft) and collected 22kg (48lb) of lunar rock and soil, the two astronauts return to the LM and launch back into orbit.

21 July 2134 GMT

The LM docks with the CSM and, once all three astronauts are safely in the CSM, the LM is jettisoned into lunar orbit.

24 July 1650 GMT

After separating from the Service Module, the Command Module splashes down in the Pacific Ocean after completing its 195-hour mission.

© NASA

Solar tsunamis

The mega-waves of energy that tear across the Sun

Solar tsunamis, also known as Moreton waves or fast-mode magnetohydrodynamic (MHD) waves, are surges of material sent crashing across the Sun as the result of a solar flare being launched into space. They can travel up to an incredible 1.6 million kilometres (1 million miles) per hour.

Solar tsunamis are made of hot plasma and magnetic energy. The first was observed by Gail Moreton in 1959, and since then several more studies have been conducted on the phenomenon by the Solar and Heliospheric Observatory (SOHO) and the Solar Terrestrial Relations Observatory (STEREO) spacecraft.

The tsunamis are formed when the Sun emits a coronal mass ejection (CME), a massive burst of solar wind commonly associated with solar flares. Around the ejection point a circular wave extends outwards in all directions travelling at a super-fast rate.

In February 2009, the two STEREO spacecraft watched as a billion-ton cloud of gas was hurled off the surface of the Sun from a CME. The result was a solar tsunami that towered 100,000 kilometres (60,000 miles) high speeding across the star's surface at about 900,000 kilometres (560,000 miles) per hour. Estimates indicate it contained the same energy as 2.4 million megatons of TNT.

Our moon reflects varying amounts of the Sun's light, depending on its position, hence why it changes shape

© NASA/ESA/LMSAL

Solar tsunamis can be thrown away from the exit point of a solar flare as it's ejected into space

Tidal locking explained

Why can we only see one face of the moon?

On Earth the same 'face' of the moon always points in our direction. Likewise, the opposite side – commonly known as the 'far side of the moon' – always faces away from us. This is because in the time it takes our satellite to orbit the Earth it completes almost exactly one revolution, so it is always aligned in this way.

This phenomenon is due to a process evident throughout the solar system, known as tidal locking. The Earth and the moon are locked gravitationally. They both pull on one another, which is the cause of tides on Earth. As the moon orbits the Earth, it pulls the part of Earth it is above towards it and creates a 'bulge'. This is noticeable on water, which is flexible, but not so on rock, which is rigid, causing parts of oceans and seas to rise where others do not. Over time, since the formation of the moon at about the same time as Earth 4.6 billion years ago, this process has slowed the rotation of the moon, as the friction caused by the gravitational pull prevented it from rotating. For this reason the moon is now locked in an orbit above Earth where one face always points towards us.

Why does the moon shine?

We take a look at our natural satellite's eerie glow

Perhaps rather bizarrely, the moon is actually very dark, and it doesn't glow for the reasons you might think. The ancients thought that the moon produced its own light, but we now know definitively that this is not the case. Rather, our moon reflects the light of the Sun in accordance with its orbit.

The entire moon does not constantly reflect light – only the half in direct view of the Sun. As the moon is tidally locked to the Earth (ie we only ever see one face), our view of the lit half changes constantly, ranging from a disc to a thin crescent. On a full moon, the Sun is directly lined up with the Earth-moon line; when we see a thin crescent, on the other hand, the Sun is illuminating just the side.

However, the moon does not reflect light quite like a mirror, although it is similar. All objects in space have an albedo, which is a measure of how well they reflect light. To give you an idea of how this works, material like ice has a high albedo, whereas soil has a low albedo. However, the moon's albedo is actually very low – similar to that of coal. Its bright glow is instead the result of something called the opposition effect. You may have come across this when seeing a car's headlights shine on a dark road: the road appears brighter than it would if light were not incident upon it. The Sun plays the part of the headlight in this case, directly shining on the moon and leading to its bright glow. The large amount of debris on the surface of the moon also contributes to its reflectivity.

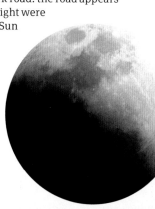

© JPL

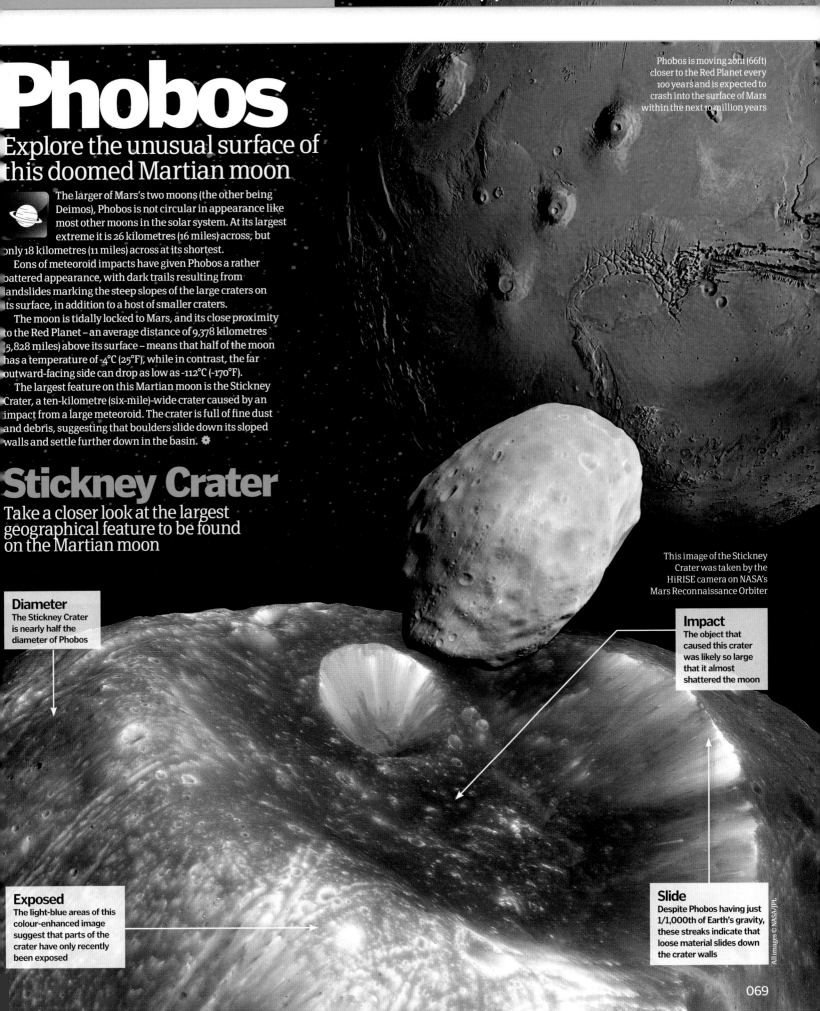

Phobos

Explore the unusual surface of this doomed Martian moon

Phobos is moving 20m (66ft) closer to the Red Planet every 100 years and is expected to crash into the surface of Mars within the next 10 million years

The larger of Mars's two moons (the other being Deimos), Phobos is not circular in appearance like most other moons in the solar system. At its largest extreme it is 26 kilometres (16 miles) across, but only 18 kilometres (11 miles) across at its shortest.

Eons of meteoroid impacts have given Phobos a rather battered appearance, with dark trails resulting from landslides marking the steep slopes of the large craters on its surface, in addition to a host of smaller craters.

The moon is tidally locked to Mars, and its close proximity to the Red Planet – an average distance of 9,378 kilometres (5,828 miles) above its surface – means that half of the moon has a temperature of -4°C (25°F), while in contrast, the far outward-facing side can drop as low as -112°C (-170°F).

The largest feature on this Martian moon is the Stickney Crater, a ten-kilometre (six-mile)-wide crater caused by an impact from a large meteoroid. The crater is full of fine dust and debris, suggesting that boulders slide down its sloped walls and settle further down in the basin. ✿

Stickney Crater

Take a closer look at the largest geographical feature to be found on the Martian moon

This image of the Stickney Crater was taken by the HiRISE camera on NASA's Mars Reconnaissance Orbiter

Diameter
The Stickney Crater is nearly half the diameter of Phobos

Impact
The object that caused this crater was likely so large that it almost shattered the moon

Exposed
The light-blue areas of this colour-enhanced image suggest that parts of the crater have only recently been exposed

Slide
Despite Phobos having just 1/1,000th of Earth's gravity, these streaks indicate that loose material slides down the crater walls

All images © NASA/JPL

069

Olympus Mons

The tallest mountain and the largest volcano in the solar system

Olympus Rupes

Caldera complex

Karzok Crater

Olympus Rupes

Pangboche Crater

© NASA

Olympic-sized mountain

Rising more than 27 kilometres above the surface, Olympus Mons is three times the height of Earth's tallest mountain, Mount Everest. It is about 550 kilometres wide, surrounded at its edges by escarpments called Olympus Rupes that are about six kilometres high. If a person were to stand on the surface of Mars, they would not be able to see the top of Olympus Mons due to its height, size and shallow slope. Olympus Mons likely grew to such an impressive height due to Mars's lack of plate tectonics. Without a shifting crust, lava piled up in one place. Mars's low surface gravity, only about 40 per cent that of Earth's, also accounts for the long lava flows that made Olympus Mons so wide.

Olympus Mons versus Mauna Loa

On Earth, the largest volcano is Mauna Loa, found in Hawaii. Another shield volcano, Mauna Loa stands just ten kilometres high above sea level and 75 kilometres wide. It's about 100 times smaller than Olympus Mons, and the entire chain of Hawaiian volcanoes could fit inside the Martian volcano. Mauna Loa is also dwarfed by Mount Everest, which is 8,848 metres high.

Mars has many interesting features, but none so striking as Olympus Mons. Astronomers believe the mountain formed fairly recently in the planet's geologic history, with the 'youngest' areas around 2 million years old. This shield volcano has a shallow slope and is wider than it is tall. It formed from very low viscosity lava that flowed over a long period of time. The peak of Olympus Mons contains a large caldera, a cavity that formed when the roof of the volcano's magma chamber collapsed and the ground above collapsed into it. More lava activity caused additional, smaller calderas that overlap the larger one, creating a caldera complex.

The volcano also has two named craters; the Karzok Crater is 15.6 kilometres wide and the Pangboche Crater is 10.4 kilometres wide. Olympus Mons lies in Tharsis, a bulging volcanic region on Mars. The area is also home to three smaller volcanoes known as the Tharsis Montes. ✿

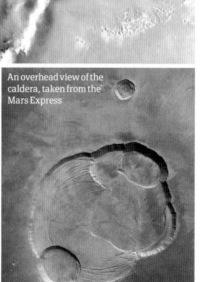

An overhead view of the caldera, taken from the Mars Express

© NASA

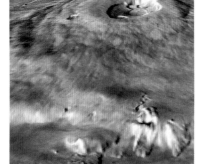

A topographical view of the Olympus Mons region

© NASA

Size comparison of Olympus Mons, Everest and the island of Hawaii

22,500m

10,200m

8,848m

Olympus Mons

Everest

Hawaii

The Martian mammoth dwarfs the mountains found on Earth

Olympus Mons diameter: 550km

1,930 KM

DID YOU KNOW? *The farthest object NASA has found is a galaxy of blue stars some 13.2 billion light years away*

Martian mudslides

Mars's barren surface isn't quite as static as we once thought...

These pictures could easily have been taken at any dusty Earth location, but they're actually snaps of Mars, taken by NASA's HiRISE (High Resolution Imaging Science Experiment) camera by mistake as scientists searched for carbon dioxide frost. The photos show four avalanches of Martian mud spilling across a strip of terrain six kilometres (3.7 miles) long and 700 metres (2,300 feet) tall, located at the Red Planet's north pole.

The landslides are actually quite small, but they've caused some excitement at NASA, partly because the planet is normally so still and lifeless that to capture these dynamic images is quite a rarity. But they have also helped to give an insight into the composition of the planet.

It's expected that the material that has fallen loose is probably more ice than red Martian dust, but by watching the debris and how rapidly it shrinks as the solids change to gas, scientists hope to apportion a precise figure over time. Also of interest to NASA scientists is the cause of the mudslide, which isn't yet clear. ✿

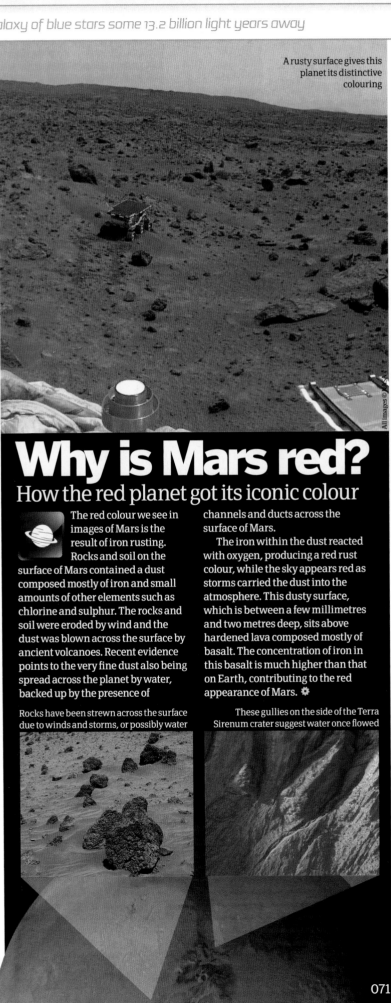

A rusty surface gives this planet its distinctive colouring

All images © NASA

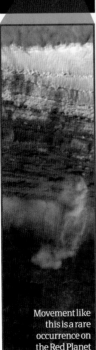

Movement like this is a rare occurrence on the Red Planet

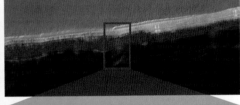

These landslides on Mars have caused quite a stir at NASA

Why is Mars red?

How the red planet got its iconic colour

The red colour we see in images of Mars is the result of iron rusting. Rocks and soil on the surface of Mars contained a dust composed mostly of iron and small amounts of other elements such as chlorine and sulphur. The rocks and soil were eroded by wind and the dust was blown across the surface by ancient volcanoes. Recent evidence points to the very fine dust also being spread across the planet by water, backed up by the presence of channels and ducts across the surface of Mars.

The iron within the dust reacted with oxygen, producing a red rust colour, while the sky appears red as storms carried the dust into the atmosphere. This dusty surface, which is between a few millimetres and two metres deep, sits above hardened lava composed mostly of basalt. The concentration of iron in this basalt is much higher than that on Earth, contributing to the red appearance of Mars. ✿

Rocks have been strewn across the surface due to winds and storms, or possibly water

These gullies on the side of the Terra Sirenum crater suggest water once flowed

Rings of Jupiter

What is encircling this gas giant?

 Jupiter's system if rings is so faint that it was more than 350 years after the planet was initially observed that it was found to have any rings at all. They are believed to have been created largely from meteoritic impacts on some of Jupiter's many moons and they're composed mostly of dust particles, as opposed to the icy, rocky debris that encircles the gas giant Saturn.

The main ring begins almost 130,000 kilometres (81,000 miles) above the centre of the planet and extends outwards a further 7,000 kilometres (4,350 miles). Inside the main ring are two of Jupiter's 64 known moons, the small Adrastea and Metis, thought to be the primary culprits of the majority of the dust present in the main ring.

Between the main ring and the cloud top of Jupiter is a region known as the halo, a faint collection of material 10,000 kilometres (6,200 miles) wide. Outside the main ring is an even fainter series of dust known as the gossamer rings, held in position by the gravity of the nearby moons Amalthea and Thebe. ✿

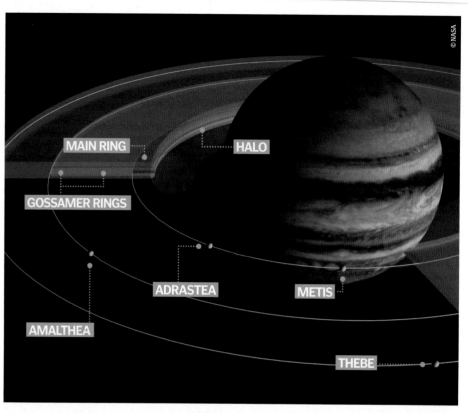

© NASA

MAIN RING
HALO
GOSSAMER RINGS
ADRASTEA
METIS
AMALTHEA
THEBE

What causes Jupiter's aurora

What scientists saw within the gas giant's northern lights

Io

Ganymede

Europa

A more familiar shot of Jupiter, our solar system's largest planet

4X © NASA

This is an image (top-left) of Jupiter's aurora, taken by NASA's Hubble Space Telescope in 1998. Auroras themselves aren't peculiar to Jupiter; they occur on Earth on both the North and South Poles and are called the aurora borealis and aurora australis, respectively.

Solar winds hitting the atmosphere and centring on the magnetic poles cause the phenomenon on Earth, but on Jupiter it's caused by the massive gas giant's own magnetic properties interacting with its upper atmosphere and exciting the gases that exist there, causing them to glow.

What makes this image particularly special is that you can also see the magnetic footprints of three of Jupiter's four largest moons within the Jovian auroral blue glow. Io, Ganymede and Europa's own auroras (which are labelled) show up as three blobs of light and the electric currents generated by these three satellites move along the magnetic field of Jupiter while bouncing in and out of the atmosphere.

This shot was taken from the ultraviolet part of the spectrum, so this particular perspective of the aurora cannot be observed with the naked eye. It shows the main oval centred on Jupiter's magnetic north pole. ✿

Head to Head
IO'S VOLCANOES

LONGEST LASTING PLUME

1. Prometheus
The nearly 100-kilometre dust plume emanating from the Prometheus volcano is thought to have been continuously erupting since at least 1979.

LONGEST LAVA FLOW

2. Masubi Fluctus
Originating from the volcano Masubi, the Masubi Fluctus is an active lava flow more than 500 kilometres long.

BIGGEST VOLCANO

3. Loki
Loki Patera is the biggest volcano depression on Io at more than 200 kilometres in diameter (126 miles).

DID YOU KNOW? Io's volcanic activity was unknown until images were taken by the Voyager spacecraft in 1979

Inside Io
Why is Io so volcanic?

3. Mountainous
Io's surface is covered with over 400 volcanoes and 100 mountains

2. Under pressure
The huge gravitational forces expelled upon Io from Jupiter's other moons cause its interior to expand and contract

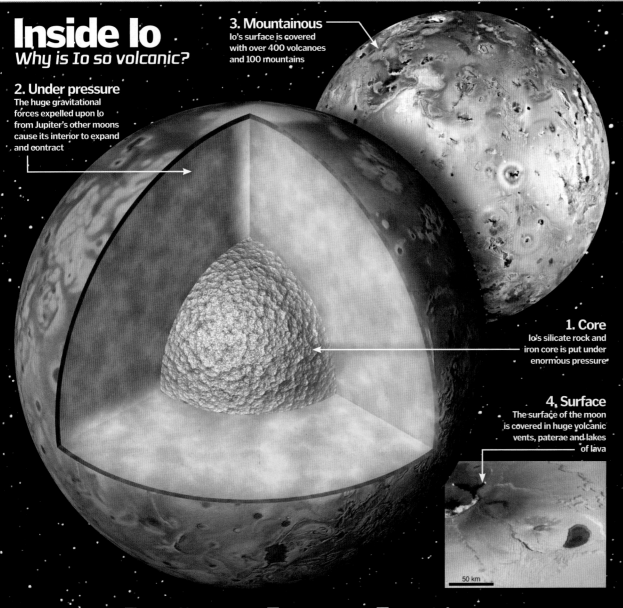

1. Core
Io's silicate rock and iron core is put under enormous pressure

4. Surface
The surface of the moon is covered in huge volcanic vents, paterae and lakes of lava

50 km

Jupiter's Galilean moons

Jupiter has 63 known moons, but its Galilean moons – Io, Europa, Ganymede and Callisto – are the four largest. Discovered by Galileo in 1620, the Galilean moons also rank among the biggest moons in the solar system. Io is known for its extreme volcanic activity as well as its unusual silicate rock and iron composition. Europa's the smallest of these moons, with a smooth surface of ice and water. It is thought to potentially harbour extraterrestrial life. Ganymede is the largest moon in the solar system, with a diameter wider than that of Mercury. Callisto is the second-largest Galilean moon, with a surface that is very old and covered in craters. Its largest crater, Valhalla, is 3,000 kilometres wide.

Io: The volcanic moon
When it comes to the landscape on Jupiter's moon Io, the only real constant is change

We often think of moons in the context of Earth's moon – cold, quiet and devoid of activity. While Jupiter's moon Io is roughly the same size as Earth's moon, it couldn't be more different. Io's main feature is its volcanic activity. The moon is covered with more than 400 volcanoes, which constantly spew plumes of sulphur, sulphur dioxide and ash as high as 500 kilometres above its surface. Io is also covered with hundreds of kilometres of lava flows and lakes, massive volcanic depressions called paterae, and openings in its crust called volcanic vents. This non-stop activity

gives Io a colourful surface that looks quite a lot like a pizza.

So what makes Io so unique? The answer is tides, but these tides are much stronger than those in Earth's oceans. Io experiences tidal heating thanks to the gravitational forces exerted upon it by Jupiter and three of its other moons: Europa, Ganymede and Callisto. Io is the innermost of these moons, so it's constantly in the centre of a tug-of-war between the planet and the other moons. These gravitational forces are so strong that they alternately compress and expand Io's interior, causing the surface to bulge in and out by as much as 100

kilometres. All of this force causes pressure and heat to build in Io's silicate rock and iron core, ultimately sending molten material spewing up through cracks in the crust.

In addition to its numerous volcanic features, Io has more than 100 mountains, some of which are taller than Mount Everest's 8.84 kilometres. These mountains may be the result of the constant resurfacing of the moon's crust due to all of the volcanic activity. A build-up of volcanic material could cause the crust to fall into the mantle, pushing chunks of it up through faults and forming a mountain. ✿

The Statistics
Io

Diameter: 3,636 kilometres
Mass: 8.93 x 10²² kilograms
Density: 3.5 grams per cubic centimetre
Average surface temperature: -143°C (130 Kelvin)
Core temperature: Estimated at up to 1,726°C (2,000 Kelvin)
Equatorial surface gravity: 0.183 g

"The temperature on the surface drops to -162°C at the equator and possibly -220°C at the poles"

Europa

Our greatest chance of finding life is possibly on this moon of Jupiter

One of Jupiter's four largest moons – the others being Io, Ganymede and Callisto – Europa is notable for its icy surface with a theorised ocean underneath. The moons all keep the same face towards Jupiter as they orbit. The layer of ice that encapsulates Europa's entire surface is as little as 5-100 miles thick. It has one of the smoothest surfaces in the solar system, with its features such as valleys and hills no larger or deeper than a few hundred metres. This suggests it is young and still actively forming like Earth.

Most of Europa is made of rock, although its core has a large iron content. Gravitational forces from Jupiter and its other three largest moons have given Europa a hot interior in a process known as tidal heating, similar to how tides are created on Earth as our moon stretches and pulls the oceans. Europa has a very thin atmosphere made of just oxygen created by particles emitted from the radiation of Jupiter striking the surface and producing water vapour.

Due to there being almost no atmosphere on Europa, which is not much smaller than our moon, the temperature on the surface drops to -162°C at the equator and possibly as low as -220°C at the poles. Absolute zero is not much colder at -273.15°C. A few miles down into Europa's ocean, the temperature could still be as cold as -30°C or as high as 0°C, meaning that any life would have to adapt to these freezing temperatures.

The large amount of radiation Jupiter exerts can severely damage any probe attempting to reach Europa. One of the only missions to study the moon was the Galileo space probe, named after the astronomer Galileo who discovered Jupiter's four largest moons in one week in 1610. It journeyed between Jupiter and its moons from 1995 to 2003, providing much of the information we know about Europa today. ✿

This picture, taken by the Cassini spacecraft, shows Europa casting a shadow on Jupiter

Into the core

Composition
The core of Europa is made of metal, specifically iron and nickel

Images courtesy of NASA

THE STATS EUROPA

YEAR OF DISCOVERY	**1610**	**ORBIT OF JUPITER**	**3.55 days**
DIAMETER	**3,122km**	**MEAN DISTANCE FROM JUPITER**	**670,900k**
		MEAN ORBITAL VELOCITY	**13.74km/second**

DID YOU KNOW? *The Galileo probe, which studied Europa, was sent crashing into Jupiter so it didn't contaminate nearby mo*

Life on Europa

The lack of impact craters on the surface of Europa but the presence of fissures and cracks means that something other than meteorites must be fracturing and altering the ice. This has led scientists to believe there is an ocean of water beneath the icy surface of Europa. It is in this ocean where life could reside. Previously, it was thought animals required sunlight to live, but the discovery of creatures living off small bacteria at the bottom of Earth's oceans have raised the possibility that animals as large as fish could be living below Europa's surface. There are two main theories as to how Europa's ocean could look, shown in the 'Under the surface' boxout.

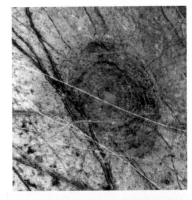

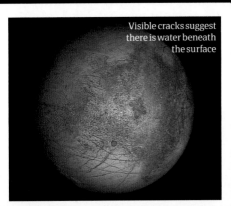

Visible cracks suggest there is water beneath the surface

Surface
The icy surface, 5-100 miles thick, has features that indicate the presence of water below

Ocean
Water in liquid or ice form is fed heat by the rock, and may harbour life

Earth-like rock
A shell of rock surrounds the core, much like on Earth

Under the surface
The two theories of Europa's structure
Thin ice sheet

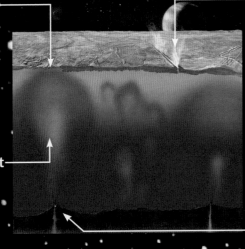

Chaos
What appear to be ice blocks on the surface of Europa, known as "chaos", may be the result of heating under the ice

Rising heat
The heat rises up through the oxygenated water, in which organisms could live

Vapour
In this theory, the ice on the surface cracks and may let out water vapour as it is heated from below

Volcanoes
The bed of the ocean may contain volcanoes, which spurt out hot gas from the core of the moon

Thick ice sheet

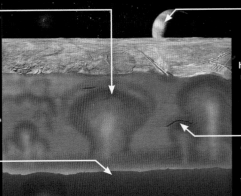

Tides
Additional heat is created by tidal heating, which forces the lower layer of ice into the surface

Core
If the ice shell is very thick, heat from the core will transfer to this lower portion of the icy surface

Jupiter
Europa's ecliptic orbit of Jupiter could be the cause of tidal heating in its core, moving the ocean up and down and thus releasing water vapour

Moving
This heat could move the lower ice layer like a tectonic plate and be the cause of the lines on Europa's surface, rather than simply volcanic heat

Sizes...
Europa's diameter is a quarter of Earth's with a mass equal to 0.008 of Earth's.

3,122km

12,756.3km

"Its diffuse Ɛ ring is truly gigantic at around 300,000 kilometres (186,000 miles) wide"

What are Saturn's rings?

The mysteries of how Saturn's rings were formed are only now revealing themselves to us...

While both Neptune and Uranus can boast of being encircled by a stellar crown of sorts, it's Saturn that is the true 'lord of the rings'. Neptune's five relatively thin rings are so small that they weren't definitively discovered until 1968, while Uranus's narrow bands were discovered even later, in 1977. By contrast, Galileo was the first person to view Saturn's rings over 400 years ago using a simple telescope.

Six of its seven rings span from 74,500 kilometres (46,300 miles) to 140,220 kilometres (87,130 miles) above the surface of Saturn, while its diffuse E ring is truly gigantic at around 300,000 kilometres (186,000 miles) wide – nearly the distance between the Earth and the moon.

Most of the rings are primarily composed of water ice that ranges in size from tiny droplets micrometres across to large chunks the size of houses. Icy moons like Enceladus that orbit Saturn help seed the enormous E ring by spouting water slush and organic compounds from beneath its frozen crust into the atmosphere and way beyond. Rock particles of a similar size, but much greater mass than the ice particles, can also be found within the rings.

One theory is that Saturn's main rings, A, B and C – the first ones that were discovered – were actually created much earlier than had been previously thought. Rather than at the time of the formation of the solar system, space scientists think the rings may have been formed a few hundred million years ago when a large moon or asteroid was broken apart by Saturn's gravity. ✿

Saturn's rings close up

Moonlets

The Cassini-Huygens mission has thrown new light on the formation of Saturn's moons. Some of the smallest moonlets that measure less than 50 kilometres (31 miles) across should have been destroyed by comets if they were captured by Saturn's gravity at the formation of the solar system, as per the old theory. Using data collected by the Cassini probe, a computer simulation suggests that the ice in the rings can piece together into large enough lumps to come under the influence of their own gravity, then continue to grow as Saturn pushes them out on a gravitational tide. It also helps explain why the biggest moons are farthest from the gas giant.

2x © NASA

Titan:
Saturn's largest moon

Discover one of the most Earth-like bodies in our solar system

Of Saturn's more than 60 natural satellites, Titan is not only the largest, but also one of the most fascinating and mysterious. It is about 50 per cent larger than Earth's moon and a few hundred kilometres larger than the planet Mercury, but Titan is often compared to Earth. It has clouds in its atmosphere that produce rain, which has resulted in large lakes at the poles. Stable bodies of water like these do not exist anywhere else but Earth. Titan also has predictable wind patterns, as well as volcanoes and evidence of plate tectonics. These processes have given it a landscape dotted with mountain ranges, dunes, valleys and shorelines.

Scientists often call Titan 'early Earth' because they believe that its atmosphere and surface – which is mostly free of impact craters – are similar to our planet around the time that life began. However, Titan only gets about one per cent of the sunlight that Earth gets, thanks to its thick, hazy atmosphere mostly made of nitrogen. Because of its distance from the Sun and its thick atmosphere, just about everything related to the moon is very frigid. Titan's average surface temperature is -179°C. Titan's rain is called a "methane drizzle", and its lakes are composed not of water, but of liquid methane and ethane. Even Titan's volcanoes are cold; instead of scorching lava made of liquid rock, it is believed that these 'cryovolcanoes' spew ammonia and water-ice. ✿

Inside Titan

Titan's internal structure is thought to be mostly ice; scientists believe that it has a rocky core (which could be hot) surrounded by a high-pressure form of ice, a liquid ammonia and water layer and a crystalline icy crust.

Atmosphere
Titan's atmosphere is mostly nitrogen, but also contains methane, hydrogen and trace amounts of other hydrocarbons and gases

Ice Ih crust
This layer comprises ice Ih, a hexagonal form of ice with a very low density. It is thought to be floating on the surface of the water and ammonia layer

Water and ammonia layer
The Hugyens probe detected extremely low-frequency radio waves (ELF), which likely reflected off this sub-surface ocean. The ammonia would keep the water as a liquid even at low temperatures

High-pressure ice layer
Pressures within the moon's structure during its formation probably created high-pressure forms of ice with tight crystalline structures

Silicate core
Titan's core is thought to comprise silicate rock approximately 5,000 kilometres in diameter

© NASA

5 TOP FACTS
TITAN

Orbit and rotation
1 Titan both rotates and orbits Saturn once every 15 days and 22 hours. It is also synchronous with Saturn, meaning that the same side of the moon always faces the planet.

Life on the moon?
2 There is speculation that Titan could support life, based on a lack of the organic compound acetylene and lower levels of hydrogen than some have previously predicted.

Observing Titan
3 Titan can be very difficult to see from telescopes on Earth because it is so close to Saturn and its countless number of rings, which are extremely bright.

Titan as a colony
4 Titan has been considered as a candidate for colonisation. This is due to its high levels of hydrocarbons, which are far beyond all of the oil and natural gas reserves on Earth.

Flying on the moon
5 Scientists believe that people could theoretically fly on Titan with wings attached to their arms due to the low gravity and the thick atmospheric haze.

DID YOU KNOW? *Titan was discovered in 1655 by a Dutch astronomer named Christiaan Huygens, who called it Luna Saturni*

The Statistics
Titan

© NASA

Diameter: 5,151 kilometres
Mass: 0.0225 Earths
Density: 1.88 grams per cubic centimetre
Average surface temperature: -178°C
Average distance from the Sun: 1,427,000,000 kilometres (9.54 AU)
Surface gravity: 0.14 g-force

Titan has a multi-layered atmosphere with very low temperatures and high pressure at its surface. Methane condenses, while surface activity such as volcanic eruptions and rain keep atmospheric gases circulating

© NASA

Orange haze

Other moons in our solar system have little-to-no atmosphere, but Titan is unique. Its atmosphere is quite dense – the atmospheric pressure is almost one and a half times that of Earth's. It is also very thick due to the moon's low gravity (lower even than our own moon's gravity), extending ten times further into space than Earth's atmosphere. Titan's atmosphere has multiple layers and is extremely complex, comprising about 98.5 per cent nitrogen, 1.3 per cent methane and 0.2 per cent hydrogen as well as traces of numerous other hydrocarbons and gases.

Both the atmosphere's orange-brown colour and thick haze are likely due to organic molecules such as tholins, which form when ultraviolet radiation from the Sun breaks apart the nitrogen and methane in the moon's upper atmosphere. The molecules that do not hang in the atmosphere fall down to the surface, contributing to the sand dunes that cover the planet.

Methane rain

Titan has rain like Earth, but it is made of methane instead of water. Scientists believe that the Sun should have converted all of Titan's atmospheric methane into tholins and other organic molecules millions of years ago. This means that there is a source of methane on the moon itself, and it is likely circulated back into the atmosphere through volcanic eruptions.

The thick, dense atmosphere and low gravity means that the methane rain falls very slowly and in drops twice as large as raindrops on Earth, mostly near the moon's poles. It doesn't rain very often on Titan – perhaps as little as once every few decades. When it does rain, however, there's a lot of it and it carves out ridges, dunes and valleys.

© NASA/Mark A. Garlick / markgarlick.com

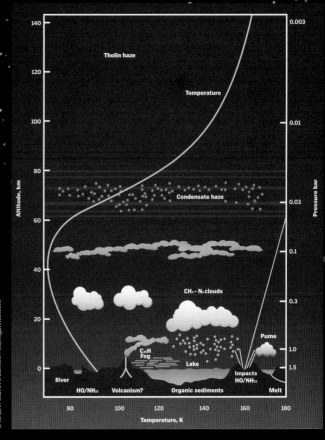

Missions to Titan

The Cassini-Huygens Mission was a joint project of NASA, the ESA and the Italian Space Agency. After several fly-bys of Titan, the Huygens probe landed on Titan's surface in 2005 and transmitted images and data back to the Cassini spacecraft. The probe provided the most in-depth look at Titan ever seen, including information about the moon's atmospheric make-up, weather and landscape. Its landing site showed a vast plain covered in water-ice rocks.

A joint NASA/ESA mission called the Titan Saturn System Mission (TSSM) has been proposed to launch as early as 2018. This mission would explore Saturn as well as Titan and another of Saturn's moons, Enceladus. It includes deploying two different types of probes on Titan: a montgolfière (or hot-air balloon) and a lander. The montgolfière would circulate in Titan's clouds and circumnavigate the moon, while the lander would splashdown in one of Titan's lakes.

© NASA

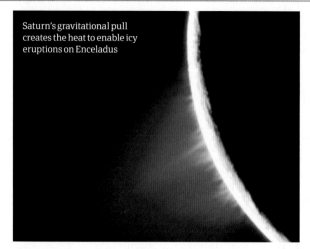

Saturn's gravitational pull creates the heat to enable icy eruptions on Enceladus

Ice volcanoes

Saturn's freezing moon Enceladus has volcanoes, but they're not what you'd expect

 They're known as cryovolcanoes, and though scientists don't have cast-iron proof that volcanoes spouting ice from a sub-zero caldera exist on Enceladus, there is strong evidence for it. The flyover by Cassini two years ago revealed jets spurting from four cracks along the moon's surface, named Alexandria, Cairo, Baghdad and Damascus. The eruptions were so high that they could easily be seen in profile from space.

Volcanoes found on Earth and also Jupiter's moon Io spout silicate lava heated by the pressure beneath the crust. Ice volcanoes work in a similar way: scientists believe that subterranean geological activity on Enceladus warms the freezing surface into a slush of water, ice and organic compounds, which is then ejected by ice sheets grinding up against one another. Enceladus has an elliptical orbit similar to our moon, so as Saturn's gravity pulls unevenly at Enceladus it creates a bulge that generates the friction and heat necessary to cause this previously unheard-of phenomenon.

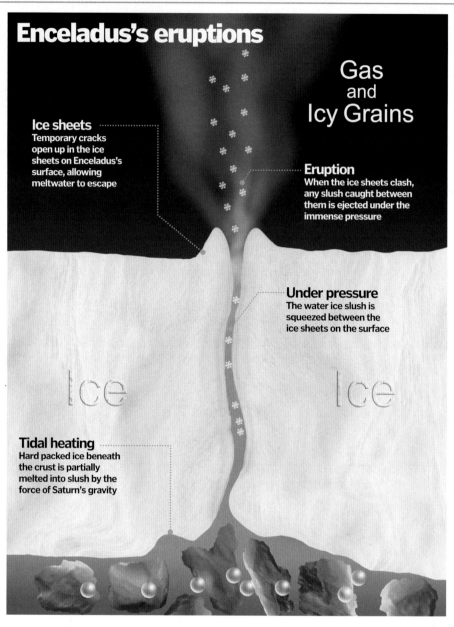

Enceladus's eruptions

Gas and Icy Grains

Ice sheets
Temporary cracks open up in the ice sheets on Enceladus's surface, allowing meltwater to escape

Eruption
When the ice sheets clash, any slush caught between them is ejected under the immense pressure

Under pressure
The water ice slush is squeezed between the ice sheets on the surface

Tidal heating
Hard packed ice beneath the crust is partially melted into slush by the force of Saturn's gravity

Ice   Ice

Why Uranus has unusual rings
What's going on around this outer planet?

 The 13 known rings of Uranus are very faint and were not known to exist until they were discovered in 1977 by a team of scientists, and later observed in more detail by the Voyager 2 spacecraft in 1986 (now in the solar system's heliosheath). Unlike the rings of other planets like Saturn, which are composed of a fine dust that reflects sunlight, the rings of Uranus consist of small boulders measuring 0.2-20m (0.7-66ft) across that reflect minimal sunlight, a major factor in their late discovery.

One reason for the large size of the ring material is that the rings are very young – no more than 600 million years old (Uranus formed roughly 4.6 billion years ago) – so they have not had much time to be broken down. They were created by one or several moons of Uranus being torn apart by its gravity, with the resultant debris being left to orbit the planet and 'shepherded' into rings by other moons. They range from a distance of about 39,000km (24,200 miles) from the centre of the planet to over 97,000km (60,300 miles) and are each just a few kilometres thick. There is no detectable material in between them, due to the shepherding effect of the nearby moons.

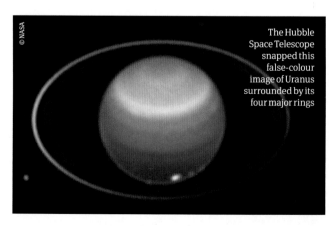

The Hubble Space Telescope snapped this false-colour image of Uranus surrounded by its four major rings

© NASA

Solar wind

How our Sun exerts its influence on the entire solar system

The Sun regularly emits a solar wind with speeds of 500 miles (800km) per second that affects the entire solar system. This wind is caused by hydrogen gas atoms being broken down into protons and electrons by the high temperatures of the Sun, which are consequently flung out of its orbit by the strong magnetic field. The tails of comets and the extension of the Earth's magnetic field are both a result of this solar wind. Solar flares and sunspots on the surface of the Sun increase the frequency and intensity of the wind during its 11-year solar activity cycle. Almost all stars in the universe have been observed to have a similar stellar wind. ✿

The Earth's magnetosphere has a tail caused by the solar wind

Why does Uranus spin sideways?

How come some objects in the solar system orbit with a retrograde rotation?

All the eight planets of the solar system (sorry, Pluto) have a counter-clockwise orbit around the Sun, and each rotates on an axis that runs between their north and south poles. Of these, six (including Earth) rotate with their poles approximately perpendicular (at a 90 degree angle) to their plane of orbit, so each side of the planet receives a roughly even amount of sunlight.

Uranus's rotational axis, however, is along its plane of orbit, a phenomenon known as 'retrograde revolution'. It takes Uranus approximately 84 Earth years to complete its orbit of the Sun, which means that the

northern and southern hemisphere each experience about 42 years of constant daylight (where the sun doesn't drop below the horizon) and darkness. The reason for this most likely occurred in the early formation of the solar system, when a large object (possibly a protoplanet – a planetary embryo) crashed into Uranus and knocked it onto its side. Venus has a similarly unusual rotation, in that it appears to rotate backwards when compared with its orbit around the Sun. ✿

> "It takes Uranus approximately 84 Earth years to complete its orbit of the Sun"

Orbit of Uranus around the Sun

As Uranus orbits on its side, no one is sure which is the north pole and which is the south

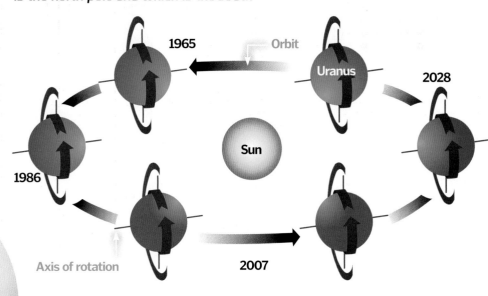

Uranus size comparison

How Uranus compares to Earth

Uranus's diameter is actually nearly five times that of Earth, with a mass equivalent to 14.5 Earths altogether.

12,756.3km   51,118km

> "There are five recognised dwarf planets in our solar system – Pluto, Eris, Makemake, Haumea and Ceres"

Dwarf planets

What is a dwarf planet and how is it distinguished from other celestial bodies?

When is a planet not a planet? Well, it's not as simple as you might think. Defining a planet into a particular category isn't easy, with the debate continuing to rage as to how exactly planets should be classified. According to the International Astronomical Union (IAU), dwarf planets are spherical objects in orbit around the Sun that are not moons, but they share their orbits with other debris which they have not been able to clear. It was the latter point that let Pluto down back in 2006, as it has other bodies within its orbit that it has not gathered. In addition, many bodies were discovered that were larger than Pluto, such as Eris, ultimately leading to its reclassification.

In simple terms, a dwarf planet can be regarded as a spherical object in our solar system exhibiting all or some of the properties of a planet, but lacking the necessary gravitational strength to have pulled other local objects into its influence.

There are currently five recognised dwarf planets in our solar system – these being Pluto, Eris, Makemake, Haumea and Ceres – but dozens more in the Kuiper belt, a disc-shaped region beyond Neptune, and the Oort cloud at the outer edge of the solar system, are being considered as candidates.

The five official dwarf planets and their unofficial brothers vary drastically in both composition and appearance, just as the main eight planets of the solar system do. Pluto is the only one of the five known to have its own moon – Charon, while Eris is the coldest of the bunch (and, indeed, the coldest known object in the solar system), with its surface temperature reaching as low as -250 degrees Celsius (-418 degrees Fahrenheit). Also of note is the dwarf planet Ceres, once regarded as a large spherical asteroid but recently promoted. Despite being the smallest dwarf planet, it is the largest object in the asteroid belt between Mars and Jupiter where it resides, accounting for about a quarter of the entire belt's mass. ✿

Size
Ceres has a diameter of 942km (585mi), which is just over one quarter the size of our moon

Mantle
It is estimated that Ceres' 100km (60mi)-thick mantle contains up to 200 million cubic kilometres (48 million cubic miles) of water-ice – one-seventh of the total volume of water on Earth

© NASA

How do the dwarf planets size up to Earth?

Mercury

Venus

Earth

Mars

Jupiter

Saturn

Uranus

Neptune

Stats
Haumea

Diameter:
1,436km (892mi)

Distance from Sun:
6.5 billion kilometres (4 billion miles)

Orbital period: 283 years

Stats
Earth

Diameter:
12,742km (7,918mi)

Distance from Sun:
150 million kilometres (93 million miles)

Orbital period: 1 year

Stats
Ceres

Diameter:
942km (585mi)

Distance from Sun:
414 million kilometres (275 million miles)

Orbital period: 4.6 years

Stats
Pluto

Diameter:
2,306km (1,433mi)

Distance from Sun:
5.9 billion kilometres (3.7 billion miles)

Orbital period: 248 years

CELEBRITY

1. Pluto
Once regarded as the ninth planet of our solar system, Pluto is now classified as a dwarf planet because it lives alongside similar-sized entities in the Kuiper belt.

© NASA

CHILLY

2. Eris
The coldest known planetary object in the solar system, the surface temperature on Eris (also found in the Kuiper belt) can drop as low as -250°C (-418°F).

© Lexicon

CLOSEST

3. Ceres
Found in the asteroid belt between Jupiter and Mars, Ceres is the closest dwarf planet to Earth but also the smallest, just one-quarter the size of our moon.

© NASA

DID YOU KNOW? In December 2011 the first planet smaller than Earth – Kepler-20e – was found outside the solar system

Inside Ceres
What's going on within the smallest dwarf planet in our solar system?

Surface
Ceres' surface bears marks of previous meteorite impacts and, despite having only a thin atmosphere, its surface temperature is about -38°C (-36°F) due to it being relatively near to the Sun, almost three times Earth's distance from the Sun

Core
Ceres has a solid rocky core. It is thought that it may once have had a hot and molten core like that of Earth, but its small size means it is unlikely that volatile material is still present due to its high rate of heat loss

Stats
Makemake
Diameter: 1,500km (932mi)

Distance from Sun: 6.9 billion kilometres (4.3 billion miles)

Orbital period: 310 years

Stats
Eris
Diameter: 2,326km (1,445mi)

Distance from Sun: 10.1 billion kilometres (6.3 billion miles)

Orbital period: 557 years

NASA's Dawn spacecraft will be the first to visit a dwarf planet, arriving at Ceres in 2015

© NASA/ESA

WHAT TYPE OF PLANET ARE YOU?
Are you a terrestrial planet, a gas giant or a dwarf planet? Or something else? Have a go at our flowchart below to find out...

START ARE YOU IN ORBIT AROUND THE SUN?

YES NO

YOU ARE... AN EXTRASOLAR PLANET
You are not from our solar system, and yet to be properly classified. You could be a super-Earth, or maybe you're made entirely of diamond. Nobody knows; you'll just have to wait to be found. Mysterious.

ARE YOU SPHERICAL? YES NO

YOU ARE... A MOON
You are a natural satellite that orbits a planet/dwarf planet. You might be the only moon or you may be one of many. You were pulled into orbit during the planet's formation and are considerably smaller than your host. Clingy.

YOU ARE... AN ASTEROID
You are a prolific potato-shaped rocky object. You're probably located in either the asteroid belt between Jupiter and Mars or the Kuiper belt beyond Uranus, where more than 90 per cent of your kind live. Sociable.

ARE YOU ICY? YES NO

ARE YOU ALSO IN ORBIT AROUND A PLANET? YES NO

YOU ARE... A TERRESTRIAL PLANET
You could be one of the rocky planets Mars, Earth, Venus or Mercury. You have a molten iron core and an atmosphere. On Venus, the climate is super-hot, but Mercury's is very cold. Atmospheric.

YOU ARE... A COMET
You're an irregular shape made mostly of ice, which melts and forms a dust tail. You have a separate tail composed of gas that always flows away from the Sun regardless of which direction you are travelling. Breezy.

HAVE YOU CLEARED YOUR NEIGHBOURHOOD? YES NO

YOU ARE... A GAS GIANT
You may be Jupiter, Saturn, Uranus or Neptune, the giants composed mostly of gas. You've cleared away all objects in your vicinity and exert an influence on everything around you due to your extremely high mass. Powerful.

ARE YOU MOSTLY MADE OF ROCK? YES NO

YOU ARE... A DWARF PLANET
You're bigger than an asteroid and spherical but generally smaller than a 'proper' planet. You don't orbit anything but the Sun, however you haven't managed to clear all local debris (or it hasn't yet formed into moons). Weakling.

© ESO

How hot is it on other worlds?

How infrared telescopes enable us to 'see' the temperatures of planets

A global temperature map, showing the white-hot heat of the equator

 Heat energy is emitted by all objects, including planets. The hotter the planet, the more radiation it gives off. Objects in space emit radiation across the electromagnetic (EM) spectrum – really hot objects, like stars and galaxies for instance, emit much of their energy in the visible, ultraviolet and x-ray range of the EM spectrum. However, celestial objects – such as planets and moons in particular – emit (or glow with) infrared radiation, which is outside the visible wavelength range. This means we cannot see this infrared light with our own eyes; we can only detect the visible light coming from the object. However, just because infrared rays are invisible, it doesn't mean they're not there.

Astronomers have put devices – such as the Spitzer Space Telescope – into orbit that collect and focus the infrared information from distant planets and display it as light we can see. The hotter the planet, the brighter the infrared light information it will produce. If you could see in infrared you would be able to 'see' variations in temperature across the surface of a planet. ✿

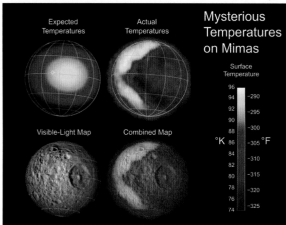

The infrared information of Saturn's moon Mimas here was collected by a composite infrared spectrometer (CIRS) on the Cassini spacecraft on 13 February 2010

How do you weigh planets?

It seems like an impossible task, but how can scientists use an orbiting moon to work out the weight of a planet?

Newton's Law of Gravitation states that every planetary body has its own gravitational field that pulls on nearby objects – such as moons or spacecraft – with a force proportional to its mass and inversely proportional to the square of the distance between the two objects. Newton also discovered that an object – a moon, for instance – will move at a constant speed and in a straight line unless acted upon by a force such as gravity that will keep the moon in orbit.

By observing the effect of a planet's gravitational attraction on an orbiting moon, scientists can measure the planet's mass. The gravitational attraction between the moon and the planet depends on their mass and the distance between their centres. The heavier the planet, the stronger its attraction to the moon and the faster the moon will travel. Measuring the distance from the planet to the moon and calculating how long it takes to orbit enables astronomers to calculate the weight of a planet. ✿

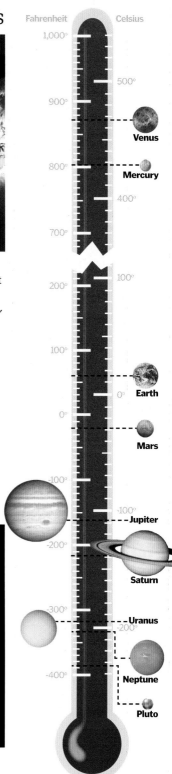

DID YOU KNOW? *The outer extent of the Oort Cloud is viewed as the edge of our solar system*

The Oort Cloud

The home of comets

The Oort Cloud is a giant sphere of icy cometary nuclei that surrounds our solar system. Its maximum distance is 1.9 light years away from the Sun, which is as far as the Sun's gravitational influence extends.

In 1950, Dutch astronomer Jan Oort developed the concept of this cloud as the origin of comets. It was created during the formation of the solar system, when planetesimal bodies gathered to form planets or moons. The gravitational influence of Uranus and Neptune sent some of these planetesimals outwards to form the Oort Cloud.

Over time the gravitational effects of the Sun, planets in the solar system and even nearby stars have caused objects to actually leave the Oort Cloud. They then either turn up in the form of comets in the inner solar system, or they are sent completely out of our system's influence altogether. Just as objects are lost from the cloud, new ones from outside the solar system can also be attracted into it. ✿

The Oort Cloud's population

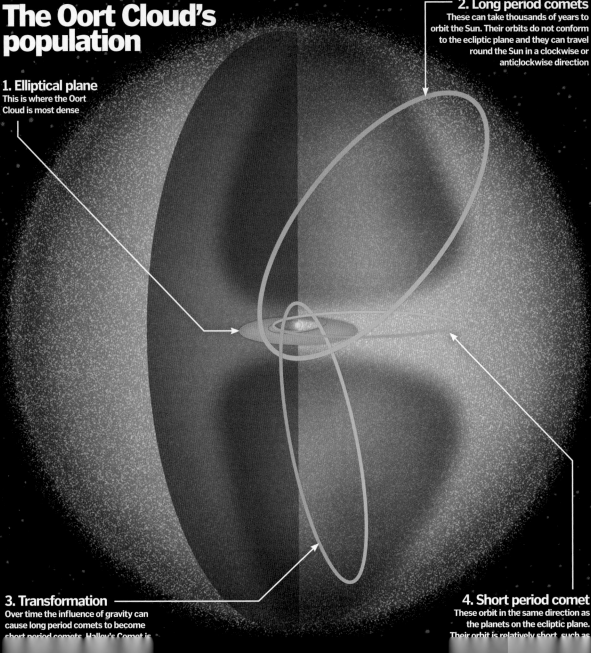

1. Elliptical plane
This is where the Oort Cloud is most dense

2. Long period comets
These can take thousands of years to orbit the Sun. Their orbits do not conform to the ecliptic plane and they can travel round the Sun in a clockwise or anticlockwise direction

3. Transformation
Over time the influence of gravity can cause long period comets to become short period comets. Halley's Comet is

4. Short period comet
These orbit in the same direction as the planets on the ecliptic plane. Their orbit is relatively short, such as

Sedna

Evidence of the Oort Cloud's existence is supported by the discovery on 14 November 2003 of the furthest object in the solar system. Named Sedna, it is currently 13 billion kilometres away from Earth. Its highly elliptical orbit around the Sun takes 11,250 years and to a maximum distance of 130 billion kilometres.

Sedna has a diameter of between 1,180 to 1,800 kilometres, making it larger than an asteroid but smaller than a planet. It is the second reddest object in the solar system after Mars, and its surface temperature is a very cold -240° Celsius.

A sticking point is that it is much closer than the predicted position of the Oort Cloud. One suggestion is that millions of years ago a rogue star passed by, causing comets and bodies like Sedna to form an inner Oort Cloud.

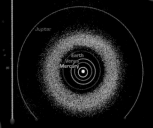

Planet killers

Remnants of failed planets, asteroids are dry, dusty and atmosphereless rocks drifting through space

Asteroids are the most numerous bodies in our solar system, with hundreds of thousands of them orbiting around the Sun in both belts and as individuals. They far outnumber our well-documented planets (and dwarf planets, to that matter) and are being studied by space agencies world wide, each of which are trying to shed some light on what historically were written off as simple floating rocks. However, asteroids are unique in the fact that they tell us much about the conditions of the universe post-big bang, how astrophysics effect space phenomena and how planets are formed, granting the scientific community great insight into our solar system's origins and workings.

FAIL
1. Asteroid
The city of Dallas, Texas, is going to be destroyed by an asteroid – the American government fires huge lasers to destroy it but only succeed in breaking it into small pieces that still go on to destroy the city.

BIG FAIL
2. Armageddon
Another asteroid is on course to destroy the world – the American government hatches a plan to plant a bomb in its core to split it in two so it will miss Earth. However, an earlier meteorite destroys Shanghai, China.

EPIC FAIL
3. Deep Impact
Yet another asteroid is on a collision course with the Earth – the American government detonates nuclear bombs to destroy it but only succeed in splitting it in two pieces, one of which destroys ¼ of the planet.

DID YOU KNOW? The first probe dedicated to studying asteroids was the NEAR Shoemaker, launched by NASA in 1997

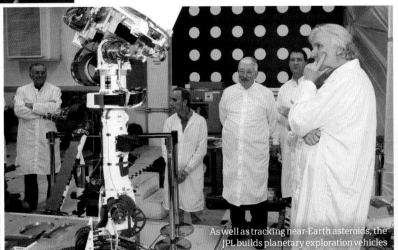

As well as tracking near-Earth asteroids, the JPL builds planetary exploration vehicles

Structures

There are three types of asteroid: carbonaceous (C-type), siliceous (S-type) and metallic (M-type) variants, each corresponding to the composition of an asteroid, be that stony, stony-iron or iron. The composition of an asteroid – be that shape or material – is dependent on when and what it was formed from, as well as if it has undergone reconstruction post collision.

Initially, at the dawn of the solar system, most asteroids were much larger than now commonly found by astronomers, with sizes more consistent with a planet such as Mars and shapes varying wildly. However, the radioactive decay of elements within the asteroid rock melted these larger bodies, and during their fluid stage, gravity pulled them into spherical shapes before they cooled. At this point, though, many smaller asteroids – which cooled more efficiently than their larger brethren – did not reach melting point and retained their uniform rocky-metallic composition and their initial irregular shape.

This process of asteroid formation can be seen vividly when contrasting many of the asteroids that modern scientists and astronomers are currently studying. Take the asteroid Ceres (Ceres was the first asteroid to be discovered and is now considered by some astronomers as a dwarf planet) for example – this is a large asteroid (it has an equatorial radius of 487km) and, in turn, is both spherical in structure and carbonaceous composition (C-class), as it was pulled apart easily and cooled slowly. However, if you compare Ceres to Ida for example, which is a small asteroid (it has a mean radius of 15.7km), you find the latter is both irregular in shape (funnily, it looks like a potato) and heavily composed of iron and magnesium-silicates (S-class).

Orbits

The majority of asteroids in our solar system are found in a concentration known as the main belt, which lies between Mars and Jupiter. This belt contains thousands of asteroids and takes roughly four and a half years to orbit the Sun on a slightly elliptical course and low inclination. Despite the fact that they all orbit in the same direction, collisions do occur at low velocities (for such large objects) and these cause the asteroids to be continuously broken up into smaller variants. Of this main belt, certain groups have been captured into peculiar orbits, such as the Trojan group of asteroids that follow Jupiter's orbit, or the Amor or Apollo groups, which cross the paths of Earth and Mars respectively and the Aten group, which sits inside Earth's own orbit.

© Science Photo Library

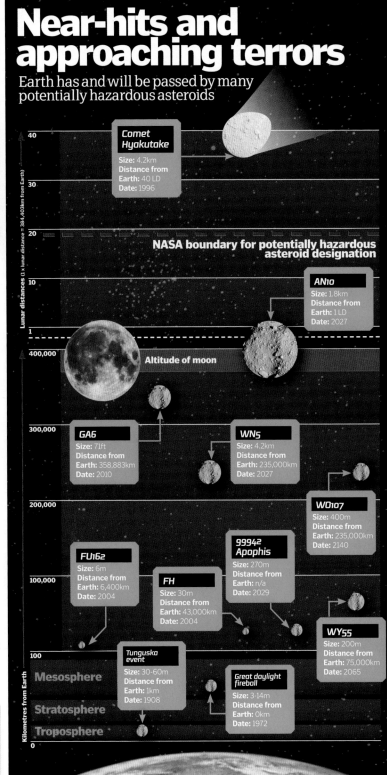

Near-hits and approaching terrors
Earth has and will be passed by many potentially hazardous asteroids

Lunar distances (1 x lunar distance = 384,403km from Earth)

Comet Hyakutake
Size: 4.2km
Distance from Earth: 40 LD
Date: 1996

NASA boundary for potentially hazardous asteroid designation

AN10
Size: 1.8km
Distance from Earth: 1 LD
Date: 2027

Altitude of moon

GA6
Size: 71ft
Distance from Earth: 358,883km
Date: 2010

WN5
Size: 4.2km
Distance from Earth: 235,000km
Date: 2027

WO107
Size: 400m
Distance from Earth: 235,000km
Date: 2140

FU162
Size: 6m
Distance from Earth: 6,400km
Date: 2004

99942 Apophis
Size: 270m
Distance from Earth: n/a
Date: 2029

FH
Size: 30m
Distance from Earth: 43,000km
Date: 2004

WY55
Size: 200m
Distance from Earth: 75,000km
Date: 2065

Kilometres from Earth

Tunguska event
Size: 30-60m
Distance from Earth: 1km
Date: 1908

Great daylight fireball
Size: 3-14m
Distance from Earth: 0km
Date: 1972

Mesosphere

Stratosphere

Troposphere

"The composition of an asteroid is dependent on when and what it was formed from"

Asteroids in our solar system

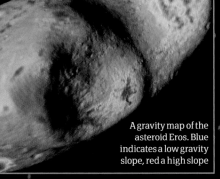

A gravity map of the asteroid Eros. Blue indicates a low gravity slope, red a high slope

Most of the asteroids in our solar system are positioned between the orbits of Mars and Jupiter, clustered in massive belts. However, some come close to Earth on their individual orbits and these are referred to as near-Earth asteroids. We take a look at some of the most notable...

Saturn's orbit

Jupiter's orbit

Earth's o

Main belt →

Mars's orbit

Direction of orbits

Eros

Dimension: 16.84km
Aphelion: 266.762Gm (1.783 AU)
Perihelion: 169.548Gm (1.133 AU)
Orbital period: 643.219 days
Escape velocity: 0.0103km/s
Temperature: -227K
Spectral type: S

With a one-in-ten chance of hitting either Earth or Mars in the next million years, Eros is one of the largest and well-studied near-Earth asteroids. In fact, Eros is one of a few asteroids to actually be landed upon by an Earth probe, and as such we have a cavalcade of information on it.

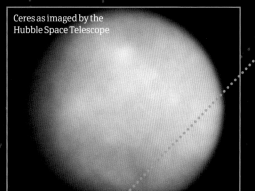

Ceres as imaged by the Hubble Space Telescope

Ceres

Dimension: 590 miles   **Aphelion:** 446,669,320km (2.9858 AU)   **Perihelion:** 380,995,855km (2.5468 AU)   **Orbital period:** 1,680.5 days   **Escape velocity:** 0.51km/s   **Temperature:** -167K   **Spectral type:** C

Technically classed as a dwarf planet, Ceres – named after the Roman goddess of growing plants and the harvest – is by far the most massive body in the asteroid belt. Indeed, it is so big compared to its neighbouring asteroids that it contains 32 per cent of the belt's total mass.

Icarus

Dimension: 1.4km   **Aphelion:** 294.590Gm (1.969 AU)   **Perihelion:** 27.923Gm (0.187 AU)   **Orbital period:** 408.778 days   **Escape velocity:** 0.000 74 km/s   **Temperature:** -242K   **Spectral type:** U

Icarus is from the Apollo asteroid sub-class of near-Earth asteroids and has the unusual characteristic that at its perihelion it is closer to the Sun than Mercury. Named after the Icarus of Greek mythology, the asteroid passes by Earth at gaps of nine, 19 and 38 years.

How to deflect an impact...

Nuclear explosion

1. Nuclear explosions
This method involves firing a nuclear bomb into the asteroid. Problems may occur if the explosion just splits the asteroid into smaller pieces.

2. Multiple explosions
Detonating multiple nuclear bombs close to impact would push the asteroid to one side and onto another, non-Earth destroying trajectory.

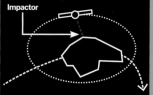

Impactor

3. Kinetic impactor
Similar to the last option, this method would involve firing a solid projectile into an asteroid in order to alter its momentum and change its course.

5 TOP FACTS
ASTEROIDS

Naked
1 The only asteroid in the main belt visible to the naked eye is Vesta, which has a mean diameter of 530km and contains nine per cent of the entire asteroid belt's mass.

Coma
2 The way comets and asteroids are distinguished relies on visual appearance, with comets displaying a perceptible coma behind them while asteroids have none.

Naming
3 Once an asteroid has been discovered it can only be named under the consultation of the International Astronomical Union, who will approve or disapprove the proposition.

Photo
4 The first true asteroids to be photographed close up were Gaspra in 1991 and Ida in 1993. They were imaged by the Galileo space probe en route to Jupiter.

New
5 The latest asteroid to be landed on is Itokawa, an S type asteroid that crosses path of Mars. The Hayabu space probe returned to E with a surface sample.

DID YOU KNOW? The asteroid Ida has its own moon, Dactyl, which orbits at a distance of 56 miles

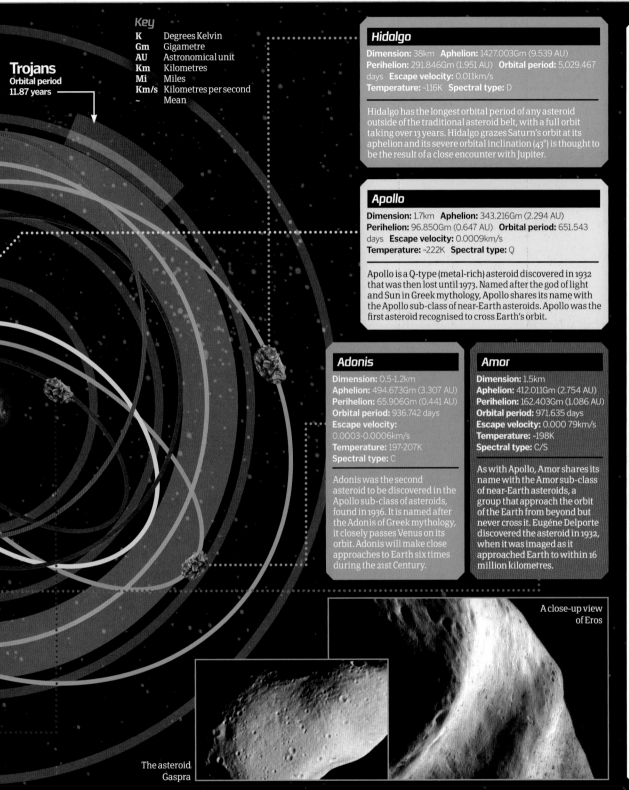

Key
K	Degrees Kelvin
Gm	Gigametre
AU	Astronomical unit
Km	Kilometres
Mi	Miles
Km/s	Kilometres per second
~	Mean

Trojans
Orbital period
11.87 years

Hidalgo

Dimension: 38km   **Aphelion:** 1427.003Gm (9.539 AU)
Perihelion: 291.846Gm (1.951 AU)   **Orbital period:** 5,029.467 days   **Escape velocity:** 0.011km/s
Temperature: ~116K   **Spectral type:** D

Hidalgo has the longest orbital period of any asteroid outside of the traditional asteroid belt, with a full orbit taking over 13 years. Hidalgo grazes Saturn's orbit at its aphelion and its severe orbital inclination (43°) is thought to be the result of a close encounter with Jupiter.

Apollo

Dimension: 1.7km   **Aphelion:** 343.216Gm (2.294 AU)
Perihelion: 96.850Gm (0.647 AU)   **Orbital period:** 651.543 days   **Escape velocity:** 0.0009km/s
Temperature: ~222K   **Spectral type:** Q

Apollo is a Q-type (metal-rich) asteroid discovered in 1932 that was then lost until 1973. Named after the god of light and Sun in Greek mythology, Apollo shares its name with the Apollo sub-class of near-Earth asteroids. Apollo was the first asteroid recognised to cross Earth's orbit.

Adonis

Dimension: 0.5-1.2km
Aphelion: 494.673Gm (3.307 AU)
Perihelion: 65.906Gm (0.441 AU)
Orbital period: 936.742 days
Escape velocity:
0.0003-0.0006km/s
Temperature: 197-207K
Spectral type: C

Adonis was the second asteroid to be discovered in the Apollo sub-class of asteroids, found in 1936. It is named after the Adonis of Greek mythology, it closely passes Venus on its orbit. Adonis will make close approaches to Earth six times during the 21st Century.

Amor

Dimension: 1.5km
Aphelion: 412.011Gm (2.754 AU)
Perihelion: 162.403Gm (1.086 AU)
Orbital period: 971.635 days
Escape velocity: 0.000 79km/s
Temperature: ~198K
Spectral type: C/S

As with Apollo, Amor shares its name with the Amor sub-class of near-Earth asteroids, a group that approach the orbit of the Earth from beyond but never cross it. Eugéne Delporte discovered the asteroid in 1932, when it was imaged as it approached Earth to within 16 million kilometres.

A close-up view of Eros

The asteroid Gaspra

Filling the gap

Franz Xaver von Zach (1754-1832), astronomer and leader of the Seeberg Observatory, Germany, believed that there was a missing planet orbiting the Sun between Mars and Jupiter. To prove his theory von Zach organised a group of 24 astronomers and gave them each a part of the celestial zodiac to search in an attempt to track down his errant planet. Unfortunately, despite such a large team, von Zach was beaten to the discovery by the Italian Catholic priest and mathematician Giuseppe Piazzi, who accidentally discovered the asteroid Ceres in 1801.

Franz Xaver Von Zach

Giuseppe Piazzi

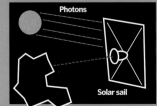
4. Solar sail
This method would involve attaching a 5,000km-wide sail to an asteroid. The constant pressure of sunlight over a large area would slowly alter its course.

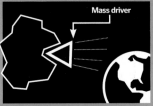
5. Mass driver
A huge space drill would be fired into the asteroid, and drill out the innards before firing them into space, altering its mass and changing the course.

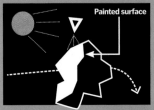
6. Paint
By coating parts of the asteroid in paint, the amounts of thermal radiation emitted by the asteroid's Sun-facing side could be increased, altering its path.

"A meteor is the visible streak of light that occurs when a meteoroid enters the Earth's atmosphere"

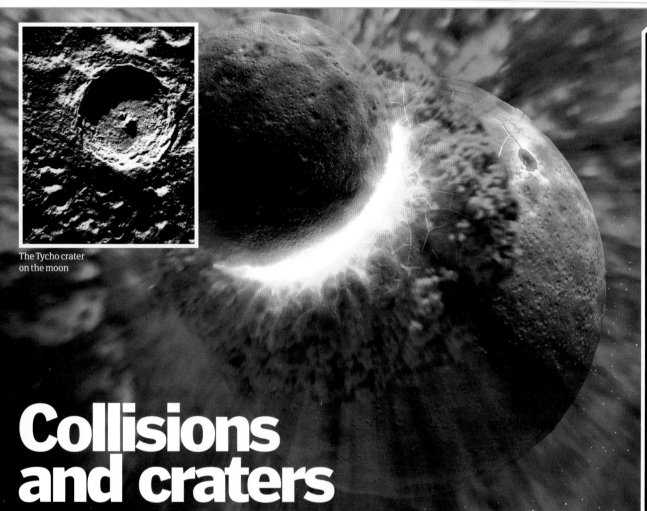

The Tycho crater on the moon

Collisions and craters

Evidence of collisions can be found everywhere

When asteroids collide with each other there are three main outcomes, each of which depends on the size of the impacting asteroid. If the incoming asteroid is 1/50,000th the size of the larger body then it will merely create a large crater, sending small fragments out into space. If the impactor is roughly 1/50,000th the size of the impacted, then the latter will fracture before breaking into rock and dust, before being pulled back together into a ball of rubble by gravity. Finally, if the incoming asteroid is larger than 1/50,000th the size of the other, larger asteroid, then it will immediately shatter into pieces and form a mini belt of smaller asteroids.

Very rarely, asteroids collide with the Earth, the most notable of which in the past 100 million years was the instigator of the Cretaceous-Tertiary extinction event that wiped out the majority of the dinosaurs 65.5 million years ago. However, there is evidence across the world of many other lesser-sized asteroids impacting the Earth, with their craters remaining a testament to their size. Importantly, their size is not directly represented by the size of the crater, which is roughly ten times the size of the impacting body. These impacts are postulated to have occurred infrequently over the Earth's 4 billion year life span.

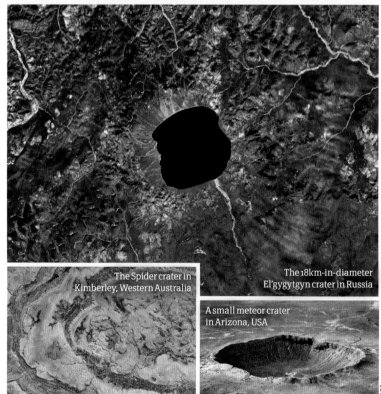

The Spider crater in Kimberley, Western Australia

The 18km-in-diameter El'gygytgyn crater in Russia

A small meteor crater in Arizona, USA

© NASA

Asteroid attack diary...
Better clear your schedule

2027

390,000km
NAME: 1999 AN10
DATE: AUGUST 2027
Soon after AN10's discovery in 1999, observations suggested it could get as close as 30,577km (18,999 miles) to Earth. Additional data puts it farther out.

800m

2028

248,000km
NAME: 2001 WN5
DATE: JUNE 2028
When WN5 zooms by, it should be bright enough to be visible with binoculars.

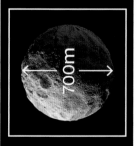
700m

2029

37,000km
NAME: 99942 APOPHIS
DATE: APRIL 2029
Astronomers calculated seven possibly hazardous encounters with Apophis. The next closest is in 2171.

270m

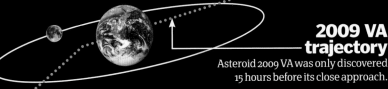

DID YOU KNOW?

Phew! Close one...
On 6 November 2009, an asteroid 22 feet in diameter passed Earth at a distance of 8,700 miles – the equivalent of a bullet missing a human by a few millimetres.

2009 VA trajectory
Asteroid 2009 VA was only discovered 15 hours before its close approach.

DID YOU KNOW? *After landing the NEAR Shoemaker was capable of moving at 1.5 metres per second on Eros' surface*

Meteor

Asteroids vs meteoroids vs comets

Despite common misconceptions, these space phenomena are different from each other. An asteroid is a small solar system body in orbit around the Sun, which are sometimes referred to or classed as minor planets. A meteoroid, however, is a sand-to-boulder-sized particle of debris drifting through space in orbit around the Sun or other bodies. They are smaller than asteroids and tend to travel at higher speeds; their composition ranging from iron to ice. Crucially, though, meteoroids differ from meteors and meteorites, although they are all part of the same body. A meteor is the visible streak of light that occurs when a meteoroid enters the Earth's atmosphere, while a meteorite is the remaining part of the meteoroid that impacts Earth.

Finally, comets are ice-based small solar system bodies that when close to the Sun display a visible coma (a nebulous temporary atmosphere) and tail of ice, dust and rock particles. Comets, unlike asteroids, generally origin in the outer solar system.

Comet

Asteroids, especially those in the main belt, are prone to collisions

Asteroid

6 x © NASA

Blast off
The Near Earth Asteroid Rendezvous (NEAR) space probe Shoemaker is launched.

JPL engineers work on the Dawn space probe pre-launch

On its trail
A chart from the JPL tracking the movement of an asteroid through space.

The asteroid finders

The Near Earth Asteroid Tracking (NEAT) program run at NASA's Jet Propulsion Laboratory has one sole purpose: to find, explore and track near-Earth asteroids

The Near Earth Asteroid Tracking program based at NASA's Jet Propulsion Laboratory has discovered thousands of asteroids during its life span, both from its range of ground-based telescopes – a good example is the GEODSS (Ground-based Electro-Optical Deep Space Surveillance) telescope located on Haleakala, Maui, Hawaii – to its deep space probes, scanning space for new asteroids and other space phenomenon. Its greatest achievement, however, has been its successful insertion of the NEAR (Near Earth Asteroid Rendezvous) Shoemaker space probe into orbit around the asteroid Eros in 2001, as well as landing upon its surface. This made it the first ever spacecraft to complete a soft-land (a landing where the probe is functional afterwards) on any asteroid.

The mission to Eros was primarily to return data on its composition, mineralogy, morphology, internal mass distribution and magnetic field. However, considering its success and time spent orbiting the asteroid, it was possible to also study its regolith properties (the loose material scattered over its surface), interactions with solar winds and spin rate. This information was garnered with the spacecraft's equipped x-ray/gamma ray spectrometer (used to measure the intensity of gamma radiation), near-infrared imaging spectrograph (used to measure and image the light properties of the near-infrared end of the electromagnetic spectrum), multi-spectral camera fitted with CCD imaging detector, laser rangefinder and

magnetometer (measures the strength and/or direction of a magnetic field). Indeed, thanks to this wealth of information, we now have more first-hand data on Eros than any other asteroid.

NASA's Jet Propulsion Laboratory in California

OUR DYING SUN

It's vital to our existence, but it's also a star progressing through its life cycle

"The Sun fuses about 620 million metric tons (683 million short tons) of hydrogen per second"

5 TOP FACTS
STAR PROPERTIES

Bigger isn't better
1 The larger the star, the shorter its life. Although bigger stars have more fuel, they have to quickly consume it through nuclear fusion to maintain hydrostatic equilibrium.

The same, but different
2 All stars are made from hydrogen and helium, and they all started out with the same proportions – they contain about 1/4 helium and 3/4 hydrogen.

More red dwarfs
3 The vast majority of stars are red dwarfs, which can have masses as low as seven per cent that of the Sun's mass. They can burn for no less than 10 trillion years.

Not yellow dwarfs
4 The name 'yellow dwarf' is a misnomer: these can range from white to yellow. The Sun is white, but it appears yellow due to the scattering of light in our atmosphere.

Second best
5 The brightest star in our s aside from the Sun is anot yellow dwarf, alpha centa which is actually a binary system about 4.2 light ye away from Earth.

DID YOU KNOW? *The Sun's death could extend the habitable zone to include planets that were previously uninhabitable*

Inside the Sun

Unlike rocky planets such as Earth, the Sun does not have a definitive outer boundary. However, the different layers beneath the Sun's surface are defined by their temperatures and density. Although the core is on average the hottest part of the Sun, the complex relationship between rising heated gases and falling cooled gases create temperature fluctuations within the layers of the Sun itself.

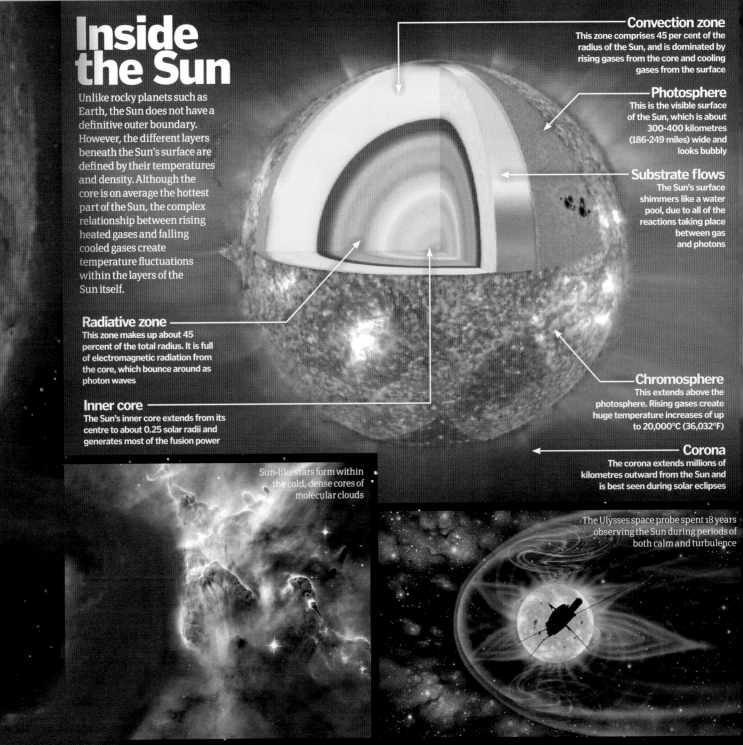

Convection zone
This zone comprises 45 per cent of the radius of the Sun, and is dominated by rising gases from the core and cooling gases from the surface

Photosphere
This is the visible surface of the Sun, which is about 300-400 kilometres (186-249 miles) wide and looks bubbly

Substrate flows
The Sun's surface shimmers like a water pool, due to all of the reactions taking place between gas and photons

Radiative zone
This zone makes up about 45 percent of the total radius. It is full of electromagnetic radiation from the core, which bounce around as photon waves

Inner core
The Sun's inner core extends from its centre to about 0.25 solar radii and generates most of the fusion power

Chromosphere
This extends above the photosphere. Rising gases create huge temperature increases of up to 20,000°C (36,032°F)

Corona
The corona extends millions of kilometres outward from the Sun and is best seen during solar eclipses

Sun-like stars form within the cold, dense cores of molecular clouds

The Ulysses space probe spent 18 years observing the Sun during periods of both calm and turbulence

 Without its existence, there wouldn't be life on Earth. In the grand scheme of things, however, our Sun is simply another star among the other hundreds of billions of stars in the universe. Officially, the Sun is a class G2V star – in other words, a main-sequence yellow dwarf. Yellow dwarfs have a temperature range of 5,000 to 6,000 degrees Celsius (9,030 to 1,080 degrees Fahrenheit), and their

mass is about 80 to 120 per cent of the mass of the Sun. That means that the Sun is one of the biggest yellow dwarfs in the group.

Like other yellow dwarfs, the Sun converts hydrogen to helium in its core through nuclear fusion, which generates massive amounts of energy and light. The Sun fuses about 620 million metric tons (683 million short tons) of hydrogen per second. Based on this speed, astronomers believe that the Sun is about halfway through

its life cycle. About 40 per cent of the hydrogen has been converted, leaving another 3 to 5 billion years before the Sun evolves into the next stage in its life cycle: a red giant.

But let's start at the beginning. The Sun formed approximately 4.5 billion years ago, at the same time as the rest of the solar system. At this time a spinning molecular cloud of dust, hydrogen and helium flattened out into a disk, with a gaseous sphere at its centre that contained most of the

mass. This sphere had a gravitational pull that attracted dust and other materials from the disk, which caused the sphere to compress until it began converting the hydrogen to helium. A star – in this case, our Sun – was born.

The Sun can't keep fusing hydrogen indefinitely, though – there's a finite supply. Nuclear fusion occurs in the Sun's core due to gravitational pressure, which heats the core to 15 million degrees Celsius (27 million degrees Fahrenheit) and splits the

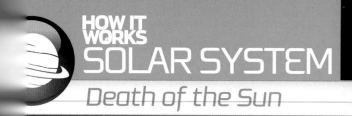
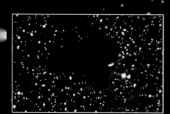

The Spitzer Space Telescope captured this image that reveals a molecular outflow of supersonic gas from a young star colliding with dust and gas from the surrounding interstellar medium and creating a nebula-type material. This stage is a particularly energetic phase of a star's life

hydrogen atoms. There's a delicate balance, known as 'hydrostatic equilibrium', between the inward compression exerted by gravity and the outward pressure from the energy created by the nuclear reactions. As the Sun's hydrogen supply is used up, the nuclear fusion in its core will decrease, and the core will contract. The core will heat up to a temperature of 100 billion degrees Celsius (180 billion degrees Fahrenheit) and begin fusing helium into carbon. The outer layers of the Sun will expand as it becomes a red giant. This means that the Sun's radius will be 250 times larger than its current radius, and it will swallow the Earth.

Astronomers once thought that because the Sun's gravitational pull will weaken when it becomes a red giant, the associated planetary movement outwards away from the Sun might spare our planet. However, the most recent projections show that the Earth would likely still be in the outer layers of the Sun, where it will be pulled in and vaporised. Even if the Earth itself is spared, astronomers still believe that the increasing heat from the Sun will eliminate life on Earth about one billion years from now. ✿

The life (and death) of a star

All stars follow the same basic pattern of their life cycle until the red giant stage. Stars bigger than the Sun go supernova and then turn into a black hole or a neutron star. Stars like the Sun progress over billions of years to a cold, dead star known as a 'black dwarf'.

1 Dense clouds start to collapse
Stars begin when giant molecular clouds full of hydrogen, helium and dust collapse into tiny fragments, which coalesce into potential stars called 'protostars'.

2 Pressure and temperature begin to rise
If there is enough released energy from the cloud collapse, these gaseous spheres become super-hot.

3 Stellar adolescence
When core temperatures reach 10 million degrees Celsius (18 million degrees Fahrenheit), nuclear fusion begins.

4 Star moves into main sequence
As nuclear fusion continues, it releases massive amounts of heat as energy, which pushes against the energy exerted by gravitational forces.

5 Hydrostatic equilibrium
Hydrostatic equilibrium – when the nuclear fusion energy is in balance with the star's gravity – is quickly reached in larger stars like the Sun. This stabilises the star.

A star is (re)born

When a star dies via supernova, it explosively ejects great volumes of material. Sometimes this matter forms a nebulae, essentially an interstellar cloud of gas and dust, which is perfect for the formation of new stars.

1. Nebulae
This floating cloud contains ionised gases, helium, hydrogen and dust particles

2. Stellar nursery
If the nebulae is dense enough and has low enough temperatures, the matter may begin to form into stars, creating a sort of stellar nursery

4. Supernova
The star goes supernova, sending gases and dust outward into the universe with the potential for creating new stars

3. Mature star
A mature star progresses through its main sequence stage, burning rapidly through its supply of hydrogen (only large stars go supernova) and becoming a red giant or supergiant

Light without the star

The light from an exploding star will not reach Earth until long after the star has died

Star light
Because the speed of light is finite, it takes time for us to see the light from an exploding star

Light source is no more
Light from the last observed supernova was seen on Earth about 20,000 years after the event

6 Star solidly on the main sequence
The mature star continues to fuse hydrogen to helium. For the Sun, this is about the rate of 620 million metric tons (683 million short tons) of hydrogen per second.

7 Expanding shell as core compresses
When the star reaches the end of its hydrogen supply, the core begins to collapse as the outer layers of the star expand.

8 Red giant
Stars like the Sun progress quickly into a red giant, typically several hundred times the size of the original star.

9 Star collapses
The helium is consumed by the core, and the resulting gravitational instability ends in a collapse.

10 White dwarf
With its outer layers sloughed off, the core of the star – usually comprising carbon and oxygen – cools down.

EXPLORATION

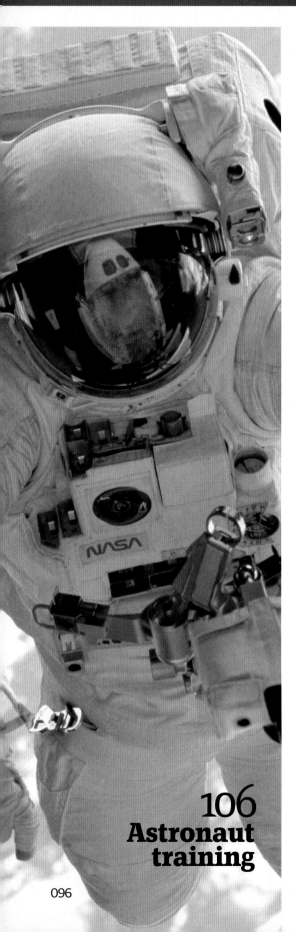

**106
Astronaut
training**

**112
Life in
space**

098
Life on Mars

132
Mega rockets

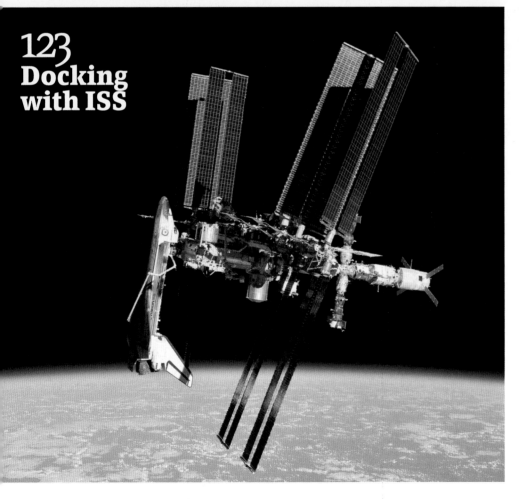

123
Docking with ISS

170
Satellites & space junk

IS THERE LIFE ON MARS?

In August 2012, NASA's Mars Science Laboratory landed on Mars. Learn how the biggest, most advanced rover yet is exploring the Red Planet and what NASA expects to find

It seemed a lonely existence just to see as far as what we thought was the edge of the universe 100 years ago. Turns out, it was just the far fringes of the Milky Way. Now our most powerful orbital telescopes can send us images of galaxies billions of light years from Earth, and though this has inspired hope in astronomers of eventually detecting intelligent life somewhere in the billions of worlds out there, until then our limited technology has left us scraping the surface of a desolate red-coloured planet that, on average, is around 225 million kilometres (140 million miles) from Earth – a mere eight light minutes. That's a cosmic heartbeat away that took the Mars rover Curiosity, also known as the Mars Science Laboratory, nine months to reach, and though the odds of mankind

discovering life on another planet within our own lifetimes are similarly astronomical, Curiosity is keeping the dream alive. Since landing, its primary mission is to study Mars for a full Martian year (about 687 days), gathering samples and exploring its surface like no other rover before it; making the most comprehensive assessment yet of whether Mars was ever capable of supporting life.

This is far from the first time NASA, or any other governmental space organisation, has undertaken a mission to investigate our second-closest planetary neighbour in the solar system. In the last 50 years, four different space agencies have sent 39 different probes, satellites and rovers to the Red Planet. The first two, Korabl 4 and 5, were Martian probes launched, respectively, on 10 October and 14 October 1960 by

the USSR, and both of which were abject failures, unable even to obtain orbit around the Earth. The USSR's next attempt in 1962, Korabl 11, achieved Earth orbit but then broke apart. Korabl 13 suffered the same fate as Korabl 11 and the US's first shot at a Mars flyby, with NASA's Mariner 3, failed to release a heat shield when it entered Earth orbit, the weight of which made it too heavy to achieve a Mars trajectory. Like so much other space junk, the terminated Mariner 3 project is now fated to orbit the Sun forever.

So it took a total of six attempts at getting to Mars before Mariner 4 flew past the planet in 1964 and took 21 photos of the surface in unprecedented detail. Since then 16 missions to Mars have overcome the difficult launch stage and achieved their goal, sending back data that has increased exponentially with our own space

THE STATS
MSL IN NUMBERS

ATMOSPHERIC ENTRY SPEED:	**21,240km/h**	COST:	**$2.5bn (£1.6bn)**
GALE CRATER DIAMETER: **154km**	LASER RANGE: **7m**	MOBILITY RANGE: **20km**	ON-BOARD CAMERAS: **17**

DID YOU KNOW? *Thanks to Spirit and Opportunity, we already know that Mars used to be much warmer and wetter*

Why Mars?

The primary reason why we're incessantly firing more investigatory craft at Mars than any other planet is that it's close to us. Not as close as Venus, but the surface of the second-closest planet to the Sun has an atmospheric pressure 92 times that of Earth and a 462°C (863°F) temperature that's hot enough to melt zinc. That was enough to put the Soviet probe Venera 7 out of action within an hour when it landed on Venus in 1970, and enough to put NASA off sending its own lander to be cooked and crushed on the deadly planet.

By contrast, the thin atmosphere and -140°C to -20°C (-220°F to 68°F) temperature range on the surface of Mars is far less hostile to our intrepid robots. Unlike Venus, Mars also exists in the same 'Goldilocks' orbital zone as the Earth, that balmy circumstellar habitable region where a planet with the right atmospheric pressure can maintain liquid water on its surface. Moreover, we've already discovered evidence for the wet stuff on Mars - and where there's liquid water, there's potential for life. So, for now, it's our still our best shot.

Curiosity's extendable arm has a variety of instruments that can analyse rocks on Mars for evidence of a previously wet environment

exploration technology. Based on the vital information gathered by the first successful soft landing on Mars, Viking 1, NASA's 1975 Viking 2 craft was able to land in a more advantageous position closer to the Martian north pole, to help take the photos that produced the Martian atlas still used today. In 1996 the Mars Global Surveyor (MGS) became one of the most successful Mars orbiters ever, taking more images than all other Mars missions put together. And it seems that NASA in particular has been getting much better at the Mars gig recently; since the turn of the millennium, the US space agency has launched five missions to Mars, all of them a resounding success and with two that have exceeded their operating lifetimes by 15 times the original NASA warranty. The Mars Exploration Rover Spirit was launched in June 2003 and

landed on Mars in January 2004, moving several kilometres across the surface before it found evidence of water existing some time in the past. Spirit's success was amplified by the fact that it hobbled with one stuck wheel in its final year, a blessing in disguise for NASA as the public warmed to the intrepid vehicle while it dutifully soldiered on despite the odds.

Opportunity was launched a month after Spirit and is still active today, having roved a 33-kilometre (20.5-mile) stretch to a crater called Endeavour that's 22 kilometres (13.7 miles) in diameter, which it is currently exploring. The tenacity of both Spirit and Opportunity bodes well for NASA's next generation of Mars rover, Curiosity, which launched on 26 November 2011 and landed on Mars on 6 August 2012. ✿

"On 5 August 2012, the MSL will enter the Martian atmosphere, 125km (78mi) above the planet"

Journey to the Red Planet

Three months after the landing of both Spirit and Opportunity, NASA began research for instruments to be used aboard the Mars Science Laboratory. But exploring and experimenting on Mars was only half the mission; first Curiosity needed to get to Mars. At the size and weight of a small car – five times that of Curiosity's predecessors – NASA couldn't simply rely on the old technology to safely deliver the rover. There were several factors to consider when sending a vehicle of this sort to another planet: how to escape Earth's gravity and set Curiosity on the right trajectory for Mars, keeping a steady course en route, entering Mars's atmosphere and then safely landing.

First of all, the launch vehicle needed to be able to provide the appropriate amount of velocity to escape the Earth's gravity. Considering the fact that the fully loaded Curiosity weighs in at 900 kg (2,000 lbs), NASA chose the tried-and-tested technology of the Atlas V 541, a variation on the Atlas V ELV (expendable launch vehicle) family with a near-perfect record since its maiden voyage in 2002. When fuelled with the liquid oxygen and kerosene propellant that makes up half of its weight, the Atlas V can provide a whopping 387,500 kg-force (854,300 lbs-force) of thrust. That was enough to launch a 6,634-kg (14,625-lbs) satellite into orbit in 2008, so Curiosity was comfortably within the Atlas V's payload limit.

Attached to the Atlas V were four solid rocket motors. These were designed to give the Atlas V the additional lift it required to achieve orbit. Their solid fuel and oxidiser propellant provided this necessary boost and, once ignited, burned until their fuel was completely expended before falling back to Earth. Once the Atlas had achieved the right altitude, the brawn of the mission had done its job and it was time for the brains to start working.

The second stage of the launch involved the Centaur, the upper-stage rocket that housed a liquid hydrogen and oxygen engine, the Curiosity payload and the flight control computer. The Centaur fired twice with up to 10,100 kg-force (22,300 lbs-force) of thrust, using the computer to precisely adjust its direction: once to insert itself into low Earth orbit and again to launch Curiosity in its spacecraft to Mars with a carefully calculated altitude and rate of spin. Having shed its protective fairing, the active part of the Mars Science Laboratory had gone from a pre-launch, complete shuttle weight of 531,000 kg (1.17 million lbs) to a cruise configuration of 3,893 kg (8,463 lbs).

The MSL cruise stage didn't work all that differently from the cruise control in a terrestrial car. Speeding along at a velocity (relative to the Sun) of 30,150 km (18,734 mi) per hour, it made a total of six corrections to its trajectory along the way; the equivalent of nudging the steering wheel to stay on course. The flight computer did this using an on-board star scanner that tracked the position of the cruise stage relative to the stars, powering up its hydrazine-fed propulsion system when required. A vital element of this part of the mission was to monitor the health of the spacecraft over the nine-month transit, pumping coolant around systems that got hot, like the solar panels and motors, while insulating instruments sensitive to the cold from the near absolute-zero temperatures of space.

On 6 August 2012, Curiosity entered the Martian atmosphere, which begins 125 km (78 mi) above the planet. Here, the aeroshell, a heatshield designed to protect the MSL during its descent, separated and began its journey through the atmosphere to the surface. A parachute deployed 11 km (6.8 mi) from the surface, while the aeroshell fell away at eight km (4.9 mi) as Curiosity approached the surface with a radar to adjust its position for optimum landing. The entire backshell, parachute and all, separated from Curiosity at an altitude of 1.6 km (0.9 mi) where a new, rocket-guided landing system slowed its descent. The final delivery system was the 'sky crane', which lowered Curiosity onto the surface for a soft landing.

1 Cruise stage
In its approach to the Mars, NASA engineers made their final calculations.

2 Cruise separation
As it entered the Martian atmosphere, the cruise phase separated from the MSL.

LANDING

Danger: Mars approaching!

The approach phase was one of the most dangerous parts of the MSL mission. Miscalculations could have seen the MSL spacecraft completely miss Mars or enter its atmosphere at a wrong angle, which would have been catastrophic either way. So, 45 days before entering Martian atmosphere, NASA engineers began approach preparations by monitoring and updating the spacecraft's attitude, as well as the correction manoeuvres that adjusted its trajectory upon entry. This was done using extra requested time from the Deep Space Network of terrestrial antennas located in Spain, Australia and the US.

3 Guided entry
Small rockets on the MSL craft fired to control its descent.

The Atlas V 541

Solid rocket motors
These four boosters increase the thrust of the rocket engine

Atlas V rocket
The main rocket that took the MSL into orbit, part of the two-stage launch vehicle created by the United Launch Alliance

The Centaur
This part of the Atlas V took the MSL into orbit and then fired it out on course for Mars

Payload fairing
A heat shield protected the MSL from air friction heat during launch then fell away

4,828KM

BIGGEST CANYON

Valles Marineris on Mars is the solar system's largest canyon at 4,828km (3,000mi) long, 8km (5mi) deep and 644km (400mi) wide. On Earth, it would cover the length of the US.

DID YOU KNOW? The MSL project cost $900m (£581m) more than its projected $1.6b (£1.03b) cost in 2006

5 Parachute deployment
At a 10km (6.2mi) Martian altitude, the MSL parachute deployed to slow its descent and the heat shield fell away.

8 Sky crane
With the landing zone in sight, the sky crane allowed Curiosity to descend from its housing on a cable.

7 Backshell separation
The backshell separated less than 2km (1.25mi) from the surface.

9 Touchdown
The sky crane lowered the Curiosity rover onto the planet, then flew clear of the zone.

4 Peak heating
The heat shield protected the MSL as it hit terminal velocity through the thickening Martian atmosphere.

6 Radar data
The MSL fired the surface with radar to judge precisely the most suitable landing site in a predetermined zone.

The landing site

Choosing a landing site was of vital importance to the mission. The last thing NASA wanted to do was to put Curiosity in a position where communication might be made difficult or in a region of less scientific interest. Although the rover is capable of articulate movement, at a speed of 144 metres (450 feet) an hour over smooth terrain, the area of Mars it can effectively explore during its mission is limited. Selection began in September 2008 with NASA profiling an ideal landing site, which should have: 'clear evidence of a past or present habitable environment', a 'favourable geologic record' – meaning preserved layers of rock exposed at the surface, evidence of past water, good accessibility for the rover and all of this located near a safe landing zone. Sites were narrowed from 100 candidates down to the final selection in 2011: Gale Crater, a 154 kilometre (96 mile)-diameter remnant of an ancient impact that has a mountain called Aeolis Mons that is five kilometres (three miles) high in its northern portion. In its 3.5 billion years it has formed sedimentary layers and evidence of a wet history. Curiosity landed on a relatively smooth plain just north of Aeolis Mons.

Martian experiments

The nature of many of NASA's future projects hinges on the success of the MSL's watershed technologies. The target landing site, for example, was an area of around 20 kilometres (12 miles) in length, a five-fold improvement in precision using the sky crane/rocket descent technique. Without this new technology, landing so close to the edge of the Gale Crater wall would have been impossible. In a worst-case scenario, should the MSL lander have failed to insert Curiosity safely or effectively into the landing zone, it may have precluded similar Martian sites in the future. As the new system is capable of landing a vehicle even bigger than Curiosity (which is five times heavier than its predecessors, Spirit and Opportunity), a proven safe delivery onto Mars became even more important.

You'd have thought that, having been developed for nearly eight years and travelled through space for the best part of nine months, the NASA team would have been keen to send the Curiosity rover off to investigate this relatively unknown area of Mars as soon as its wheels touched the ground. But as much as the scientists would have liked to get stuck into sucking up samples and zapping Martian rocks with the ChemCam's mounted laser, the engineers needed to run a host of system checks that meant the Curiosity remained stationary for over two weeks after its landing. During this time, engineers had to ensure that Curiosity's wheels weren't stuck and that the rover was capable of moving away from its landing position without embedding itself in soft sand, an irrevocable situation its predecessor Spirit found itself in two years ago. But once that was done, the fun part of the MSL mission began.

The nature of this mission is one of discovery, so NASA hasn't carved in stone exactly what Curiosity will be doing in its 680 or so Earth days on Mars, though scientists do have a plan. Apart from maintenance and a 20-sol period (a Martian day, referred to as a 'sol', is nearly 40 minutes longer than Earth's) when Mars is on the far side of the Sun (a superior solar conjunction), Curiosity's activities are prioritised according to what it can find. Curiosity has a much bigger range of movement than Spirit or Opportunity, rated for roaming up to 20 kilometres (12.4 miles) from the landing site and a major portion of its time will be taken up driving to scientifically interesting sites, specifically around its primary mission target Mount Sharp, and taking samples.

There is a huge range of possible ways that the MSL mission might unfold in the single Martian year it spends investigating the area around Gale Crater – so many that NASA cannot possibly account for every positive and negative scenario. However, using what we already know about Mars and the mission site, NASA has compiled a number of day-to-day activities into logical sequences that form five separate scenarios, measured in tactical windows known as sols. Traverse sols mostly involve roving between target sites, triggered by a ChemCam observation. Reconnaissance sols involve surveying a site prior to detailed study, triggered again by the ChemCam plus the Mars Hand Lens Imager (MAHLI). Approach sols are triggered by a previous sol and place a patch of soil or rock within the working area of the Curiosity's robotic arm, while contact sols incorporate the arm-mounted instruments on the MSL measuring and observing a target.

Sampling and analysis sols will most likely prove the most fascinating of these five scenarios. The MSL will spend some time passing rock and soil samples through a sieve and into CheMin and Sample Analysis at Mars (SAM). Here, a suite of instruments in SAM will check for the presence of hydrogen, oxygen, nitrogen and other elements associated with life, while CheMin will check for minerals like gypsum and jarosite, which indicate the presence of water and might point to a previous Martian environment that supported life.

The Curiosity and its payload
A closer look at some of the key equipment

■ **Rover:** Curiosity will traverse the Martian terrain, guided by its cameras, and collect samples

■ **MSL:** The Mars Science Laboratory, on board the Curiosity rover, will analyse the samples in depth

Power
A radioisotope thermoelectric generator (RTG) uses the predictable rate of plutonium's radioactive decay to generate electricity from heat

ChemCam
The mast head includes a pair of cameras used to help navigation, but the star of the show is the ChemCam. This checks out rocks and soil from a distance, before blasting the surface with a laser. The resulting plasma can be analysed for its composition with an on-board spectrometer.

Vital statistics...

Curiosity rover

Cost:	$2.5bn (£1.61bn)
Weight:	900kg (1,984lb)
Scientific payload:	57kg (125lb)
Size:	3 x 2.7 x 2.2m (10 x 9 x 7ft)
Arm reach:	2.2m (7ft)
Wheels:	6
Top speed:	144m/ph (450fph)
Power:	Plutonium RTG (radioisotope thermoelectric generator)

Wheels
Six wheels with a 'rocker-bogie' system help Curiosity balance over uneven terrain, while cleats on the tread provide grip

MEDLI
Like RAD, MEDLI (or MSL Entry, Descent and Landing Instrument suite) provides data vital to future missions to Mars. It's made up of two parts. One measured atmospheric pressure on the heat shield during descent to help determine the spacecraft's orientation, while the other measured heat during entry and descent to determine the composition of future heat shielding.

Sojourner
The Mars Pathfinder rover landed on 4 July 1997 and communications were lost two months later on 27 September 1997.

Spirit
The Mars Exploration rover landed on 4 January 2004 and its last communication was on 22 March 2010.

Opportunity
Spirit's twin has been on Mars since 25 January 2004 and is still going, nearly eight years after the original mission limit.

DID YOU KNOW? In Victorian times, it was widely believed that life flourished on Mars

The WEB
The body of the rover is called the Warm Electronics Box, which contains its computer and electronics

The computer
The brains of Curiosity regulates systems, calculates movement and enables communications with mission control

SAM
Sample Analysis at Mars (SAM) is a major piece of kit. At around 30 kilograms (over 60 pounds) it takes up more than half of Curiosity's scientific payload and is more than Spirit and Opportunity's entire scientific payloads combined. It's a kind of mobile chemistry set that includes a mass spectrometer, gas chromatograph and laser spectrometer for analysing samples.

Curiosity's first drive

After landing, but just before it took its first 'steps' across the Martian landscape, engineers needed to run some tests on Curiosity. Of primary concern was its initial footing and the terrain, which were assessed so that Curiosity could be moved safely away from the landing site. Then Curiosity went through a start-up sequence that included measuring the air temperature, testing communications, unfolding the mast that carries the navigation camera, shooting images of its immediate surroundings and helping mission control pinpoint its precise location. Only then was Curiosity able to make its first foray across Mars.

REMS
The Rover Environmental Monitoring Station (REMS) is the Curiosity's own weather vane, providing measurements on atmospheric pressure, UV radiation, wind speed and more.

Surviving winter on Mars

Martian winters are more brutal than even the coldest place on Earth, Antarctica. It can plummet as low as -143°C (-225°F) in the negligible atmosphere of the polar ice caps. It gets so cold that the carbon gas in the atmosphere freezes at certain times in the Martian calendar, causing the atmospheric pressure to drop.

The main problem with Spirit and Opportunity wasn't the cold, though – it was that they were solar powered, which meant that during the dark periods they went into a state of hibernation with little or no activity. Curiosity has an independent power source, so its mission won't have to work around the same constraints.

The coldest recorded temperature on Earth is -89°C (-129°F), while on Mars it can get as low as -143°C (-225°F)

Hazcam
Two cameras – one on the front and one on the rear – capture three-dimensional images that help avoid crashes

RAD
The Radiation Assessment Detector (RAD) is one of the more radical (excuse the pun) instruments on board the Curiosity. It detects and measures high-energy radiation, both from space and irradiated surfaces. It's being used with the specific intent of preparing NASA for human exploration of Mars in the future.

> "Curiosity's capable of examining scientifically interesting sites from a distance then moving to them"

Life – but not as we know it...

Curiosity is a very versatile machine. It can measure the atmospheric pressure, humidity, wind speed and UV levels on Mars, detect radiation levels dangerous to humans, scan for minerals and gases trapped beneath the surface and take many gigabytes' worth of images and video.

It's especially tactile too, capable of examining scientifically interesting sites from a distance then moving to them, scooping up soil samples, collecting and sifting through Martian rock, drilling into the rock to remove samples with a mechanical arm, blasting the surface of boulders with a powerful laser and examining the plasma that comes off it. It can then analyse everything it's zapped, drilled, scooped and sucked up in a portable laboratory housed in its body that could rival a university chemistry lab. We know it can collect masses of useful scientific information, but what can we expect to find, and what can we conclude from that information?

NASA's major goal in all the experiments that the MSL will conduct in its Martian year is to assess whether the processes on Mars indicate a planet that was ever capable of supporting life. A lifeless planet (or moon, such as Earth's) that proves completely inert for billions of years could never have supported life, for example. We know Mars has been subject to geological and atmospheric changes for millions of years, so MSL is there to see what other changes the planet has experienced and examine the finer details. Among other things, it will analyse any sedimentary rock found to see whether water was once present and look for evidence of ancient microbes, the simplest of life forms, in the rocks that will leave behind geological signatures, like the ancient organisms that made calcium carbonate (chalk) deposits on Earth.

From a broader perspective, we're very subjective judges of the conditions that lead to life – we only know for sure that the conditions on Earth led to life here. So one of the goals of the MSL project is to build up a new picture of how other forms of life might evolve on other planets, to help in the search for potential life around the cosmos. From MSL and Mars, NASA has other targets in its long-term future: within our own Solar System, Titan, Europa and Enceladus, the frigid moons that orbit Saturn and Jupiter. Then maybe in the very distant future, we'll be able to send a space laboratory beyond our own system to those exoplanets with life potential, perhaps discovering the conditions for life somewhere else in the universe, whatever form it may take.

Surface
Mars is very rocky and iron-rich, resulting in a high iron oxide soil content that gives the planet its characteristic red colour

Crust
The crust is believed to be much thicker than the Earth's, at 14-129km (9-80mi) deep

Gravity
Mars is much smaller and, significantly, has less mass than Earth, meaning gravity is around 38 per cent that of our planet's

Poles
Like Earth, Mars has north and south polar regions, which are covered in frozen water

Mars deconstructed

Mars has a lot in common with Earth and yet has just as many features that starkly contrast our own planet. It has a day/night cycle of a very similar length to Earth's (24 hours, 39 minutes and 35 seconds) but a Martian year is nearly twice as long as our own. Mars tilts at a similar angle to the Earth (25.19 degrees and 23.45 degrees, respectively) yet has an elliptical orbit that means the distance between the two planets can vary from 56 million kilometres (35 million miles) to as far as 482 million kilometres (300 million miles). This is one of the reasons MSL has chosen Mars to see whether there is potential for life under realistic, non-terrestrial conditions.

Missions to Mars
Past, present and future 'soft' landings on Mars

'71
Russian lander touches safely, then shortly stopped transmitting.

1976
Viking 1 is a complete success for NASA, lasting over six Earth years.

1997
NASA's Mars Pathfinder successfully lands its 10.5kg (23lb) rover, Sojourner.

2004
Mars Exploration Rovers A and B, Spirit and Opportunity, landed three weeks apart

2008
The last spacecraft to successfully land on the surface of Mars was the Phoenix lander

TERRAFORMING MARS

Scientists at NASA believe making Mars fit for human habitation is possible. The atmosphere would need thickening and temperature raising, but this could be achieved using a giant orbital mirror to melt the ice caps, releasing carbon dioxide gas and triggering a greenhouse effect.

DID YOU KNOW? Mars is much smaller than Earth, but because it has no oceans, has about the same land surface area

Core
Unlike Earth, Mars has very little magnetic field, indicating a solid or partly solid core

Keep it clean

Why would you bother keeping the MSL clean? Keeping any scene of investigation clear of external influence is vitally important to a scientist. NASA is searching for the potential for Martian life, so keeping as little terrestrial contamination from the scene was a major priority for the MSL project. Contaminants are measured as 'spores' and might include Earth bacteria, dust and synthetic material that has dropped off the lander or vehicle. Throughout the project, NASA went to great lengths to keep the MSL as clean as possible, resulting in a spore count less than half the maximum set by NASA Planetary Protection regulations.

Communicating with NASA

To receive commands and send data back to NASA, Curiosity makes use of terrestrial and Martian infrastructures. On Earth, three enormous antenna arrays consisting of dishes up to 70 metres (230 feet) in diameter make up the DSN (Deep Space Network). These are based in the US, Spain and Australia. Communicating directly with the DSN can be costly in terms of Curiosity's energy consumption and, due to the orbital position of Mars relative to the Earth and the Sun, it might not always be possible. So sometimes Curiosity will uplink to two satellites orbiting Mars: the Mars Odyssey and the Mars Reconnaissance Orbiter. These are between 257 and 400 kilometres (160 and 250 miles) above the surface of Mars, so are not only costing the Curiosity less energy to send messages to, but they have Earth in their field of view for a lot longer, allowing a larger window of communication.

Mars Odyssey, one of the two satellites in orbit around the Red Planet that Curiosity will use to communicate with Earth

All images © NASA

Atmosphere
A thin Martian atmosphere is made up of 95 per cent carbon dioxide and five per cent nitrogen, argon and oxygen and water vapour. It's poisonous to humans

Interior
Scientists think Mars has a similar, triple-layer interior to Earth's, with a crust, mantle and core

Interview
John Grotzinger
– Project scientist

A key member of the MSL science team offers some first-hand insight

Q: First, what does your role as project scientist on the MSL involve?

John Grotzinger: Probably the best way to think about it is like being the chief scientist. What that means is that we've got the rover, with all its capabilities and all the science instruments, and nine principal investigators who were responsible for building it and developing those instruments, calibrating them and establishing protocols and procedures for how we're going to operate them [on Mars]. My responsibility is to co-ordinate all this interaction and oversee the science team of 300-plus members.

Q: Your area of expertise is ancient surface processes on Earth and Mars – can you tell us why this was so relevant to this project?

JG: Basically, since the primary objective for the mission is the search for habitable environments on Mars – and the emphasis is strongly in the area of ancient Mars, which is why we chose the landing site – it's kind of exactly what I do on Earth. As a geobiologist, before I got involved in Mars projects, we head off into a particular field area that we select in advance, usually involving some of the oldest rocks on Earth. Then we set up our equipment, make maps and collect samples that we bring back to the lab for analysis.

Q: How do you investigate possible life?

JG: We borrow quite heavily from these [geobiology] principles and use them for our guidance. The search for a habitable environment involves looking for evidence of an aqueous environment because water is important for all microbes. You're often trying to establish some source of energy that, if the microbes had been there, would have been used for metabolism. Then you're looking for carbon because this is a building block for life as we know it. So you take those elements as the key ingredients along with some other 'proper' elements like nitrogen, hydrogen, oxygen, sulphur and phosphorus. Then you're looking for the geological context that can present those [such as a mass of layered rock]. We hope that, as we work our way through the layers at Mount Sharp in Gale Crater we'll [uncover] the physical and chemical properties that tell us about what kind of ancient environment this once was.

Visit **http://bit.ly/RHeUF9** for the entire interview

2012
The Curiosity rover landed successfully on Mars on 6 August 2012.

2014
Finland's MetNet plans to initiate a multi-lander network.

2016
Europe's ESA will use the Trace Gas Orbiter to place a lander on Mars.

2018
As part of the same ESA ExoMars project, Russia plans to deploy a rover.

2023
Mars One is an ambitious private project that plans to establish a human colony on Mars.

"They're taken for a joyride in the infamous KC-135, aka 'the weightless wonder', aka 'the vomit comet'"

If you think you have what it takes to be an astronaut, think again

Astronauts run the systems engineering simulator in front of a full-sized projection of interactive International Space Station components

Virtual reality programs let astronauts practice mission-specific duties hundreds of times before flight

Engineers test a new extra-vehicular space suit with a partial gravity simulator

Astronaut training

It's been nearly half a century since Russian cosmonaut Yuri Gagarin became the first man in space, but with the rare exception of a few billionaire civilians, space travel is still a well-guarded privilege.

As NASA initiates a new long-term mission to return to the Moon and push on to Mars, the space agency is looking for a few good men and women who contain the rare mix of hyper-intelligence, marathon stamina and good old-fashioned guts to board the brand-new Ares I-X rocket and blast off to the uncharted depths. ✿

Applications at the ready!

Becoming an astronaut isn't easy. Firstly you'll have to be selected from thousands of applicants, and if you're successful train for two years, after which you may be chosen for an astronaut programme.

This huge centrifuge doesn't test the g-force limits of astronauts, but replicates up to 3.5g for flight simulation exercises

American and Russian astronauts train for spacewalks in the massive Hydrolab at the Gagarin Cosmonaut Training Center

NASA basic training

NASA astronaut training is much like cramming for final exams at MIT while simultaneously enduring basic training for the Green Berets. Candidates begin their training in the classroom, taking advanced courses in astronomy, physics, mathematics, geology, meteorology and introductions to the Space Shuttle guidance and navigation systems. Sorry, no poetry electives.

Both pilots and non-pilots are trained to fly T-38 jets, highly acrobatic aircrafts that can reach 50,000ft. Pilots must log 15 hours of flight time a month, plus extra practice landing the Shuttle Training Aircraft (100 more hours). Non-pilots must log a minimum of four hours a month in the T-38.

But before astronaut candidates even step foot in a flight simulator, they need to be trained in military water survival. That means scuba certification and the proven ability to swim three lengths of an Olympic size pool in full flight gear and shoes. To cover all contingencies, astronaut candidates are also trained in wilderness survival, learning how to navigate by the stars and to live on nuts and berries.

The torture isn't over yet. To weed out the weaklings, candidates are subjected to extremes of high and low pressure and trained to deal with the 'consequences'. Then they're taken for a joyride in the infamous KC-135, aka 'the weightless wonder', aka 'the vomit comet', to experience 20-second shots of weightlessness. Some people love it, some people are violently sick.

After that it's time to brush up on a couple dozen equipment manuals in preparation for intense training with full-size, fully functional simulators,

everything from flight controls to hydraulic arms, even down to how to use the toilet. Every single astronaut candidate is trained in every phase of space flight, ranging from pre-launch diagnostics to emergency landing procedures.

Candidates also train in the Johnson Space Center's Neutral Buoyancy Laboratory, an immense pool that faithfully simulates near-weightlessness. Here, they prepare for both the extraordinary and mundane aspects of space life. They conduct underwater 'space walks' in full space gear and practice making freeze-dried snacks in the tiny Shuttle kitchen.

Finally comes the mission-specific training, where each member of the team runs countless simulations within his or her area of expertise. Scientists conduct their experiments over and over. Engineers do hundreds of mock space walks to make repairs to space station components. And pilots pretty much live in the flight simulators. After two years of full-time training, the candidates receive a silver lapel pin indicating they are officially astronauts. After their first flight, it's swapped for a gold one.

This centrifuge is designed to test the effects of linear acceleration on visual function in space

So you want to be an astronaut?

In the late Fifties, when NASA began its internal search for the first seven astronauts, it drew from the ranks of the most experienced Air Force pilots. A lot has changed since the dawn of space flight, and so have the résumés of modern astronauts.

There are still some military pilots in the ranks, but they're in the minority. Today's astronauts are more likely to be academics, scientists and engineers of all stripes – particularly astronautical engineers.

Astronaut candidates are chosen through a rigorous application process and there is no career path that guarantees admission into the programme, although many current astronauts work for years within the NASA research and development ranks before suiting up themselves.

Head to Head

THE YOUNGEST, OLDEST AND MOST EXPERIENCED ASTRONAUTS IN HISTORY

YOUNGEST

1. Gherman Stepanovich Titov

Age: 25
Facts: Only the second man in space after Yuri Gagarin, this charismatic young Russian cosmonaut was the first to make multiple orbits (17, in fact) of the Earth on 6 August 1961. He is probably most famous for his in-flight exuberance, repeatedly calling out his codename: "I am Eagle! I am Eagle!"

OLDEST

2. John Glenn

Age: 77
Facts: On 20 February 1962, John Glenn piloted NASA's very first manned orbital mission of the Earth, whipping around the globe three times in under five hours. Fast forward 36 years to 29 October 1998, when the retired US senator took his second space flight, a nine-day mission exploring – among other things – the effects of space flight on the aging process.

MOST TIME IN SPACE

3. Sergei Konstantinovich Krikalev

Total duration: 803 days
Facts: Cosmonaut Krikalev crushes all competitors in the category of most time spent in space. He flew six missions between 1985 and 2005, notching up over two years in space, including the first joint Russia/US Space Shuttle flight in 1994. The uber-experienced Krikalev now runs the Gagarin Cosmonaut Training Center in Star City, Russia.

How cleanrooms stay pristine

Why do these rooms need to be so spotless when engineers work on space equipment?

A cleanroom is a secured environment where the level of particulate matter in the atmosphere is strictly controlled. All pollutants such as dust, chemical vapours, airborne microbes and aerosols are permanently monitored and eradicated by an internal conditioning system, which includes a combination of filters (HEPA and ULPA), extraction fans, airlocks, air showers and protective clothing for its workers.

Via this system, a controlled number of particles per cubic metre (and of a specific size) can be ensured, with higher-class facilities capable of delivering smaller and fewer particles. For instance, an ISO 1 cleanroom – the highest grade; there are nine in total – allows no more than two two-micrometre particles per cubic metre. For perspective, a typical urban environment has 35 million particles of all sizes per cubic metre.

Cleanrooms are used by NASA when building, testing and integrating spacecraft components to ensure no contamination or damage is inadvertently done to the sensitive and expensive equipment – technology that once launched into space cannot be decontaminated. Indeed, while tiny specks of dirt may seem insignificant, past experiences and studies have shown that even the tiniest piece of pollen, sand, hair or flake of skin can imbalance a star-tracking unit, damage an exhaust port or even lead to a spacecraft's thruster becoming blocked.

As such, whenever a NASA engineer comes into work on the latest space technology, far from simply hanging up their coat and getting down to business they must first change into their protective clothing, pass through an air shower – essentially a human-sized hand-dryer that removes any particles stuck to the suit, proceed through a secure airlock equipped with extraction fans, and then finally pass through a temperature and humidity-controlled room to the assembly area. Only then, and under the constant filtering process of a laminar flow filtration system, can they begin work. ✿

A team of engineers working on the SM4 mission to the Hubble Space Telescope in the High Bay Cleanroom (the world's largest)

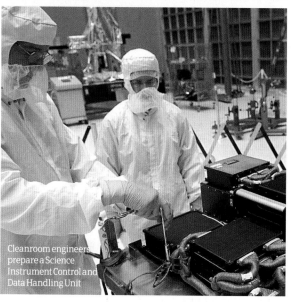

Cleanroom engineers prepare a Science Instrument Control and Data Handling Unit

How space pens write in zero gravity

The anti-gravity pen adopted for countless space missions explained

In the Fifties, American Paul Fisher noted that ballpoint pens relied on gravity, and that they could not function properly without it. This meant that the ballpoint pen was very limited in its use, so Fisher decided to develop his own idea for an anti-gravity pen.

Inside the ink cartridge of a space pen is pressurised nitrogen that continuously feeds ink into the head of the pen, a tungsten carbide ball, in place of gravity. Fisher also used thixotropic ink, which is very thick and viscous when stored in the pen (so it doesn't flow out), but free-flowing when pressure is applied. This also means the pens can write upside down and on almost any surface, including wet materials, snow, underwater and on plastic. NASA was so impressed with the design that it began using them on its space flights, starting with Apollo 7 in 1968. ✿

The Fisher space pens are available to buy and use here on Earth

© NASA

Apollo computers

How did a machine with a calculator's computational power fly a spacecraft to the Moon?

In 1969, NASA tasked the MIT Instrumentation Lab with creating the world's first integrated circuit computer that, while orbiting the Moon at 3,500kmph, could land a 13,000kg spacecraft on the Moon's surface and return to orbit on its first attempt with the equivalent of 4kb of RAM. It devised two computers for the Apollo capsule that were largely automated, but allowed some input from the astronauts.

The computer worked by completing tasks in four milliseconds and then checking for new, higher-priority tasks every 20 milliseconds. Commands such as firing the boosters were pre-programmed into the machine, meaning that when the landing began, the computer already had a specific sequence of tasks to carry out.

The computers had very little memory, so different components performed multiple time-dependent tasks at varying points during the mission, unprecedented multitasking for a computer of that age. The system was designed to retain the most crucial information if it had to reboot and perform the highest-priority task. This proved invaluable during the first landing, when a fault repeatedly restarted the machine. With ground control unsure of whether to abort the mission or not, it transpired that the computer would still be able to operate and land the Lunar Module, and so the mission went ahead.

The display and keyboard unit (DSKY)

Memory
The computer's fixed and erasable memory was made with iron cores woven into copper wires and encased in plastic, with the erasable memory using magnets to alter its data

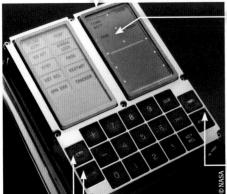

Display
Warning lights displayed in the upper-left, while a display containing data and commands was in the upper-right

Fixed
Fixed memory contained 75kb of vital programs and co-ordinates, the equivalent of four seconds of a three-minute MP3 song

Verb
To input a command, such as manoeuvring the module, an astronaut would press the Verb button, followed by the corresponding numerical button for that action

Noun
The Noun button, followed by a number, would allow astronauts to input data into the computer to be re-used at a later date

Vostok 1

We look back at how the first man ventured into space

On 12 April 1961, Yuri Gagarin became the first man to reach low-Earth orbit, otherwise known as 'space'. He travelled there inside a metal sphere known as Vostok 1, the world's first manned spacecraft, beating American Alan Shepard into space by just 25 days.

Vostok 1 was a spherical cabin, coated entirely in an ablative material to act as a heat shield as it re-entered the atmosphere. There was a window out of which Gagarin could view the Earth, and an ejector seat for his return (as he would separate from the capsule as it re-entered the atmosphere). Beneath Vostok 1 was a service module containing the chemical batteries and rockets to manoeuvre the spacecraft. After almost one complete orbit of Earth, lasting 68 minutes, the spacecraft re-entered the atmosphere and landed in Kazakhstan an hour and 48 minutes after launch.

As Gagarin ejected from the spacecraft before it landed, under FAI (Fédération Aéronautique Internationale) rules it did not qualify as an actual space flight, although the Russians kept this quiet for several years after. Nonetheless, Gagarin was still the first human to venture into space.

The Russians beat the Americans in the space race

Inside Vostok 1

How the spacecraft that took the first man into space worked

Instruments
A variety of instruments allowed Vostok's pressure, temperature and position above Earth to be continuously monitored during the mission

Out of control
Gagarin had no control over the spacecraft as scientists were unsure how humans would operate in weightlessness, although he did have an emergency override key

Life support
Spherical oxygen and nitrogen tanks provided breathable air for Gagarin, in addition to propulsion for the spacecraft

© DK Images

Antennas
External radio antennas provided continuous communication with ground control, transcripts of which show Gagarin repeatedly assure controllers he was fine

Portholes
In addition to a visor to view the world, three portholes gave Gagarin a view of his surroundings

Entry hatch
Upon re-entry, this hatch was blown off and Gagarin's ejector seat fired him to safety, landing by parachute

Such a groundbreaking event was headline news

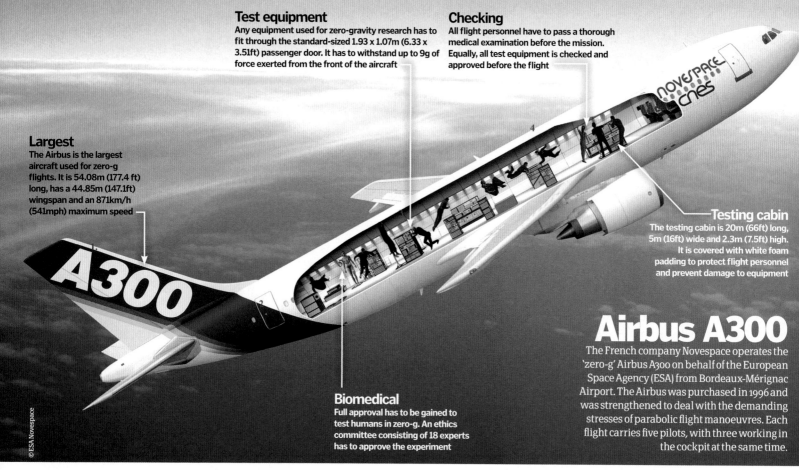

Test equipment
Any equipment used for zero-gravity research has to fit through the standard-sized 1.93 x 1.07m (6.33 x 3.51ft) passenger door. It has to withstand up to 9g of force exerted from the front of the aircraft

Checking
All flight personnel have to pass a thorough medical examination before the mission. Equally, all test equipment is checked and approved before the flight

Largest
The Airbus is the largest aircraft used for zero-g flights. It is 54.08m (177.4 ft) long, has a 44.85m (147.1ft) wingspan and an 871km/h (541mph) maximum speed

Testing cabin
The testing cabin is 20m (66ft) long, 5m (16ft) wide and 2.3m (7.5ft) high. It is covered with white foam padding to protect flight personnel and prevent damage to equipment

Biomedical
Full approval has to be gained to test humans in zero-g. An ethics committee consisting of 18 experts has to approve the experiment

Airbus A300
The French company Novespace operates the 'zero-g' Airbus A300 on behalf of the European Space Agency (ESA) from Bordeaux-Mérignac Airport. The Airbus was purchased in 1996 and was strengthened to deal with the demanding stresses of parabolic flight manoeuvres. Each flight carries five pilots, with three working in the cockpit at the same time.

©ESA Novespace

How a vomet comet trains astronauts

Find out how fixed-wing aircraft can simulate zero-gravity conditions for astronaut training

When an aircraft follows a parabolic flight path, it creates a weightless period for several seconds. This is ideal for providing astronauts with the sensation of zero gravity and testing equipment for use in outer space. A typical three-hour training mission makes at least 30 parabolic flights. They can simulate zero-g for 25 seconds, one-sixth g (lunar-g) for 30 seconds or one-third g (martian-g) for 40 seconds.

In 1959, NASA used a Convair C-131 Samaritan aircraft to train the Mercury programme astronauts. It was quickly nicknamed the 'vomit comet', as one in three passengers became violently sick.

Most aircraft used for such flights are adapted versions of transport or commercial passenger aircraft. NASA currently uses a McDonnell Douglas C-9 and the European Space Agency uses an Airbus A300.

Since 2004, commercial companies started offering such flights to the public, and NASA offers a scheme for students to design and fly micro-gravity missions.

The parabolic flight manoeuvre

1. Entry pull-up phase
Flying at an altitude of 5km (16,404ft) at a speed of 825km/h (513mph), the aircraft ascends at 47 degrees. Up to 2g is experienced.

2. Injection point
In 20 secs, at an altitude of 7km (22,966ft), the aircraft reaches the injection point. Engine thrust is reduced and in five secs enters the zero-g phase. Speed drops from 570km/h (354mph) to 370km/h (230mph).

3. Zero-gravity phase
At the microgravity phase, lasting 20 secs, zero-g is experienced. Using a video link, pilots can control the aircraft to keep objects free-floating in the testing cabin.

4. Pull-out phase
The free-falling aircraft is pulled out of the zero-g phase, and in 20 secs it descends at 42 degrees to its original cruising speed and altitude.

5. Repeat
After returning to normal-level flight for two mins, the parabolic manoeuvre is repeated. 30 can be done in a three-hour flight.

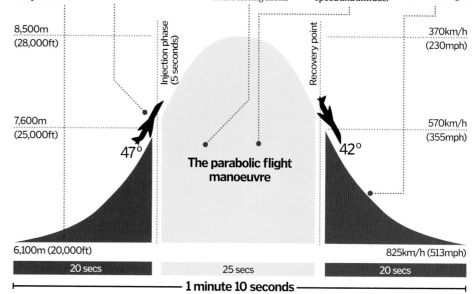

8,500m (28,000ft)

7,600m (25,000ft)

6,100m (20,000ft)

Injection phase (5 seconds)

Recovery point

370km/h (230mph)

570km/h (355mph)

825km/h (513mph)

47°

42°

The parabolic flight manoeuvre

20 secs | 25 secs | 20 secs

1 minute 10 seconds

Accidentally on purpose

Luna 1 carried the Soviet coat of arms and was initially intended to impact with the Moon's surface. However, it missed by about 9,656km (6,000 miles) and accidentally became the first spacecraft to fall into orbit with the Sun.

© NASA

DID YOU KNOW? Luna 1 was the first man-made object to reach the escape velocity of Earth – 40,234km/h (25,000mph)

Luna 1

How did the first spacecraft to reach the Moon work?

'Luna' was the name of the series of Russian spacecraft that made the journey to the Moon from 1959 onwards, starting with Luna 1 on 2 January that year. It flew by the surface of the Moon at a distance of just under 10,000km (6,000 miles) after a 34-hour journey.

Luna 1 made some key discoveries in its pioneering mission, including the lack of a magnetic field around the Moon and a flow of ionised plasma emanating from the Sun that we now know to be solar wind. It also provided useful data on the Van Allen radiation belts surrounding the Earth.

Interestingly, when it was 180,000km (111,847 miles) from Earth, Luna 1 released a 1kg (2lb) golden-orange cloud of sodium, allowing astronomers to track the motion of the probe from Earth in addition to serving as an experiment on the behaviour of gas in space. In doing so, Luna 1 became the first ever artificial comet. ✿

The spacecraft is one of the crowning achievements of the USSR's space missions

Luna 1 was the first in the Soviet's Moon exploration program

The launch vehicle

Luna 1 was strapped atop a modified intercontinental ballistic missile called the R-7 Semyorka, known as the SS-6 Sapwood in the west. It carried out many successful launches including Sputnik 1 and Vostok 1, the latter of which housed Yuri Gagarin, the first man in space.

The statistics...

R-7 Semyorka

Retired:	1964
Missions:	13
Height:	30.84m (101.18ft)
Weight:	281,375kg (620,326lb)
Payload:	4,730kg (10,428lb)
Thrust:	3,894 kilonewtons

© Sergei Arssenev

Inside Luna 1

Communication
Radio equipment and a tracking transmitter provided communication with ground control

Propulsion
Luna 1 had no propulsion system, achieving all of its speed from the initial launch from orbit

Scintillator
A piece of equipment known as a scintillator detected the presence of high-energy particles in the outer Van Allen radiation belt

Stages
Once the rocket had set Luna 1 on a path for the Moon, it detached from its container to ensure that its equipment did not overheat

Cone
A cone protected the rocket from overheating when passing through the atmosphere. It was discarded in space

Radiation
A Geiger counter on board Luna 1 let scientists measure the intensity of the Earth's radiation belts

Magnetometer
The discovery of the lack of a magnetic field surrounding the Moon was made possible by the magnetometer

Power
Luna 1 used chemical batteries for power, which ran out of juice a day after it passed the Moon

Dust
On 3 January 1959, Luna 1 ejected a cloud of sodium so that it could be observed from the ground

© Science Photo Library

SURVIVE THE COSMOS
LIFE IN SPACE

Humans have had a presence in space in some form or another for half a century, but learning to live in the cosmos has been a steep learning curve. We take a look at what it's like to live in space, and how we've adapted over the years

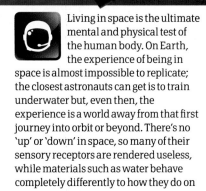

Living in space is the ultimate mental and physical test of the human body. On Earth, the experience of being in space is almost impossible to replicate; the closest astronauts can get is to train underwater but, even then, the experience is a world away from that first journey into orbit or beyond. There's no 'up' or 'down' in space, so many of their sensory receptors are rendered useless, while materials such as water behave completely differently to how they do on

Earth. So, how do astronauts cope, and what's it like to actually live in space? We're about to find out.

Since Yuri Gagarin became the first man to leave the Earth in 1961, life in space has altered and improved dramatically. Gagarin spent the entirety of his 108-minute flight encased in a spacesuit, but nowadays astronauts can wear the same shorts and T-shirts they'd wear at home. The first space station, Russia's Salyut (launched in 1971), saw astronauts eat food from freeze-dried

packets and stay only briefly on the station in order to survive. Now, astronauts aboard the International Space Station (ISS) can eat pizza and curry, reuse and recycle many of their utilities and can stay in orbit for hundreds of days.

Before the ISS there were many unknowns about living in space. Indeed, on the earlier space stations Mir and Skylab, procedures and equipment were much less advanced than they are now. For one thing, it was quickly realised that

Head to Head
SPACE RECORDS

CUMULATIVE

1. 803 days
Russian Sergei Krikalev, aged 53, has spent a grand total of 803 days, 9 hours and 39 minutes in space across six different missions.

CONTINUOUS

2. 437 days
The record of longest single spaceflight in history is currently held by Russian Valeri Polyakov, 69, who spent 437 days and 18 hours aboard the Mir space station.

CANINE

3. 22 days
Veterok and Ugolyok jointly hold the record of longest canine spaceflight, spending 22 days in orbit in 1966 before returning to Earth.

DID YOU KNOW? You grow taller in space because your spine elongates – some reports suggest by an inch in just ten days

Space bodies
How does living in space affect the human body?

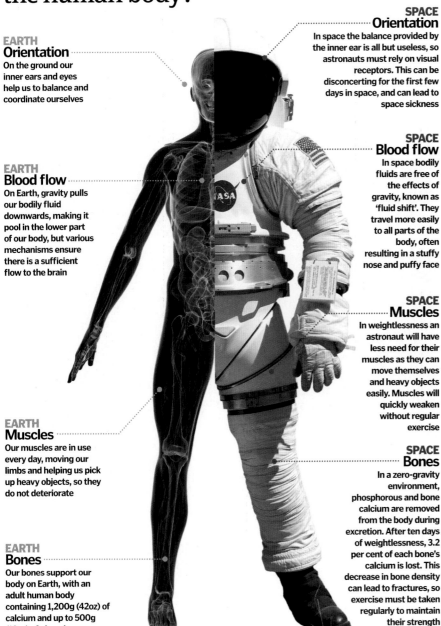

EARTH
Orientation
On the ground our inner ears and eyes help us to balance and coordinate ourselves

EARTH
Blood flow
On Earth, gravity pulls our bodily fluid downwards, making it pool in the lower part of our body, but various mechanisms ensure there is a sufficient flow to the brain

EARTH
Muscles
Our muscles are in use every day, moving our limbs and helping us pick up heavy objects, so they do not deteriorate

EARTH
Bones
Our bones support our body on Earth, with an adult human body containing 1,200g (42oz) of calcium and up to 500g (18oz) of phosphorous

SPACE
Orientation
In space the balance provided by the inner ear is all but useless, so astronauts must rely on visual receptors. This can be disconcerting for the first few days in space, and can lead to space sickness

SPACE
Blood flow
In space bodily fluids are free of the effects of gravity, known as 'fluid shift'. They travel more easily to all parts of the body, often resulting in a stuffy nose and puffy face

SPACE
Muscles
In weightlessness an astronaut will have less need for their muscles as they can move themselves and heavy objects easily. Muscles will quickly weaken without regular exercise

SPACE
Bones
In a zero-gravity environment, phosphorous and bone calcium are removed from the body during excretion. After ten days of weightlessness, 3.2 per cent of each bone's calcium is lost. This decrease in bone density can lead to fractures, so exercise must be taken regularly to maintain their strength

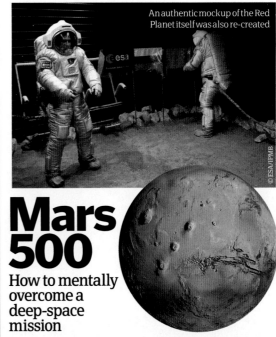

An authentic mockup of the Red Planet itself was also re-created

Mars 500
How to mentally overcome a deep-space mission

In 50 years of space exploration, the furthest a human has been from Earth is the far side of the Moon. While astronauts have spent hundreds of days aboard the ISS, the complexities of tackling a deep-space mission are relatively unknown. As a result, projects such as the Mars 500 mission have been given increasing precedence.

The Mars 500 mission was an important study to ascertain the mental and physical strain on humans in closed isolation on a long-haul trip. The mission was a joint project between the ESA and Russian Institute for Biomedical Problems, which ran from 3 June 2010 to 4 November 2011. Six candidates were sealed in an isolation chamber for 520 days, the approximate journey time for a real trip to and from the Red Planet. The chamber contained several modules designed to replicate a Martian spacecraft and the surface of Mars itself. The volunteers were subjected to some of the conditions they would experience, such as delayed communications and confined quarters. The results will be used to develop countermeasures to remedy potential problems.

The astronauts carried out the same day-to-day routine they would on a real-life mission to Mars

Space was very limited in the Mars 500 'shuttle'

astronauts must sleep near a ventilation fan. If they don't they run the risk of suffocation. This is because, as they sleep, warm air does not rise in a weightless environment. In a badly ventilated area they would be surrounded by a bubble of their own exhaled carbon dioxide. A regular supply of air (oxygen) is needed to allow for regulated breathing.

Over the years sleeping methods have changed, from slumbering in a sleeping bag attached to a wall, on NASA's Space Shuttle, for example, to having their own small compartment on the ISS. Sleeping isn't easy, either. Astronauts experience a sunrise and sunset every 90 minutes as they fly at 24,945km/h (15,500mph) around the Earth, so clocks on the ISS are set to GMT and astronauts live their days just as they would on Earth. They work for over eight hours on weekdays, but on weekends they are given much more leisure time, although work must still be done to keep the ISS safe and operational, in addition to checking on experiments. Life in space isn't tough just for humans; animals have struggled as well. On NASA's Skylab space station in the Seventies, spiders were taken up

2 x images © ESA/IPMB

113

"The ISS's life-support systems recycle as much waste as possible, including urine"

to see how they would cope in a weightless environment. While disoriented they still managed to spin a web, even if it was a little wonky. More famous was the first living animal to be sent into space from Earth, Laika the dog from Russia. Sadly, she perished in orbit, but she was said to cope well with the experience of weightlessness. At the very least, Laika proved that animals could survive in space, providing the basis for Gagarin's later mission and all future human missions into the cosmos.

Each human consumes 0.9kg (2lbs) of oxygen daily, which is enough to fill a 3.5 cubic metre (123.6 cubic feet) room, and drinks 2.7kg (6lbs) of water. Therefore, the life-support systems on board the ISS recycle as much waste as possible, including that from urine and condensed moisture in the air, both of which are purified and reused, often after being broken down by electrolysis to provide fresh oxygen. However, not all water can be reused, and thus astronauts must rely on regular re-supply vehicles to bring cargo to the station. These have been performed by several spacecraft over the years, such as NASA's Space Shuttle until its retirement in July 2011, but they are now largely carried out by the ESA's Automated Transfer Vehicle (ATV). The ATV brings fresh food, clothes, water and equipment to the station. Once the cargo has been delivered, astronauts fill the vehicle with 5,896kg (12,998lbs) of waste and it is sent to burn up in Earth's atmosphere.

These are just some of the many ways that astronauts have adapted to life in space, and as more and more time is spent on the International Space Station, our capabilities to perform in a weightless environment will no doubt improve. The ultimate goal of sending humans to an asteroid and Mars in the 2030s is looking like an increasingly achievable objective thanks to the tireless work of space agencies worldwide over the last 50 years.

A DAY IN SPACE

Astronauts aboard the ISS experience 15 'dawns' every day, but while they're on board the station they operate according to GMT so they can stay in direct contact with the ground at operational hours. Here's how a typical day pans out for an astronaut on the station

08:00
Daily conference/work
In the morning astronauts perform the first of their daily tasks assigned by ground control. They often have a daily conference where they discuss their jobs for the day. Their work consists of supervising experiments that would not be possible on Earth or performing routine maintenance on equipment to ensure the survival of the crew. On some days they take video calls from Earth. These are often simply to friends and family but, on rare occasions, they may talk to schoolchildren, the US president or even the Pope.

06:40
Breakfast/getting ready
Astronauts eat their first meal of the day, which is nothing like the freeze-dried food of the Apollo missions. Fresh fruit and produce are stored on the ISS, while tea and coffee are available in packets. Astronauts can wear anything from shorts and T-shirts to trousers and rugby shirts. However, there are no washing machines, so clothes must be allocated for specific days (although in such a clean environment they pick up very little dirt). Most clothes are disposed of every three days, but socks can be worn for up to a month, while a pair of underwear must be taken for each day on the station.

The ESA-built Cupola is a popular module where astronauts can get a fantastic view of Earth

All Images © NASA

06:00
Post-sleep
Astronauts are woken up at 6am. On the ISS most astronauts have their own sleeping compartments, small spaces where the astronaut can lie vertically (although this doesn't matter as there is no 'up' or 'down' on the station). After waking they will get washed and dressed before eating breakfast, much like a regular day on Earth. There is a shower on the ISS, although most washing is done with a simple wet cloth. In the shower, water is squirted out from the top and 'sucked' by an air fan at the bottom, but water must be used sparingly. Grooming techniques such as shaving are difficult on the ISS, as surface tension makes water and shaving cream stick to an astronaut's face and the razor blade in globules.

16:00 & 17:00
Physical exercise

Astronauts must exercise regularly, at least 2.5 hours a day, to keep their body in optimum condition while in space. As explained previously, bones and organs can become frail and weak in a weightless environment. Therefore astronauts on the ISS have a variety of exercise machines, like treadmills and cycling machines, to keep them strong.

13:00 Lunch

Prolonged microgravity dulls tastebuds, and the white noise doesn't help (like being on an aircraft), so foods with strong flavours (such as spicy curries) are often the preferred choice for meals.

19:00
Back to work

On rare occasions astronauts will have to leave the station on an extra-vehicular activity (EVA). For this astronauts will don a spacesuit and perform work outside the ISS. Before they leave they must exercise for several hours in a decompression chamber to prevent suffering from the 'bends' on entering space. Work outside the station ranges from maintenance to installing or upgrading a component.

19:30
Pre-sleep

In the evening astronauts eat dinner in a communal area. This is an important time for social interaction, as often many hours are spent working alone on the station. Before sleep, they also have a chance for a bit of entertainment, which can range from watching a DVD to playing guitar.

21:30 Sleep

In space no one can hear you scream, right? Well, in an orbiting craft, space is actually very loud, with a multitude of fans and motors ensuring that the space station remains in the correct operational capacity. At 21.30pm astronauts head off to their designated sleeping compartments to grab some rest and, while reassuring, these noises can take a while to get used to for astronauts staying on the station for the first time, much like living next to a busy main road on Earth.

"Skylab required only one unmanned launch to be complete"

Skylab

How NASA's first space station provided the groundwork for the ISS

Following on from the success of the Apollo missions, and using the same equipment, NASA launched its Skylab space station in 1973 to observe the effects on a human during a prolonged period in orbit around the Earth. It was also intended to provide more astronomical information than could be provided from Earth-based observations. It was operational until 1979, completing more than 300 experiments in the process with three different three-man crews inhabiting the station. Unlike the ISS, which has taken over 12 years to build and is still ongoing, Skylab required only one unmanned launch to be complete and needed no assembly in space.

The shell of Skylab was a modified Saturn V rocket used to go to the moon. It was also initially launched on top of a Saturn V, but the later manned missions used a Saturn 1B rocket. An Apollo spacecraft transported the crew to the station and returned them to Earth. The success of Skylab missions proved that humans could be a positive asset when working in space, demonstrating excellent mobility and limited space-related problems barring a few bouts of space sickness. Skylab also, for the first time, showed that the resupply of space vehicles was indeed possible.

The crew were able to produce unprecedented data on the Earth and the Sun using the equipment on board like the Apollo Telescope Mount (ATM), which acted as a solar observatory, giving views of the Sun and stars with no atmospheric interference. The crew exceeded all expectations, performing unplanned experiments such as observing a nearby comet. The station also famously had two spiders on board which showed that they could build a near-perfect web, if slightly irregular, in space.

Although a successful six-year mission, the station did encounter problems on launch when its meteoroid shield ripped off and damaged the station's solar protection. When astronauts first arrived the station was a rather sweltering 52 degrees centigrade. A sun-parasol had to be deployed to lower the temperature. ✿

Inside Skylab

Discover the layout of this groundbreaking space station

Apollo Telescope Mount
Housing a number of solar telescopes which were used primarily in attempting to observe solar flares which were of great interest to NASA. It was successful on several occasions

Multiple Docking Adaptor
Provided a primary and secondary docking port for the Apollo spacecraft. Also contained control panels for the Apollo Telescope Mount

Command and service module
Used as a workstation, the crews also used this module to travel to and from the station. The last crew, knowing the space station might not survive, packed it with valuable equipment that would have been lost

© NASA

Some experiments were attached to the outside of Skylab and collected by astronauts

© NASA

1. Skylab
LONG
Three crews manned the station (although not continuously) for 171 days and 13 hours, a record at the time. The longest stay was 84 days.

2. ISS
LONGER
Broke Mir's record for uninterrupted human presence in space (3,644 days) on 23 October 2010, and could remain operational for at least another ten years.

3. Mir
LONGEST
Occupied for 4,592 days (not continuously) from 1986 to 2001. Mir was one of the Soviet Union's major achievements in space.

DID YOU KNOW? A story written by Edward Everett Hale in 1869 pioneered the idea of placing a manned space station into orbit

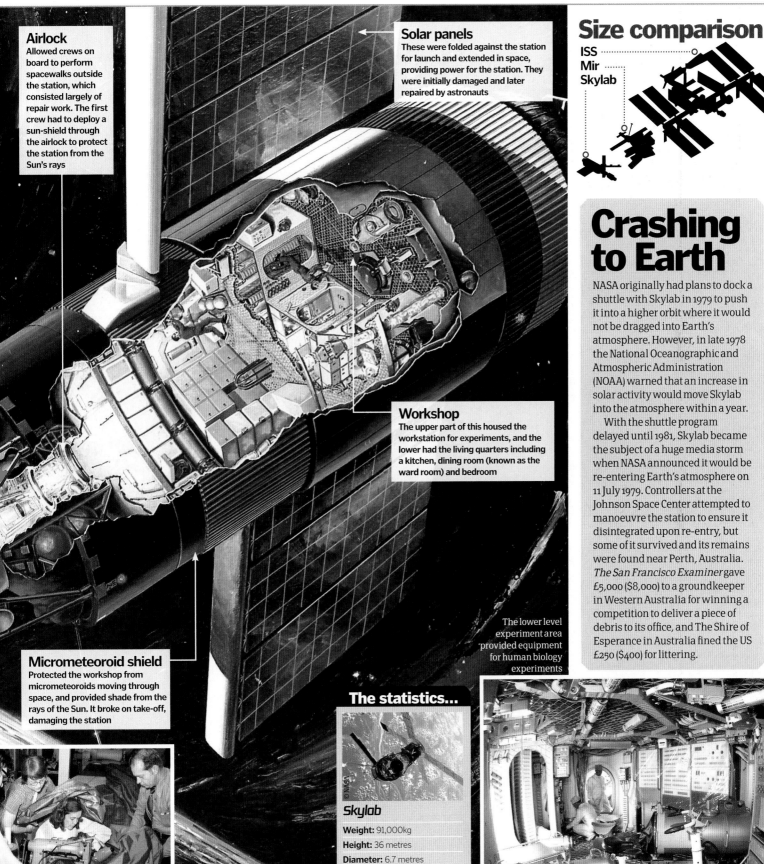

Airlock
Allowed crews on board to perform spacewalks outside the station, which consisted largely of repair work. The first crew had to deploy a sun-shield through the airlock to protect the station from the Sun's rays

Solar panels
These were folded against the station for launch and extended in space, providing power for the station. They were initially damaged and later repaired by astronauts

Workshop
The upper part of this housed the workstation for experiments, and the lower had the living quarters including a kitchen, dining room (known as the ward room) and bedroom

Micrometeoroid shield
Protected the workshop from micrometeoroids moving through space, and provided shade from the rays of the Sun. It broke on take-off, damaging the station

The lower level experiment area provided equipment for human biology experiments

A solar sunshade is sewn to be deployed on Skylab

Size comparison

ISS
Mir
Skylab

Crashing to Earth

NASA originally had plans to dock a shuttle with Skylab in 1979 to push it into a higher orbit where it would not be dragged into Earth's atmosphere. However, in late 1978 the National Oceanographic and Atmospheric Administration (NOAA) warned that an increase in solar activity would move Skylab into the atmosphere within a year.

With the shuttle program delayed until 1981, Skylab became the subject of a huge media storm when NASA announced it would be re-entering Earth's atmosphere on 11 July 1979. Controllers at the Johnson Space Center attempted to manoeuvre the station to ensure it disintegrated upon re-entry, but some of it survived and its remains were found near Perth, Australia. *The San Francisco Examiner* gave £5,000 ($8,000) to a groundkeeper in Western Australia for winning a competition to deliver a piece of debris to its office, and The Shire of Esperance in Australia fined the US £250 ($400) for littering.

The statistics...

Skylab
Weight: 91,000kg
Height: 36 metres
Diameter: 6.7 metres
Living space: 283 cubic metres
Altitude: 270 miles
Orbital period: 93 minutes

On board the International Space Station

What's it like to live in space?

Man has had a continuous presence in space since 2000 on the International Space Station. In 1998, the Zarya module was launched into orbit by the Russian Federal Space Agency. This was the first piece of the ISS. Now that it is complete but for one more module, the ISS is the largest satellite to ever orbit the Earth. Due to be finished in 2012, the ISS is the most expensive object to ever be constructed.

The ISS wasn't the first space station, however; in 1971 the Soviet Union launched the Salyut, which was the first in a series of space stations. Two years later, NASA launched Skylab. However, both of these programmes were single modules with limited life spans. In 1986, the Soviet Union launched the Mir, which was intended to be built upon and added to over time. The United States planned to launch its own space station, Freedom, just a few years later, but budgetary restraints ended the project. After the fall of the Soviet Union, the United States

began negotiating with Russia, along with several other countries, to build a multinational space station.

Until Expedition 20 in May 2009, crews on the International Space Station consisted of two-to-three astronauts and cosmonauts, who stayed for six months. Now the ISS is large enough to support a six-man crew, the stay has been reduced to just three months. The current ISS crew is a crew of six: NASA commander Sunita Williams and flight engineers Yuri Malenchenko (RKA), Akihiko Hoshide (JAXA), Kevin Ford (NASA), Oleg Novitskiy (RKA) and Evgeny Tarelkin (RKA).

The crew typically works for ten hours a day during the week and five hours on Saturdays. During their eight scheduled night hours, the crew sleeps in cabins while attached to bunk beds, or in sleeping bags that are secured to the wall. They also have to wear sleep masks, as it would be difficult to sleep otherwise with a sunrise occurring every 90 minutes.

All food is processed so it is easy to reheat in a special oven, usually with the addition of

water. This includes beverages, which the crew drinks with straws from plastic bags. Exercise is a very important part of daily life for the crew of the ISS because of microgravity's adverse effects on the body. The astronauts and cosmonauts may experience muscle atrophy, bone loss, a weakened immune system and a slowed cardiovascular system, among other problems. To help counteract this, the crew exercises while strapped to treadmills and exercise bicycles.

Research is the main reason for the station's existence in low Earth orbit (about 330 kilometres above the planet's surface). Several scientific experiments spanning fields including astronomy, physics, materials science, earth science and biology take place on the station simultaneously. Between September 2012 and March 2013, for example, the current expedition crew (33) and the next expedition crew (34) will be working on over 100 experiments in a wide range of fields, spanning biology and biotechnology, the

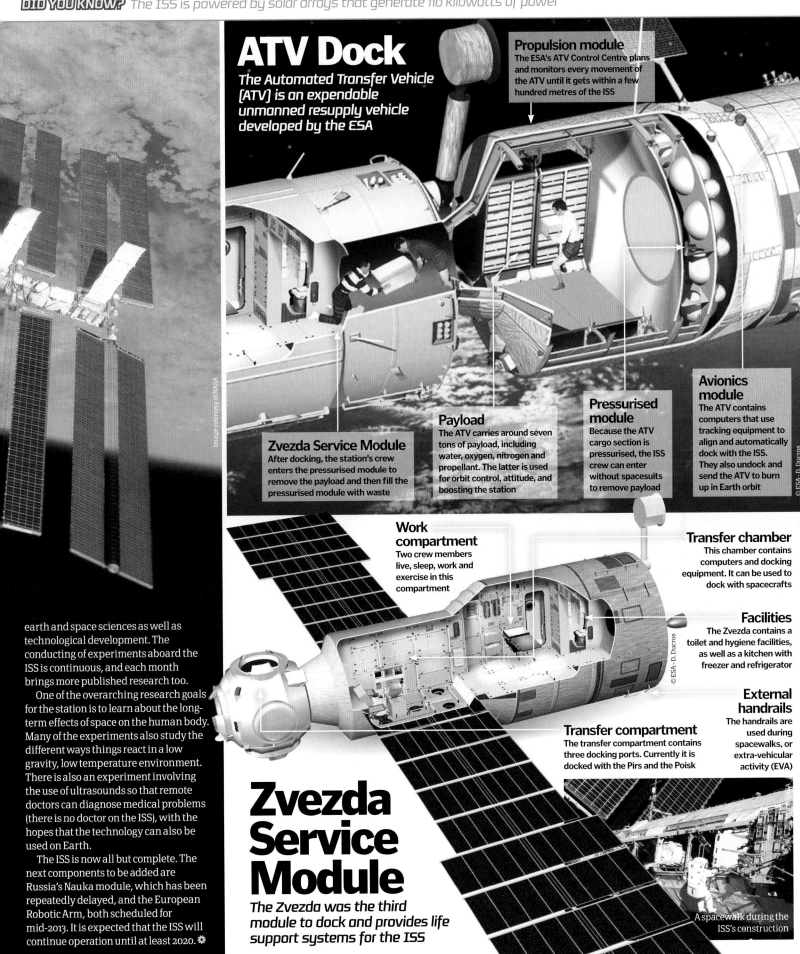

ATV Dock

The Automated Transfer Vehicle (ATV) is an expendable unmanned resupply vehicle developed by the ESA

Propulsion module
The ESA's ATV Control Centre plans and monitors every movement of the ATV until it gets within a few hundred metres of the ISS

Zvezda Service Module
After docking, the station's crew enters the pressurised module to remove the payload and then fill the pressurised module with waste

Payload
The ATV carries around seven tons of payload, including water, oxygen, nitrogen and propellant. The latter is used for orbit control, attitude, and boosting the station

Pressurised module
Because the ATV cargo section is pressurised, the ISS crew can enter without spacesuits to remove payload

Avionics module
The ATV contains computers that use tracking equipment to align and automatically dock with the ISS. They also undock and send the ATV to burn up in Earth orbit

Image courtesy of NASA

© ESA– D. Ducros

Work compartment
Two crew members live, sleep, work and exercise in this compartment

Transfer chamber
This chamber contains computers and docking equipment. It can be used to dock with spacecrafts

Facilities
The Zvezda contains a toilet and hygiene facilities, as well as a kitchen with freezer and refrigerator

External handrails
The handrails are used during spacewalks, or extra-vehicular activity (EVA)

Transfer compartment
The transfer compartment contains three docking ports. Currently it is docked with the Pirs and the Poisk

© ESA – D. Ducros

Zvezda Service Module

The Zvezda was the third module to dock and provides life support systems for the ISS

A spacewalk during the ISS's construction

earth and space sciences as well as technological development. The conducting of experiments aboard the ISS is continuous, and each month brings more published research too.

One of the overarching research goals for the station is to learn about the long-term effects of space on the human body. Many of the experiments also study the different ways things react in a low gravity, low temperature environment. There is also an experiment involving the use of ultrasounds so that remote doctors can diagnose medical problems (there is no doctor on the ISS), with the hopes that the technology can also be used on Earth.

The ISS is now all but complete. The next components to be added are Russia's Nauka module, which has been repeatedly delayed, and the European Robotic Arm, both scheduled for mid-2013. It is expected that the ISS will continue operation until at least 2020. ✿

> "A series of complex treaties and agreements govern the ownership, use and maintenance of the station"

The Columbus Module

The Columbus is a research laboratory designed by the ESA – its largest contribution to the ISS

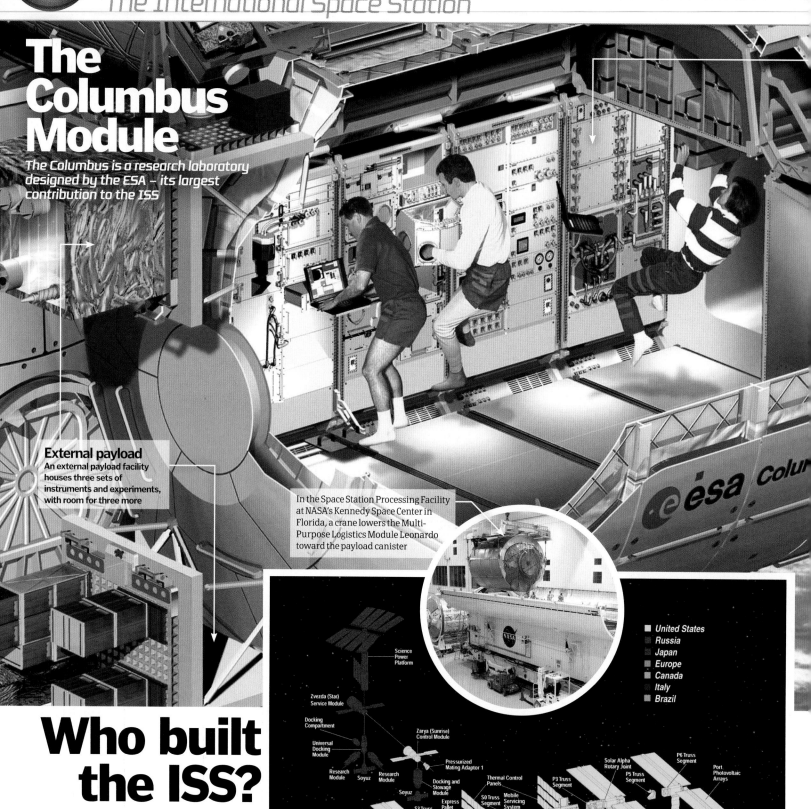

External payload
An external payload facility houses three sets of instruments and experiments, with room for three more

In the Space Station Processing Facility at NASA's Kennedy Space Center in Florida, a crane lowers the Multi-Purpose Logistics Module Leonardo toward the payload canister

esa Colu

United States
Russia
Japan
Europe
Canada
Italy
Brazil

Science Power Platform

Zvezda (Star) Service Module

Docking Compartment

Universal Docking Module

Research Module

Soyuz

Research Module

Zarya (Sunrise) Control Module

Soyuz

Pressurized Mating Adaptor 1

Docking and Stowage Module

Express Pallet

Thermal Control Panels

S0 Truss Segment

Mobile Servicing System

P3 Truss Segment

Solar Alpha Rotary Joint

P5 Truss Segment

P6 Truss Segment

Port Photovoltaic Arrays

S6 Truss Segment

S3 Truss Segment

S5 Truss Segment

S1 Truss Segment

Unity (Node 1)

Z1 Truss Segment

CSA Remote Manipulator System

P1 Truss Segment

P4 Truss Segment

Centrifuge Accommodation Module

Starboard Photovoltaic Arrays

Cupola

S4 Truss Segment

Solar Alpha Rotary Joint

Node 3

Airlock

U.S. Lab Destiny

Kibo (Hope) JEM Experiment Logistics Module–Pressurized Section

Kibo (Hope) JEM Remote Manipulator System

Kibo (Hope) JEM Experiment Logistics Module–Exposed Section

Kibo (Hope) JEM Exposed Facility

Kibo (Hope) JEM Pressurized Module

Crew Return Vehicle

Pressurized Mating Adaptor 3

Habitation Module

Node 2

European Lab – Columbus Orbital Facility

Pressurized Mating Adaptor 2

Multi-Purpose Logistics Module

Who built the ISS?

The ISS currently comprises 15 pressurised modules and an Integrated Truss Structure. The modules are contributions from the Russian Federal Space Agency (RKA), NASA, the Japanese Aerospace Exploration Agency (JAXA), the Canadian Space Agency (CSA) and the Eurpopean Space Agency (ESA), which includes 18 member countries. A series of complex treaties and agreements govern the ownership, use and maintenance of the station. A further four modules are scheduled to be added.

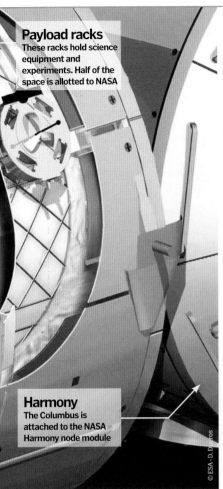

Payload racks
These racks hold science equipment and experiments. Half of the space is allotted to NASA

Harmony
The Columbus is attached to the NASA Harmony node module

© ESA - D. Ducros

Creating water in space

For the crew of the ISS it's better not to think where their next glass of water is coming from

The ECLSS (Environmental Control and Life Support System) provides water with the Water Recovery System (WRS). Water from crew member waste, condensation and other waste water is distilled, filtered and processed. This water is then used for drinking, cooking, cleaning and other functions. An Oxygen Generation System (OGS) separates water into oxygen and hydrogen. An experimental Carbon Dioxide Reduction Assembly (CReA) uses the leftover hydrogen with carbon dioxide filtered from the crew cabins to produce usable water and methane. In addition, the ECLSS filters the cabin air, maintains cabin pressure and can detect and suppress fires.

Anatomy of the Space Station

The ISS is a configuration of modules, trusses and solar arrays

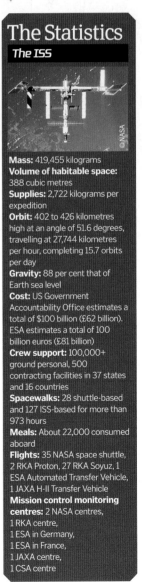

© ESA - D. Ducros

1. Zarya
The Zarya, launched in 1998 and built by the RKA, is now a storage component. As the first module it provided storage, power and propulsion.

2. Unity
Built by NASA and launched in 1998, Unity was the first node module to connect to the Zarya. It provides a docking station for other modules.

3. Zvezda
The RKA-built Zvezda launched in 2000. It made the ISS habitable by providing crew cabins and environmental control as well as other systems.

4. Destiny
The Destiny is a NASA laboratory. Launched back in 2001, it also contains environmental controls and works as a mounting point for the Integrated Truss Structure.

5. Quest
The 2001 NASA-built Quest is an airlock used to host spacewalks. The equipment lock is used for storing the spacesuits, while the crew lock allows exit to space.

6. Pirs
A mini-research module called Pirs was launched in 2001 by the RKA. It can dock spacecraft and also host spacewalks by cosmonauts.

7. Harmony
Harmony, built by NASA in 2007, is a node module. It serves as a berthing point and docking station for modules and spacecraft.

8. Columbus
The Columbus, launched in 2008, is an ESA laboratory specifically designed for experiments in biology and physics. It provides power to experiments mounted to its exterior.

9. Kibo Experiment Logistics Module
This JAXA module (also known as JEM-ELM) is part of the Japanese Experiment Module laboratory and was launched in 2008. It contains transportation and storage.

10. Kibo Pressurised Module
Also launched in 2008, the JEM-PM is a research facility and the largest module on the ISS. It has an external platform and robotic arm for experiments.

11. Poisk
The RKA-built Poisk (MRM2) launched in November 2009. In addition to housing components for experiments, it serves as a dock for spacecraft and a spacewalk airlock.

12. Integrated Truss Structure
The ISS's solar arrays and thermal radiators are mounted to this structure, which is more than 100 metres long and has ten separate parts.

13. Mobile Servicing System
Also known as the Canadarm2, this CSA-built robotic system used to move supplies, service equipment and assist astronauts on spacewalks.

14. Special Purpose Dexterous Manipulator
The SPDM, or Dextre, is a robot built by the CSA and is extremely dextrous. It can perform functions outside the ISS that had previously required spacewalks to happen.

15. Tranquillity
The Tranquillity is NASA's third node module, and was successfully launched in February 2010. It contains the ECLSS as well as berthing stations for other modules.

16. Cupola
The seven windows of this observatory module, launched with Tranquility in February 2010, make it the largest window ever used in space.

17. Rassvet
Launched in May 2010, this second RKA mini-research module also serves as storage.

18. Leonardo
A pressurised multipurpose module, the Leonardo was installed in March 2011. It serves as a storage unit and frees up space in the Columbus.

19. Nauka (MLM)
Scheduled to be launched with the European Robotic Arm in mid-2013, this multipurpose research module will be a rest area for the crew as well as doubling up as a research laboratory too.

20. Solar Arrays
These arrays convert sunlight into electricity. There are four pairs on the ISS.

21. Thermal Radiators
The Active Thermal Control System (ATCS) removes excess heat from the ISS and vents it out into space via these radiators.

The ISS in early construction while in orbit in 1999

© NASA

The Statistics
The ISS

© NASA

Mass: 419,455 kilograms
Volume of habitable space: 388 cubic metres
Supplies: 2,722 kilograms per expedition
Orbit: 402 to 426 kilometres high at an angle of 51.6 degrees, travelling at 27,744 kilometres per hour, completing 15.7 orbits per day
Gravity: 88 per cent that of Earth sea level
Cost: US Government Accountability Office estimates a total of $100 billion (£62 billion). ESA estimates a total of 100 billion euros (£81 billion)
Crew support: 100,000+ ground personal, 500 contracting facilities in 37 states and 16 countries
Spacewalks: 28 shuttle-based and 127 ISS-based for more than 973 hours
Meals: About 22,000 consumed aboard
Flights: 35 NASA space shuttle, 2 RKA Proton, 27 RKA Soyuz, 1 ESA Automated Transfer Vehicle, 1 JAXA H-II Transfer Vehicle
Mission control monitoring centres: 2 NASA centres, 1 RKA centre, 1 ESA in Germany, 1 ESA in France, 1 JAXA centre, 1 CSA centre

"Dextre weighs 1,560kg and cannot be assembled on Earth"

Dextre as attached to the International Space Station

All images courtesy of NASA

Dextre being unpacked and readied for launch

Dextre the space robot

The robot that will fix the International Space Station

And you thought fixing your toaster was a challenge! On the International Space Station, components sometimes need repair or must be moved for scientific tests. Late 2010, the Special Purpose Dexterous Manipulator, or Dextre, became operational after about two years of testing.

Why send a repair robot into space? The primary reason has to do with saving time for human astronauts, who can focus on science experiments on the space station and because the robot is impervious to radiation and other space hazards. "Dextre also helps reduce the risk from micrometeorites or suit failures that astronauts are exposed to during an EVA (Extravehicular Activity)," says Daniel Rey, the manager of Systems Definition for the Canadian Space Agency in charge of the project.

Dextre is an electrical robot – as opposed to the common hydraulic and pneumatic robots found on Earth – because the robot itself won't require as much maintenance, space station repairs require precise movement, and there is no leakage. The robot has two large, electrically controlled arms, each with seven degrees of movement.

Each joint is controlled by a separate computer processor and runs a set of predetermined computer code. "CPUs control co-ordinated movements," says Rey, explaining that the robot is mostly controlled from the ground but does have some autonomous behaviour. "All the joints are rotary joints so they have to move in a co-ordinated fashion." The 3.67-metre tall robot weighs 1,560 kilograms and had to be 'orbitally assembled'. The colossal bot has four main tools it will use for repairs. Rey described the two important characteristics of Dextre which makes it the ultimate space repairbot.

First, Dextre uses an inverse kinematic engine to control joint movement. The 'inverse' is that the joints are instructed on the final place to move one of its repair tools, and then must work backwards and move joints to arrive at that position. Rey described this as similar to instructing a human to put a hand on a doorknob, and then knowing that you need to move an elbow, forearm, and shoulder to that position. A second characteristic is called forced moment sensor, which measures the forces applied on the joints and is used for correcting inputs from an astronaut to avoid errors and joint bindings. ✿

The Statistics
Dextre

Height: 3.67 metres
Weight: 1,560 kilograms
Arm length (each):
3.35 metres
Handling capability:
600 kilograms
Crew: 98
Average operating power:
1,400 watts

Docking with the ISS

How do shuttles link up with the International Space Station?

Docking with the ISS can potentially be catastrophic. Suffice to say, precision-manoeuvring a manned shuttle onto a space station docking ring while orbiting the Earth is just a little more complicated than parking your car in the garage. Fortunately, the world's space agencies tend to recruit many pilots into their ranks, whose skills and flight experience make this task a lot less hazardous.

Whenever a shuttle delivering equipment, supplies or new crew needs to dock at the ISS, there's a strict procedure to which the pilot must adhere. First, orbital manoeuvring and reaction control systems are used to thrust the shuttle into an orbit approximately 110 metres (360 feet) below the station, before the reaction control system finishes the approach. Firing rockets located in the nose and tail sections to alter the pitch, yaw and roll, the shuttle is stopped 50 metres (164 feet) from the station. Then it awaits clearance from mission control to continue.

Once it has clearance, the pilot moves the shuttle at a much slower rate of five centimetres (two inches) per second until it's ten metres (33 feet) from the ISS. Here, the pilot will stop for a few minutes to fine-tune the final approach: the station's docking target is lined up in the viewer with a cross mounted 30 centimetres (11.8 inches) above the target, called the stand-off cross. When aligned, the shuttle is manoeuvred the remaining distance onto the docking ring, where a series of hooks fixes it in place. The passage takes two hours to pressurise, after which the crew can open the hatch to pass between space station and shuttle. ✿

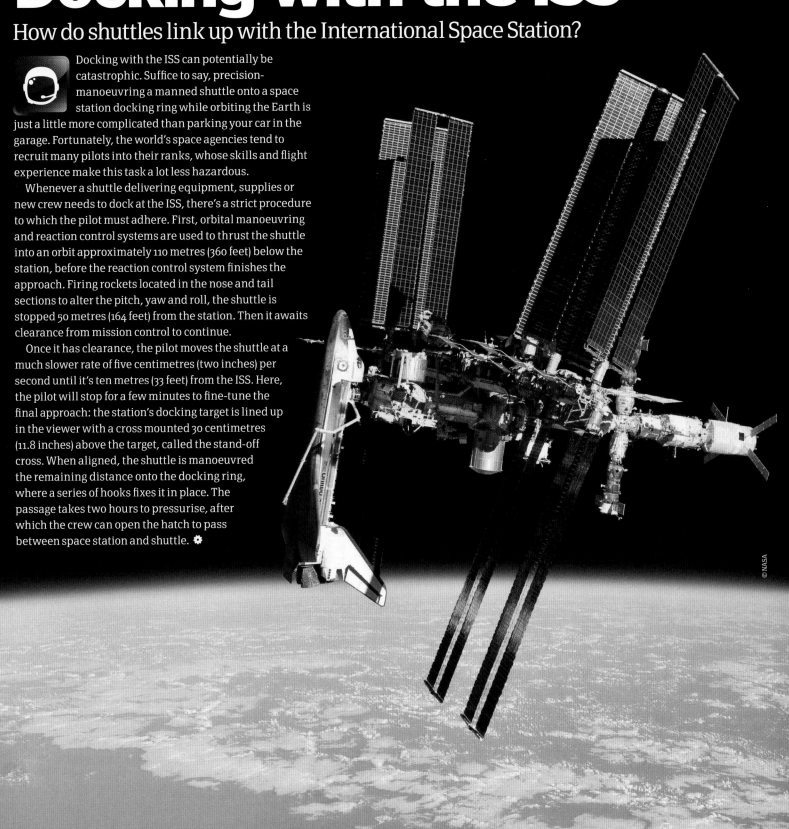

© NASA

A holiday that's out of this world

SPACE VACATIONS

Will space tourists choose LEO or the ISS? You decide

The statistics...

SpaceShipTwo

Manufacturer: Scaled Composites

Length: 18 metres

Wingspan: 8 metres

Tail height: 4.5 metres

Top speed: Mach 3.5 (2,600mph)

Required fuel: Hybrid rocket using liquid nitrous oxide and a solid rubber compound

G-force: 3.8g entering space, 6g on re-entry while reclining

Body construction: 100 per cent carbon composite

Windows: 17" and 13" in diameter

Passenger cabin: 3.6m long and 2.3m wide

The space tourism industry has really taken off, so to speak, within the last three years. A dozen major companies are competing for a race to space with tourists on board. Seven space tourists to date have already been flown to the International Space Station, which is the only space tourism option open right now.

However, for shorter duration adventures in the near future, several companies such as Virgin Galactic (a division of Virgin Airlines) have already flown successful test flights with an expected rollout to paying consumers to follow.

At this time two different space tourist packages will be offered including orbital space (200 miles up aboard the ISS) or sub-orbital space (60 miles up in low Earth orbit). Orbital space flights to the ISS of 10-14 days cost around $20 million.

Suborbital space flights to LEO (low Earth orbit) can last from 30 minutes to 2.5 hours, depending upon the company offering the flights, and cost between $100,000 and $400,000.

Virgin Galactic has teamed up with a company called Scaled Composites (the builders of the vehicles) and are the frontrunners right now in leading tourists into low-Earth orbit (LEO). Scaled Composites has developed a unique approach in carrying tourists to space which it says is safer than the traditional rocket launch.

Scaled Composites is using both an aircraft and a spacecraft to transport tourists on a 2.5 hour space adventure. The WhiteKnightTwo (or Virgin Mothership Eve) is the aircraft and the SpaceShipTwo (or VSS Enterprise) is the spacecraft. Both vehicles are made from carbon fibre composites which are

Head to Head
SPACE TOURISTS

OLDEST

1. John Glenn
Former astronaut and US Senator John Glenn, at 77-years-old, was the oldest non-paying space tourist who travelled on the Space Shuttle Discovery.

FIRST PAYING

2. Dennis Tito
Multimillionaire Dennis Tito was the first paying space tourist, coughing up $20 million to spend almost eight days orbiting the Earth.

FIRST FEMALE

3. Anousheh Ansari
Anousheh Ansari was the first female space tourist and she and her family were the largest multimillion dollar donors to the X Prize for space tourism.

DID YOU KNOW? US astronaut John Glenn was a non-paying space tourist

SpaceShipTwo features

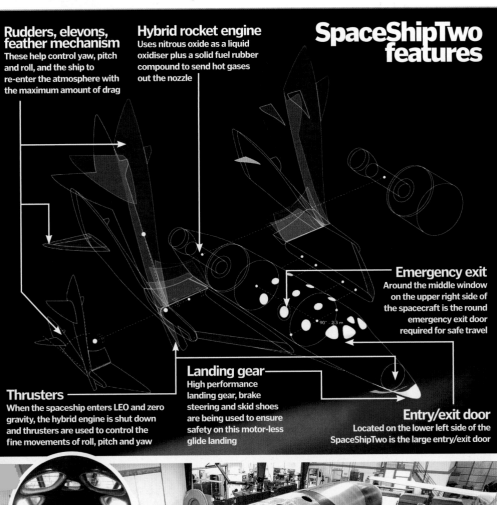

Rudders, elevons, feather mechanism
These help control yaw, pitch and roll, and the ship to re-enter the atmosphere with the maximum amount of drag

Hybrid rocket engine
Uses nitrous oxide as a liquid oxidiser plus a solid fuel rubber compound to send hot gases out the nozzle

Emergency exit
Around the middle window on the upper right side of the spacecraft is the round emergency exit door required for safe travel

Thrusters
When the spaceship enters LEO and zero gravity, the hybrid engine is shut down and thrusters are used to control the fine movements of roll, pitch and yaw

Landing gear
High performance landing gear, brake steering and skid shoes are being used to ensure safety on this motor-less glide landing

Entry/exit door
Located on the lower left side of the SpaceShipTwo is the large entry/exit door

SpaceShipTwo begins to take shape

Space Adventures training program

The Yuri Gagarin Cosmonauts Training Center in Star City, Russia is where space tourists, in the Space Adventures program, will undergo up to six months of training before they are allowed to travel in a Soyuz spacecraft to the ISS.

As a prospective space tourist, you can expect not only thorough medical exams but training in zero gravity, communications systems within both the Soyuz and ISS, and centrifuge simulator training (launching into orbit).

Specific space training will be conducted in a simulator for the Soyuz TMA with experienced spacecraft pilot trainers. And additional training will be provided in a hi-tech International Space Station simulator.

Centrifuge simulator training takes place in Star City

Because the carbon composite material reduces friction and because of the unique feathered tail configuration the spacecraft automatically accounts for drag and temperature, passengers are no longer submitted to a "lean forward, grab your ankles and then hope for the best" experience when it comes to re-entering the Earth's atmosphere.

What is also unique about the SpaceShipTwo compared to ground-launched spacecraft is that there are no parachutes or water landings. SpaceShipTwo is designed to "lower its tail-feather" at around 21,300 metres and glide back into the spaceport from where it started, which initially will be Spaceport America in New Mexico. So, even though WhiteKnightTwo and SpaceShipTwo are being constructed and tested by Scaled Composites in the Mojave Desert of California, actual flights will take off and land in New Mexico.

Now, for those with a larger budget – say in the tens of millions of dollars – Space Adventures will carry passengers to the ISS (and get a closer look at the constellation Leo). To date, Space Adventures has transported seven paying space tourists including Guy Laliberte, Charles Simonyi, Richard Garriott, Anousheh Ansari, Greg Olsen, Mark Shuttleworth and Dennis Tito.

Adventures into orbital space are a bit more complicated than LEO in that journeys are longer,

stronger and lighter than steel plus resistant to heat. WhiteKnightTwo has two fuselages, 15 metres apart and will carry SpaceShipTwo in-between them. The aircraft and spacecraft will both travel up to 15,000 metres above sea level before SpaceShipTwo is launched into LEO.

Some of the safety advantages of this two-stage system that Virgin Galactic points out are that SpaceShipTwo can be lighter and carry less fuel than ground-launched rockets. In addition, there is less drag on the vehicle when launching it from 15,000 metres above the ground and the unique design and materials used in SpaceShipTwo make for less friction (and heat) during re-entry.

The hybrid rocket is another feature that integrates top thrust and the safety features of using a combined liquid fuel and solid fuel engine. The liquid that is used in the hybrid rocket engine is nitrous oxide and the solid fuel is a benign rubber compound. Unlike solid rocket fuel engines, hybrid rocket engines can be shut down any time. SpaceShipTwo carries a pilot, a copilot and six tourists, each with identical seating. This means that each tourist has a window seat as well as a window above to enjoy. After several minutes of weightlessness tourists will re-enter Earth's atmosphere in less traumatic fashion than astronauts and cosmonauts of old.

"Space tourists travel at over 17,000mph"

A holiday that's out of this world

Spaceport America

Spaceport America, declared open on 18 October 2011, is the world's first spaceport built specifically for the space tourism industry. Even though it was still under construction in October 2010, the New Mexico Spaceport Authority (NMSA)

dedicated the runway, which is two miles in length, and named it the "Governor Bill Richardson Spaceway" after the current governor.

Spaceport America is located 30 miles east of Truth or Consequences, New Mexico (a bit of an ironic name

associated to this high risk and reward location). The terminal hub of the spaceport has been built to certified Gold LEED standards, meaning that it is very energy efficient with a small carbon footprint. Virgin Galactic's operational headquarters

are located at Spaceport America, where White Knight Two and the SpaceShipTwo aircrafts reside. Since August 2012 there have been 12 successful suborbital launches from Spaceport America. Virgin Galactic's first launch will be from the port.

Want to avoid airport queues? Take your holidays in space!

© Spaceport America Conceptual Images URS-Foster + Partners

Runway
Spaceport America's runway is 61 metres wide and 3,000 metres long. That's almost two miles

SpaceShipTwo
Virgin Galactic's SpaceShipTwo will be flying from Spaceport America for at least the next 20 years

Big bucks
The estimated construction cost of the world's first purpose-built spaceport is $198 million

Administrative centre
Virgin Galactic's HQ is at Spaceport America. It is also home to the New Mexico Spaceport Authority visitor area

© Mark Greenberg/Spaceport America Conceptual Images URS-Foster + Partners

take place further out from the Earth and involve more people. Even though Space Adventures is a US-based company, it launches passengers in a Soyuz spacecraft from the Baikonur Cosmodrome in Kazakhstan. Right now, Space Adventures is using a Soyuz TMA space capsule which contains three modules. Three cosmonauts (two professional cosmonauts and a space tourist cosmonaut) ride in the descent module to and from the ISS.

Like the cosmonauts, the space tourist will be wearing a fully pressurised spacesuit, have to endure g forces upon liftoff and re-entry, adapt to weightlessness and once docked they will journey from the Soyuz space capsule to the ISS. Aboard the ISS, space tourists travel at over 17,000mph and orbit the Earth every 90 minutes.

Space tourists to the ISS typically undergo 6-12 months worth of training at the Yuri Gagarin

Cosmonauts Training Center in Star City, Russia before travelling on board the Soyuz rocket. Typical space trips are in the 10-16 day range. Before entering the Soyuz capsule with the two cosmonauts in charge of the vehicle, the tourist will have to have already undergone a series of extensive medical tests to be cleared for the flight. Second, the equipment will be tested, such as pressurised spacesuit tests, and the passenger will be quarantined shortly before take-off.

So, what can you do in space on the ISS? In the past, space tourists have used their time to document and communicate their own personal experiences, run experiments and call awareness to a cause or promote a business. The most recent space tourist, Guy Laliberte, the CEO of Cirque du Soleil, used his video blog to promote "Poetic Social Mission" calling awareness to water-related

challenges facing the Earth and to promote his business. As if this didn't got far enough, he also wore a red clown nose while making his videos before, during and after his spaceflight.

Google cofounder Sergey Brin has put a $5 million down payment with Space Adventures for a future flight. Presumably he will be calling awareness to environmental issues (Google Green Initiatives), promoting space flight (Google Lunar X Prize) and promoting his search engine company in general. And right now Space Adventures is offering something that no one else has offered yet, which is

3 TOP FACTS
SPACE TOURISM FACTS

Before space tourists
1 After astronauts had flown into space and before the first tourist ventured to the ISS, a couple of payload specialists flew aboard the NASA Space Shuttle in 1983.

Opposition to space tourism
2 Former astronaut John Glenn was a notable vocal opponent to the prospect of space tourism saying that it would cheapen space flight and the legacy of those who worked for NASA.

Cheapening space tourism
3 The most recent space tourist Guy Laliberte, CEO of Cirque du Soleil has been accused of cheapening the space experience by wearing a red clown nose while on-board the International Space Station.

DID YOU KNOW? Some companies use a Boeing 727 aircraft at high altitude to create the feeling of zero gravity

You'll have to catch it if you want to drink it

Zero gravity and weightlessness

Passengers aboard SpaceShipTwo will experience weightlessness for about six minutes where they can free themselves from their constraints and float about the cabin. For many this will come with a euphoric feeling of freedom. For a few, however, this could mean temporary space sickness so they will need to be sure to use their motion sickness pills, patches or beads beforehand just in case. A person can experience a short dose of weightlessness going over the hump on a rollercoaster or in an aeroplane when rising from the seat unsupported.

Weightlessness in SpaceShipTwo will be achieved in zero gravity conditions as the vehicle orbits the Earth and the passengers inside are going the same speed as the spacecraft. Since human bodies are adapted for gravitational force on Earth the feelings of weightlessness may seem odd and exhilarating at first as reported by astronauts, cosmonauts and the space tourists who have made it to the International Space Station.

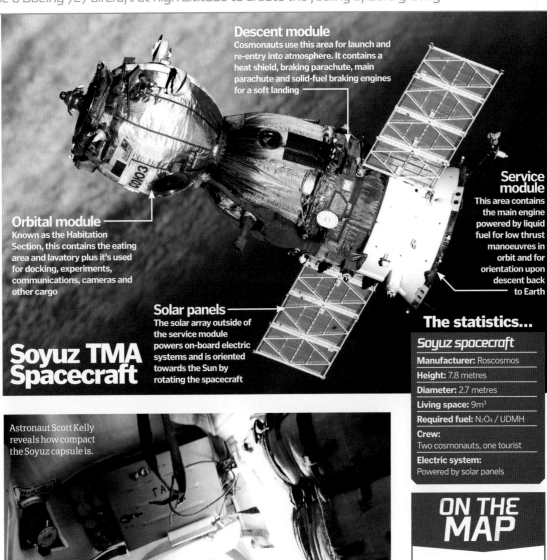

Descent module
Cosmonauts use this area for launch and re-entry into atmosphere. It contains a heat shield, braking parachute, main parachute and solid-fuel braking engines for a soft landing

Orbital module
Known as the Habitation Section, this contains the eating area and lavatory plus it's used for docking, experiments, communications, cameras and other cargo

Service module
This area contains the main engine powered by liquid fuel for low thrust manoeuvres in orbit and for orientation upon descent back to Earth

Solar panels
The solar array outside of the service module powers on-board electric systems and is oriented towards the Sun by rotating the spacecraft

Soyuz TMA Spacecraft

Astronaut Scott Kelly reveals how compact the Soyuz capsule is.

2 x Soyuz © NASA

The statistics...

Soyuz spacecraft	
Manufacturer:	Roscosmos
Height:	7.8 metres
Diameter:	2.7 metres
Living space:	9m³
Required fuel:	N_2O_4 / UDMH
Crew:	Two cosmonauts, one tourist
Electric system:	Powered by solar panels

ON THE MAP

World spaceports
Go here for your space holiday
1 Baikonur Cosmodrome, Kazakhstan
2 Spaceport America, New Mexico, USA
3 Spaceport Singapore, Singapore
4 Spaceport Sweden, Kiruna, Sweden
5 Vostochny Cosmodrome, Russia
6 United Arab Emirates Spaceport, Dubai

to be the first private citizen in history to take a spacewalk. None of the previous space tourists have made this claim so this milestone is still up for grabs. The spacewalk from the ISS will last around 90 minutes, will cost an additional $15 million and will add another six to eight days to the trip. One advantage of tourists on the ISS is that they will get a good dose of zero gravity weightlessness that you cannot experience in LEO.

According to some of the previous space tourists, including Guy Laliberte, getting used to zero gravity takes several hours, as does manoeuvring around the station and trying not to break anything. So, in the near future budding space tourists will have a choice between whether to spend a few hundred thousand dollars and go into low Earth orbit, or instead cough up a few million dollars and travel to the International Space Station. Most of the major players right now are betting on making a lion's share of the money on LEO on what is projected to be a multibillion dollar business by 2025.

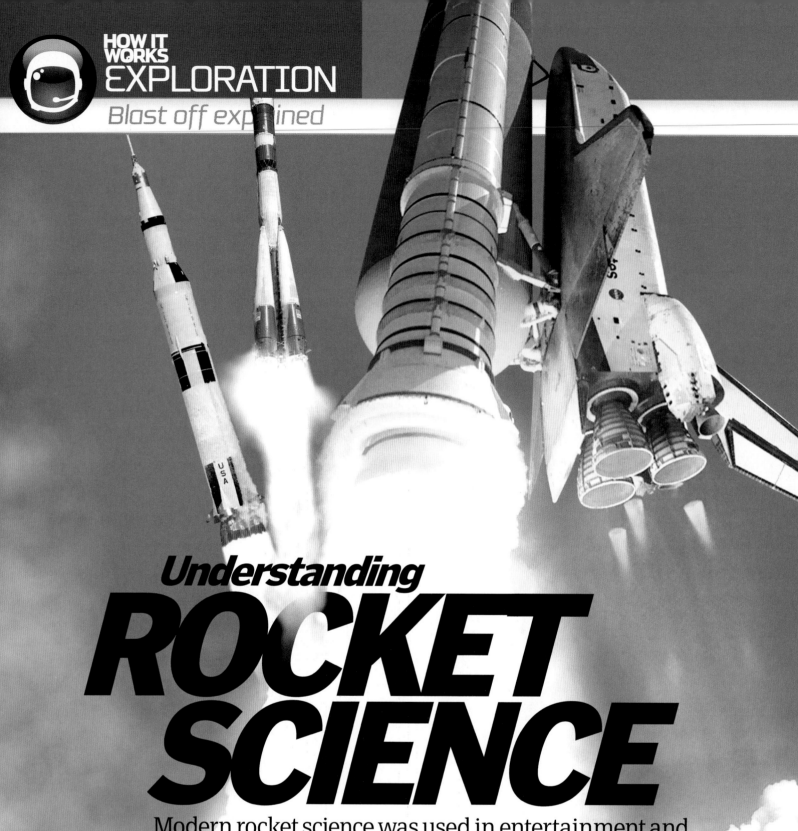

Understanding
ROCKET SCIENCE

Modern rocket science was used in entertainment and weaponry, long before the realms of space travel

 Rocket science has been around since the 280s BCE, when ancient Chinese alchemists invented gunpowder. Initially used in fireworks, gunpowder was soon put to use in weaponry as fire-arrows, bombs and more. Through the centuries, rockets continued to be used as weapons until the early-20th Century. In 1912, Robert Goddard built the first liquid-fuel rocket (previous rockets were solid-fuel) and began the age of modern rocketry. To date, there have been about 500 rocket launches from NASA's Cape Canaveral, and more than five thousand satellites launched by rockets from spaceports around the world.

While the term 'rocket' can be used to describe everything from cars to jet packs, most of us think 'space travel' when we see 'rocket'. Most rockets follow the same basic design.

Typically they are tube-like, with stacks of components. Rockets carry propellants (a fuel and an oxidiser), one or more engines, stabilisation devices, and a nozzle to accelerate and expand gases. However, there's a lot of variation among those basic elements.

There are two main types of rockets: solid-fuel and liquid-fuel. The former have some similarities to those early gunpowder rockets. For space applications, solid-fuel rockets are often used as boosters to lower the amount of needed liquid fuel and reduce the overall mass of the vehicle as a whole. A common type of solid propellant, used in the solid rocket boosters on the NASA space shuttles, is a composite made of ammonium percholate, aluminium, iron oxide and a polymer to bind it. The propellant is packed into a casing. Solid-fuel

5 TOP FACTS
ROCKET FIRSTS

Liquid-fuel rocket
1 Robert Goddard built and launched the first liquid-fuel rocket on 26 March 1926. It was fuelled by gasoline and liquid oxygen, the flight lasting 2.5 seconds.

True rocket
2 In 1232 BC, the Chinese used rocket-arrows propelled by burning gunpowder in their war with the Mongols. While not very effective, they were likely a frightening sight.

Launch into Earth orbit
3 On 4 Oct 1957, the R-7 ICBM was the first rocket to launch an artificial satellite – Sputnik 1 – into orbit. This marked the start of the Space Race between the US and the USSR.

Launch into space
4 Germany launched the first rocket capable of reaching space, the V-2 rocket, in 1942. The missile was launched at sites in England and Belgium as part of the WWII effort.

Private launch, Earth orbit
5 Space X, a company pioneering commercial space travel, launched Falcon 9 on 10 Dec 2010. With an unmanned capsule, it orbited Earth twice before landing in the Pacific.

DID YOU KNOW? *Advances in gunnery left rockets forgotten until an Indian prince used them in the Mysore Wars (late 1700s)*

rockets are used alone sometimes to launch lighter objects into low-Earth orbit, but they cannot provide the type of overall thrust needed to propel a very heavy object into Earth orbit or into space. They can also be difficult to control and to stop once ignited.

The difficulty in getting off the ground is due to the strength of Earth's gravity. This is why thrust – a rocket's strength – is measured in pounds or Newtons. One pound of thrust is the amount of force that it takes to keep a one-pound object at rest against Earth's gravity. A rocket carries fuel that weighs much more than the object that it's trying to move (its payload – a spacecraft or satellite). To understand why, think about what happens when you blow up a balloon and then release it. The balloon flies around the room

because of the force exerted by the air molecules escaping from it. This is Newton's third law in action (see boxout on the following page). But the balloon is only propelling itself; rockets need to generate thrust greater than their mass, which includes the weight of the fuel. For example, the space shuttle in total weighs about 4.4 million pounds, with a possible payload of about 230,000 pounds. To lift this, rocket boosters provided 3.3 million pounds of thrust each, while three engines on the main tank each provided 375,000 pounds of thrust.

Liquid-fuel rockets have the benefit of losing mass over time as their propellant is used up, which in turn increases the rate of acceleration. They have a higher energy content than solid-fuel rockets. Typically they

consist of a fuel and an oxidiser in separate tanks, mixed in a combustion chamber. Guidance systems control the amount of propellants that enter, depending on the amount of thrust needed. Liquid-fuel rockets can be stopped and started.

Launch location can also help rockets become more efficient. European Space Agency member country France chose to build a spaceport in French Guiana not only for its location near water, but also its location near the equator. Launching a rocket near the equator, in an easterly direction, makes use of energy created by the Earth's rotation speed of 465m per second. This also means that putting a rocket into geosynchronous orbit is easier, because few corrections have to be made to its trajectory. ⚙

Liquid-fuel rocket

The components of a liquid fuel rocket and how they work

Fuel
Common fuels used today include kerosene (RP-1), liquid hydrogen and hydrazine

Oxidiser
The oxidiser may be liquid hydrogen, or in the case of hydrazine, nitrogen tetroxide

Pumps
These pumps move the fuel and oxidiser into the combustion chamber

Combustion chamber
Jets of fuel and oxidiser meet here, where their ignition creates a high-pressure stream of gases

Nozzle
The gases are further accelerated in the nozzle, which directs them from the engine

© DK Images

Escape velocity
How rockets break free of Earth's gravity

Throw an apple into the air and it will keep travelling away from planet Earth until gravity overcomes the force of your throw. At this point the apple will fall back down to the

ground. If, however, you launched that apple from a cannon at a speed of 25,000mph (40,000kph) – that's a nippy seven miles (11km) per second – the apple will reach what's known

as escape velocity. At this speed, the force of gravity will never be stronger than the force causing the apple to move away from Earth, and so the apple will escape Earth's gravity.

Escaping other bodies

Escape velocity depends on the mass of the planet or moon, meaning that each planet's escape velocity is different

Ceres
Mass (Earth = 1):
0.00015
Escape velocity:
1,430mph (2,301kph)

The Moon
Mass (Earth = 1):
0.012
Escape velocity:
5,320mph (8,561kph)

Earth
Mass (Earth = 1):
1
Escape velocity:
25,038mph (40,000kph)

The Sun
Mass (Earth = 1):
333,000
Escape velocity:
1,381,600mph (2,223,469kph)

1. Gravity
An object fired from a cannon is returned to Earth by gravity, in the direction of Earth's core

2. Mid-range
The greater the object's speed, the further it travels before returning to Earth (falls at the same rate of acceleration)

3. Long-range
With enough velocity, the object reaches the horizon, at which point the ground 'falls away' (due to Earth's curve) and the object travels further before landing

8. Escape velocity
At escape velocity, the object will break free of Earth's gravitational pull

5. Orbital velocity
At this speed the object's gravitational fall is balanced with the curvature of the Earth

6. Circular orbit
The object travels so fast it falls all the way around the world. It is now in orbit

7. Elliptical orbit
Object speed is greater than orbital velocity but less than escape velocity. The object continues to circle the Earth

Newton's cannon
How an object's velocity helps it escape Earth's gravitational pull

4. Half orbit
Earth's surface falls away from the object nearly equal to gravity's rate of acceleration

"There are two main types of rockets: solid-fuel and liquid-fuel"

The three laws of motion

Rockets have been around for thousands of years, but the science behind them wasn't understood until Isaac Newton's 1687 book *Philosophiae Naturalis Principia Mathematica*. In it, Newton explained three laws that govern motion of all objects, now known as Newton's Laws of Motion. Knowing these laws have made modern rocketry possible.

FIRST LAW

The first law states that objects that are at rest will stay at rest, while objects that are in motion will stay in motion unless an external, unbalanced force acts upon it. A rocket is at rest until thrust unbalances it; it will then stay in motion until it encounters another unbalanced force.

SECOND LAW

Force equals mass times acceleration. Force is the pressure from the explosions. It accelerates the rocket's mass in one direction and the mass of the expelled gases in the other. Mass decreases as it burns up propellants, while acceleration increases.

THIRD LAW

The third law states that for every action, there is an equal and opposite reaction. When a rocket launches, the action is the gas expelling from its engine. The rocket moves in the opposite direction, which is the reaction. To lift off, the thrust must be greater than the rocket's mass.

Saturn V: The biggest and most powerful

Rockets like Saturn V, the one used to launch NASA's Apollo and Skylab programs, are multi-stage liquid-fuelled boosters. The Saturn V is considered to be the biggest, most powerful and most successful rocket ever built. It was 110.6m tall, 10.1m in diameter and had a payload of 119,000kgs to low-Earth orbit.

There were three stages, followed by an instrument unit and the payload (spacecraft). The total mission time for this rocket was about 20 mins. The centre engine was ignited first, then engines on either side ignited. The first stage lifted the rocket to about 70km and burned for 2.5 mins. When sensors in the tanks sensed that the propellant was low, motors detached the first stage. The second stage continued the trajectory to 176km and burned for six mins. About halfway through this stage's ignition, the instrument unit took control of calculating the trajectory.

Second stage complete, solid-fuel rockets fired it away from the third stage. The third stage burned for 2.5 mins and stayed attached to the spacecraft while it orbited the Earth, at an altitude of 191.2km. It continued to thrust and vent hydrogen before ramping up and burning for six more minutes, so the spacecraft could reach a high enough velocity to escape Earth's gravity.

Launch Umbilical Tower
Built as part of the MLP (but removed and installed permanently at the launch site for the shuttle missions), the Launch Umbilical Tower contains swing arms to access the rocket, a crane and a water suppression system

Payload
The Saturn V payload was either Apollo spacecraft or the Skylab space station. With the former, it carried both the Command Service Module (CSM) and the Lunar Module (LM)

Instrument unit
The instrument unit, containing telemetry and guidance systems, controlled the rocket's operations until the ejection of the third stage

Third stage
The third stage is S-IVB. It only had one engine but also used liquid hydrogen and liquid oxygen. Fully fuelled, it weighed 119,000 kilograms

Second stage
The second stage, or S-II, also contained five engines and was nearly identical to the first stage. However, it was powered by liquid hydrogen and liquid oxygen and weighed 480,000 kilograms

First stage
The first stage was also known as S-IC. It contained a central engine, four outer engines, RP-1 fuel (kerosene) and liquid oxygen as the oxidiser. Fully fuelled, it weighed 2.3 million kilograms

© DK Images

Crawler Transporter
This tracked vehicle moved spacecraft from the Assembly Building to the launch complex along a path called the Crawlerway, and then moved the empty MLP back to the VAB

Mobile Launcher Platform (MLP)
A three-story platform designed to support and launch the Saturn V (and later, the space shuttle). Spacecraft are built vertically, in a ready-for-launch configuration, in the Vehicle Assembly Building (VAB)

DID YOU KNOW? In 100 BCE the Greek inventor Hero created the aeolipile, a rocket-like jet engine that ran on steam

6. Payload launched
Ariane's payload, a satellite, is released by steel springs. The rocket is also capable of carrying and launching dual satellites and also delivered a spacecraft to the International Space Station

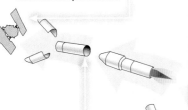

4. Third stage
This third stage is known as the storable propellant stage. It contains two propellant tanks of nitrogen tetroxide and hydrazine, which feed an engine that provides the energy to release the payload

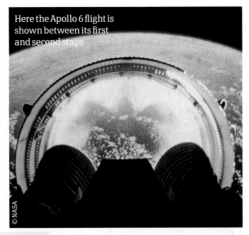
Here the Apollo 6 flight is shown between its first and second stage
© NASA

5. Fairing
The fairing protects the upper stages and payload from thermodynamic and acoustic pressure during launch. It falls off about three minutes after liftoff, at an altitude of about 100km

3. Main stage
Ariane's main, or second, stage comprises two separate compartments, containing liquid oxygen and liquid hydrogen. These power an engine that burns for ten minutes until the stage separates, at an altitude of 145km

2. Solid rocket boosters
These solid rocket boosters provide 110 tons of thrust. At an altitude of 60km, about 130 seconds after liftoff, the boosters are spent and detach from the main stage

Multi-stage rockets

Multi-stage rockets are essentially multiple rockets (each with their own engines and fuel systems) stacked on top or beside each other. Sometimes this assembly is known as a launch vehicle. As the fuel burns, the container holding it becomes dead weight. When a stage separates from the main body, the next stage is capable of generating more acceleration. The downside of a multi-stage rocket is that they're more complex and time-consuming to build, and there are multiple potential failure points. However, the fuel savings are worth the risk. This example shows the ESA's Ariane rocket launching a satellite in Earth orbit.

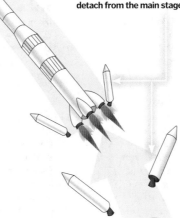

1 Payload packed
Any external features of a payload (such as solar panels) will remain folded up until it reaches orbit

THE FINAL COUNT DOWN
Liquid-propellant rockets have come a long way since their inception...

1981
STS
NASA's Space Transportation System, which took the shuttle into orbit, was retired in July 2011 after a mighty 135 missions.

1967
Saturn V
The most powerful space rocket to date, Saturn V was taller than a 36-story building and launched every Apollo Moon mission.

1957
Sputnik
The Soviet Union's Sputnik Rocket launched the world's first satellite, Sputnik 1, a major landmark at the start of the 'Space Race' with the USA.

1944
V-2 Rocket
Developed by Germany for use at the end of WWII, the V-2 was the first rocket to achieve sub-orbital spaceflight.

1926
The first modern rocket
American Robert Goddard built the first successful liquid-propellant rocket. It climbed 12.5 metres before landing in a nearby cabbage patch.

Ion engine propulsion

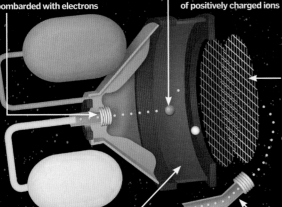

Propellant injection
Ion engines use a propellant fuel, which is injected into a discharge chamber and bombarded with electrons

Collision
The collision of propellant atoms and electrons results in the release of positively charged ions

Multi-aperture grids
This series of grids extracts the positively charged ions and electrically accelerates them into ion jets, generating thrust

Magnetic field
Magnetic rings generate a magnetic field that facilitates the ionisation process

Cathode
A hollow cathode injects negatively charged electrons into the positively charged ion beam to render it neutral

Both solid-fuel and liquid-fuel rocket engines generate thrust through chemical reactions, but in the future, rockets may be powered by ion engines while in space. An ion engine uses either electromagnetic or electrostatic force to accelerate ions, atoms with a net positive or negative charge. While the amount of thrust generated is comparatively low, the engine is more efficient and can last for a very long time.

© NASA

The Delta II rocket launched with the Dawn spacecraft in 2007 to explore asteroids Vesta and Ceres

The new breed of propulsion system that will take us to Mars and beyond

MEGA ROCKETS

 The hardest part of exploring the final frontier is actually getting there in the first place. While mankind has been undertaking space-faring missions for over 50 years now, our methods of propulsion to escape Earth's influence have barely changed at all, and the fundamental problem of overcoming our planet's gravity is still readily apparent. When, years ago, people dreamed of regular space planes flying every week or space elevators lifting cargo into orbit, limitations and complexities have seen our forays beyond Low Earth Orbit (LEO) rely solely on vertically launching rockets. Unfortunately, these themselves bring with them a number of limitations – notably the amount of thrust that is needed to transport cargo into orbit and the cost considering that most rockets are almost entirely non-reusable. And so, as is the way with most things, the solution to take more cargo into orbit was relatively simple: make the rockets bigger. Much bigger.

Giant rockets are used predominantly to take loads such as satellites into orbit. Different rockets can travel to differing heights, with larger payloads unable to be transported into further orbits, while smaller payloads can be taken out to geosynchronous orbits over 32,000 kilometres (20,000 miles) above the surface of the Earth, and even beyond.

One of the major problems with rocket-powered flight is the sheer cost involved in taking even just a single kilogram into orbit. Most rockets that fly today are all but wholly non-reusable. This means the boosters that are

1. Johannes Kepler ATV
This unmanned ISS resupply vehicle is Europe's heaviest ever space payload, weighing almost 20,000kg (44,092lb).

BIGGER

2. Apollo 16
The penultimate manned mission to the Moon was also the heaviest, at 47,000kg (103,607lb), owing to the lunar rover and satellite it carried.

BIGGEST

3. Skylab
NASA's first space station weighed in at a mighty 77,100kg (169,976lb). Incredibly, the entire thing was launched in one go by a Saturn V rocket in 1973.

DID YOU KNOW? The Delta IV Heavy holds 483,500 gallons of fuel but only does the equivalent of 0.00087mpg

The ESA's Ariane 5 heavy-lift rocket

Inside NASA's Space Launch System

Payload
Preliminary specifications allow for a payload of 70 tons, but eventually this will be closer to 130 tons, equivalent to 75 SUVs

J-2X
In advanced versions of the Space Launch System, NASA will attach a J-2X engine (an upgraded version of the J-2 engine used on the Saturn V rocket) to achieve even more power

Solid
Some heavy-lift rockets, like the Space Launch System, use two or more additional solid fuel rockets to harness a greater amount of thrust

Liquid
The core of NASA's heavy-lift rocket uses five of the engines that powered the Space Shuttle for thrust, fuelled by liquid hydrogen and oxygen

Heavy lifting
How do giant rockets differ from the norm?

There are three major classes of rocket that are used to reach space. Light and medium launch vehicles are generally used for smaller satellite launches to LEO, whereas heavy-lift launch vehicles are used for deep-space missions and to haul larger objects into higher orbit. These rockets can do what others cannot, namely taking mega payloads into orbit. NASA's Saturn V rocket lifted an entire space station – the Skylab – in 1973.

One major benefit of heavy-lift rockets is the ability to lift a satellite to geostationary orbit. At this height – 35,406 kilometres (22,000 miles) above Earth – satellites stay in the same position, which is crucial for communications satellites. Heavy-lift rockets can also take vehicles, or even humans, to other planetary bodies. The Saturn V rocket could take 130 tons to Earth orbit or 50 tons to the Moon, and was imperative in the Apollo missions. NASA's next mega rocket, the Space Launch System, will be able to lift a comparable load and is planned to take astronauts to the Moon, an asteroid and Mars.

However, not all heavy-lift rockets can travel these large distances. NASA's Space Shuttle, although extremely powerful, did not have the propulsion to escape LEO, and thus it was used to take large payloads into orbit such as the Hubble Space Telescope and many modules for the ISS.

jettisoned as the rocket makes its way to the cosmos are left to burn up in the atmosphere or, occasionally, are recovered from the sea where they have splashed down, but they are rarely designed to be flown again and again.

One company planning to tackle this problem is SpaceX, a US-based manufacturer that has been developing its own rockets for several years. The first of these, the Falcon 9, has already flown several times, but the next development will be the Falcon Heavy, a giant rocket employing three of the Falcon 9's Merlin engines to take about 50,000 kilograms (110,231 pounds) of mass into orbit. The ultimate goal of SpaceX is to make the rocket fully reusable. Their plan is to use rockets attached to each stage to carry out controlled ground landings and recover each component of the rocket. This has never been done before, but for good reason, as making a rocket that can survive the forces of re-entry intact is incredibly difficult.

Other innovations in the world of heavy-lift rockets have largely focused on new propulsive fuels and advanced technologies to make better use of what is already available. One example of this is NASA's new J-2X engine. The original J-2 engine was used on the Saturn V Moon rocket, the most powerful rocket of all time, but the new J-2X engine employs advanced capabilities to harness the power of this old workhorse and turn it into a modern marvel.

The only way for humans to venture beyond LEO, where the International Space Station (ISS) currently resides, is to use a heavy-lift rocket. NASA's long-term plan is to use its new Space Launch

"One major benefit of heavy-lift rockets is the ability to lift a satellite to geostationary orbit"

©NASA

"The advancement of heavy-lift launch vehicles promises to usher in an exciting era for space exploration"

System to take astronauts first to the Moon, then to an asteroid, and finally to Mars by the 2030s. SpaceX aims to challenge NASA's deep-space exploration plans by launching its own variant of the Falcon Heavy in the coming years. Known as the Red Dragon mission, this would see the soon-to-be completed Falcon Heavy taking a specially designed Dragon capsule, SpaceX's human transportation vehicle, to Mars by the 2020s. It all depends who finishes their heavy-lift launch vehicle first, but its entirely possible that the first human on Mars will be flown by a private technology company, which would be no small feat, to put it mildly.

Heavy-lift launch vehicles have a number of advantages over their smaller brethren, not least their size. Were it not for NASA's Space Transportation System rocket, used to take the Space Shuttle into orbit, the ISS would be some way from completion. It was thanks to the high operating capabilities of this launch system that NASA was able to contribute more than 90 per cent of the orbiting outpost and ensure that it reached completion this year.

Heavy-lift rockets, like regular-sized rockets, have a number of stages to take the vehicle into orbit. The first stage gets the rocket off the ground. This is usually composed of several booster rockets strapped together, like the Delta IV Heavy which uses three of the boosters seen on the smaller Delta III.

The advancement of launch vehicles promises to usher in an exciting era for space exploration. Bigger, more powerful rockets will enable us to visit once unreachable worlds. A human mission to Mars looks more and more likely, and as the rockets are developed further, the goal of landing humans on the Red Planet in the next decade or two might just be achievable. ✿

NASA's J-2X engine, being tested here, will play a key role in the Space Launch System

THE PAST
How man's most powerful rocket took astronauts to the Moon

The Saturn V is the most powerful rocket of all time... for the time being

© NASA

To date there has been no rocket that has matched, let alone exceeded, the lifting capabilities of the Saturn V Moon rocket. Of course, this will change in the future with the arrival of several new super-heavy-lift rockets, but for now the Saturn V retains the title of most powerful rocket of all time. Capable of lifting 130 tons into orbit, the Saturn V was used to take Apollo astronauts to the Moon throughout the Sixties and Seventies.

Undeniably the most well-known heavy-lift launch vehicle of all time, though, is the Space Transportation System (STS), used to take the Space Shuttle into orbit. The Space Shuttle could take a payload weighing 30 tons into orbit, and it was pivotal in the construction of the ISS. Now retired, the STS was one of the most powerful rockets of the modern era. It used solid rocket propellant and its initial rocket boosters were recoverable when they landed in the ocean, allowing for up to 20 more uses before they were deemed unsafe to fly.

THE PRESENT
The modern workhorses that laun satellites and resuply the ISS

Russia's heavy-lift Proton rocket is currently the longest-serving rocket in activity, completing its first flight in 1965. It has a formidable success rate: 88 per cent across over 300 launches. It has been one of the few successes of Russia's Space Program, which has otherwise been riddled with failures and a lack of advancement, particularly in missions beyond LEO.

Another hugely successful rocket has been Boeing Delta series. The largest of these, the Delta IV Heavy, can take over 20 tons of cargo into orbit. The Delta IV

The Delta IV can take 21,772kg (48,000lb) of cargo into Low Earth Orbit (LEO)

© NASA

Heavy uses two strap-on rocket boosters to achieve higher orbits and greater payload capabilities. In Europe, the ESA's Ariane rocket continues to make great strides to being the most reliable heavy-lift rocket around. It uses a cryogenic main stage, holding liquid oxygen and hydrogen, to produce a thrust of 115 ton-forces, while two solid rocket boosters provide additiona thrust. These heavy-lift vehicles have been instrumental in the modern space era and wil continue to launch countless satellites and craft into the cosmos.

One of the huge boosters used on the Delta rockets

ROCKET SIZE COMPARISON

Height (metres): 120, 90, 60, 30, 0

Saturn V
Manufacturer: NASA
Payload: 118,000kg
Operation: 1967-1972
Launches: 13

Space Transportation System
Manufacturer: NASA
Payload: 24,400kg
Operation: 1981-2011
Launches: 135

Delta IV Heavy
Manufacturer: United Launch Alliance
Payload: 22,950kg
Operation: 2004-present
Launches: 4

Titan IV
Manufacturer: Lockheed Martin
Payload: 21,682kg
Operation: 1989-2005
Launches: 35

Inside the Ariane 5

Take a look at the inner workings of this ESA rocket

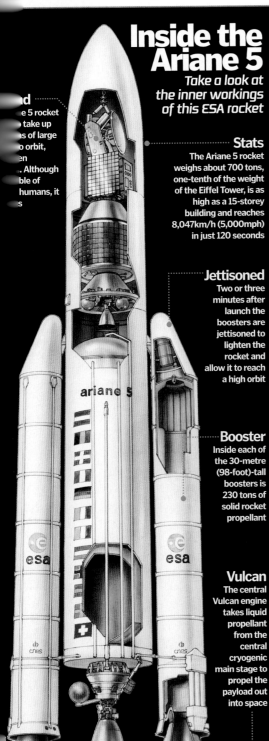

ariane 5

esa

esa

cnes

cnes

[...]ad

[...]e 5 rocket
[...] take up
[...]s of large
[...]o orbit,
[...]en
[...]. Although
[...]ble of
[...]humans, it
[...]s

Stats

The Ariane 5 rocket weighs about 700 tons, one-tenth of the weight of the Eiffel Tower, is as high as a 15-storey building and reaches 8,047km/h (5,000mph) in just 120 seconds

Jettisoned

Two or three minutes after launch the boosters are jettisoned to lighten the rocket and allow it to reach a high orbit

Booster

Inside each of the 30-metre (98-foot)-tall boosters is 230 tons of solid rocket propellant

Vulcan

The central Vulcan engine takes liquid propellant from the central cryogenic main stage to propel the payload out into space

THE FUTURE

Which rockets will take us to the Red Planet and beyond?

With NASA's Space Shuttle retired in July 2011, the next step for the agency is to build a rocket comparable in size and power to the Saturn V. This comes in the form of the Space Launch System (SLS).

One of the major advancements of NASA's new mega rocket is its shift to liquid propellants over solid ones. Liquid propellants, while more expensive, allow for a greater power yield. In addition, solid propellants cannot be stopped burning when lit, a potential problem if a disaster were to occur, whereas liquid propellants can be throttled for the required speed. NASA is reusing old, tried-and-tested components to keep costs down. For example, the main booster core of the SLS will use five of the main engines that had been used to take the Space Shuttle into orbit. This booster core uses a liquid hydrogen/oxygen combination, a very efficient way of getting to orbit with minimal toxic waste produced. The second stage of the SLS will use a modified version of the engine used to take astronauts to the Moon aboard the Saturn V rocket. This will be the J-2X engine, an advancement of the old Saturn V J-2 engine. At first the SLS will be able to carry 70 tons to orbit, but eventually it will be able to handle 130 tons.

American manufacturer SpaceX is also making strides with heavy-lift rockets. Having already successfully flown the smaller Falcon 9 rocket, they plan to begin flying their Falcon Heavy in the coming years. With twice the payload capability of NASA's Space Shuttle, the Falcon Heavy promises trips to space at a fraction of the cost of current rockets.

It will use three Merlin engines – the Falcon 9 rocket only uses one – and with 1.7 million kilograms (3.8 million pounds) of thrust it will be equivalent to 15,747 jumbo jets operating at full power. The ultimate goal of SpaceX's Falcon Heavy is to make the rocket fully reusable. The company's plan is to use rockets attached to each stage to carry out controlled ground landings and recover each component. If successful, the Falcon Heavy will be one of the cheapest rockets to launch of all time.

Concept art of SpaceX's Falcon Heavy mega rocket

The predecessor to the Falcon Heavy, the Falcon 9

A visualisation of NASA's Space Launch System due to be completed by 2017

Proton
Manufacturer: Roscosmos
Payload: 21,682kg
Operation: 1965-present
Launches: 326

Ariane 5
Manufacturer: EADS Astrium
Payload: 21,000kg
Operation: 1996-present
Launches: 56

Falcon Heavy
Manufacturer: SpaceX
Payload: 53,000kg
Operation: Due in 2013
Launches: 0

Space Launch System
Manufacturer: NASA
Payload: 130,000kg
Operation: Due in 2017
Launches: 0

One of the two modified Boeing 747s used to transport the space shuttles between the landing site and the launch complex

© NASA

How the space shuttle worked

NASA's most successful spacecraft was retired on 8 July 2011, 30 years after the launch of the first space shuttle mission. We take a look back at how this marvellous space machine worked

In January 1972, the US president Richard Nixon announced a plan to create the first reusable spacecraft. Ten years later, on the 20th anniversary of the first human space flight, NASA had its first successful mission with the orbiter Columbia. This flight demonstrated that the space transportation system (STS) was viable. The space transportation system was designed by Maxime Faget, the same American engineer who designed all of NASA's previous spacecraft systems. Since then, the program had 135 launches and experienced some significant successes, but also encountered devastating losses and setbacks.

Although we think of the winged, plane-like spacecraft as the 'shuttle', it is actually the orbiting part of the entire space shuttle system. The spacecraft's design came about in part because of the need for a large payload capacity, from which satellites could be deployed. Its unique design meant that it launched and flew like a rocket, but landed like a plane. The orbiter and solid rocket

boosters were recovered and reused, making it more efficient than previous spacecraft systems.

Originally the first orbiter was going to be named the Constitution, but fans of the cult television show *Star Trek* staged a write-in campaign and convinced NASA to change its name to that of the sci-fi show's spaceship, the Enterprise. This orbiter was not designed to fly into space, but NASA intended to upgrade it to do so as needed after testing. However, enough significant design changes were made between test flights and the first fully functional launch to require the building of a new orbiter, the Columbia. The Enterprise is still on display at the United States National Air and Space Museum in Washington DC.

NASA's space shuttle program ended on 8 July 2011. Potential replacement spacecraft, such as NASA's Orion, are in progress with targets of completing a lunar mission by the early 2020s. However, with funding always a concern, there will be a gap of several years before the US is fully re-engaged in space travel and exploration.

The shuttle's main parts

At launch, the space shuttle system, or 'stack', comprises three main components: a black-and-white orbital vehicle (OV) containing payload and crew, as well as the space shuttle main engines (SSMEs) and orbital manoeuvring engines (OMEs), two white solid rocket boosters (SRBs) and an orange external tank (ET) carrying liquid fuel oxidiser and liquid hydrogen.

Orbiter
The orbiter is the only part of the space shuttle system that actually goes into space. It transports a crew of up to seven astronauts as well as payload such as satellites, ISS components and experiments materiel

Fuel tank
The external fuel tank stores fuel for the orbiter's main engines. It contains more than 700,000 kilograms of liquid oxygen and liquid hydrogen, separated into two separate tanks. The tank is insulated with foam to shield the fuels from heat

© NASA

Rocket boosters
The solid rocket boosters provide nearly 75 per cent of the thrust required to lift the rest of the shuttle system off the launch pad. They have a jointed structure and contain solid rocket fuel, a catalyst, instruments, a parachute and explosive charges

Crawler transporters
NASA uses these tracked vehicles to move the space shuttle from the assembly building to the shuttle launch pad. They travel on a special pathway called the 'crawlerway' and have been in use since 1965. Each crawler transporter is very heavy, weighing nearly 3,000 tons

5 TOP FACTS
IMPORTANT MISSIONS

STS-1
1 12 April 1981 marked the start of the space shuttle era, taking John Young and Bob Crippen into low-Earth orbit. STS-1 and STS-2 were the only missions to have a white rocket booster.

STS-51-L and STS-107
2 Challenger and Columbia perished in 1986 and 2003 respectively, losing all crew. The former exploded 73 seconds after launch and the latter burned up on re-entry.

STS-31
3 On 24 April 1990, space shuttle Discovery took the Hubble Space Telescope into Earth orbit, spending five days deploying and testing the famous telescope.

STS-71
4 Atlantis docked to Russian space station Mir in 1995, delivering two Russian cosmonauts and taking a NASA astronaut and two other cosmonauts back.

STS-88
5 On 4 Dec 1998 Endeavour became the first shuttle to visit the ISS, delivering America's first module (the Unity node) and attaching it to Russia's Zarya module.

DID YOU KNOW? As some shuttle missions were delayed, the numbering of STS missions did not always run in order

THE FINAL LAUNCH

"The first was the Columbia, launched on 12 April 1981, followed by the Challenger, Discovery, Atlantis and Endeavour orbiters"

The Shuttle orbiter

14. Hydrazine and nitrogen tetroxide tanks

8. Vertical stabiliser
Much like on an aeroplane, the vertical stabiliser is designed to reduce side slip. It also holds a rudder and speed brake to assist with deceleration during re-entry

5. Payload Bay
The payload bay contains the Canadarm, a robotic arm used to retrieve and deploy payloads. The bay's doors contain heat radiators and remain open when in orbit to help with thermal control

11. Space radiators

6. Space Shuttle main engines (SSMEs)
These engines are fuelled by liquid hydrogen and liquid oxygen from the external fuel tank. They are used solely to propel the orbiter during its ascent

7. Orbital manoeuvring engines (OMEs)
The OMEs are located in the aft fuselage near the SSMEs. These engines are used to help send the orbiter into orbit and adjust the orbit as necessary

10. Main gear
Upon re-entry, the crew manually deploys the orbiter's landing gear in the form of three sets of wheels through the heat shield

Endeavour after launch for mission STS-118

9. Elevons
The elevons are located on the edges of the wings. They are used for both roll control and pitch control during landing

Inside the Shuttle
Under the skin of the Shuttle's surface

5 TOP FACTS
SPACE SHUTTLE MISSIONS

STS-7: Space Shuttle Challenger
1 Launched on 18 June 1983, this marked the first time that an American female astronaut entered space with the inclusion of Sally K. Ride.

STS-31: Space Shuttle Discovery
2 Launching on 24 April 1990, the crew of the Space Shuttle Discovery deployed the Hubble Space Telescope during STS-31.

STS-71: Space Shuttle Atlantis
3 On 27 June 1995, the Atlantis launched STS-71. This mission marked the first time that the Space Shuttle docked with the Russian space station Mir.

STS-88: Space Shuttle Endeavour
4 Launched on 4 December 1998, STS-88 was the first mission to the ISS. As its payload, it carried the first US node for the ISS, Unity.

STS-95: Space Shuttle Discovery
5 Discovery's 25th flight launched on 29 October 1998. It is also well-known as John Glenn's return to space at the age of 77.

DID YOU KNOW? *Upon re-entry, the external Shuttle skin withstands temperatures as high as 1,648° Celsius*

NASA's main spacecraft fleet was retired in 2011. Find out about the history of these iconic vehicles

What we think of as the 'Space Shuttle', NASA calls the Space Shuttle transport orbital vehicle or orbiter (STS-OV, or just OV). It was a reusable winged plane-like spacecraft. In addition to its engines and thrusters, it also had a three-level crew cabin and a payload bay.

The orbiter fleet had five different craft. The first was the Columbia, launched on 12 April 1981, followed by the Challenger, Discovery, Atlantis and Endeavour orbiters (the latter built to replace Challenger). Although all of the orbiters were similar, rotating maintenance meant that each was somewhat unique. The Endeavour was the youngest orbiter, first launched on 7 May 1992.

On 28 January 1986, the Challenger was destroyed a little more than a minute into its tenth mission. A seal on one of the SRBs failed, which caused it to leak flames onto the external fuel tank. The orbiter veered and was torn apart by as much as 20Gs of aerodynamic force, which resulted in the death of its seven-member crew.

On 1 February 2003, the Columbia was destroyed upon re-entry into the atmosphere, killing its seven crew members. This occurred when gases entered one of the orbiter's wings through a hole made by a piece of foam during launch and caused a structural failure.

Atlantis was the last to fly into orbit, completing the final flight of the space shuttle program on 8 July 2011.

Discovery approaches the ISS for docking

12. Manipulation arm

4. Crew cabin
The crew cabin includes the flight deck with controls. The mid-deck has areas for work, sleeping and hygiene. An airlock contains spacesuits and allows for the crew to perform spacewalks

A simulation of handling large objects in space

2. RCS thrusters
The reaction control system (RCS) comprises 44 small thrusters located around the orbiter. They are used for close manoeuvring such as docking, orientation and altitude control

1. Nose cap
The orbiter's nose is made of a carbon fibre and graphic composite known as reinforced carbon-carbon (RCC), which protects the orbiter from the 1,650° Celsius heat during re-entry

3. Surface tiles
The orbiter's thermal protection system (TPS) includes black high-temperature reusable surface insulation (HRSI) tiles on its underside. They are made of silica ceramic and vary in thickness depending on their location

13. Electrical system fuel cells

Where the action is
Crew on the flight deck perform duties ranging from piloting the Shuttle to satellite launches

The orbiter's flight deck seats the mission's commander, pilot and two mission specialists. It looks much like the cockpit of an aeroplane, but with more controls – over 2,000 buttons, switches, dials and displays in total. In addition to forward controls in front of the commander and pilot, the flight deck also has displays and controls on its aft side. These are used to operate payloads.

The duties of the commander, pilot and specialists while on the flight deck depends on the details of the mission. In addition to firing the orbital manoeuvring engines (OMEs) to take the Shuttle in and out of orbit, the pilot also steers the Shuttle to rendezvous with the ISS or other crafts. Mission specialists may conduct experiments or retrieve and release satellites from the payload bay.

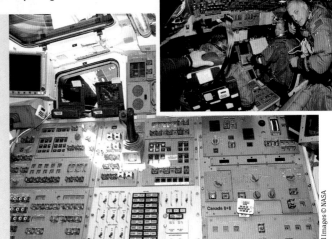

All Images © NASA

"The crew module will use parachutes and air bags to allow a cushioned touchdown"

The Orion spacecraft

How the replacement for NASA's Space Shuttle will take us to the Moon and beyond

The primary goals of the Orion spacecraft, which has been contracted to technology company Lockheed Martin by NASA, are to deliver crew and cargo to the International Space Shuttle and return astronauts to the Moon after almost a 50-year wait. Orion is scheduled to make its first test flight before 2014 and complete a lunar mission by the early 2020s.

The Orion crew module is similar in design and appearance to the Apollo Command Module that first took astronauts to the Moon. It is three times the volume of the Apollo module with the same 70° sloped top, deemed to be the safest and most reliable shape for re-entering Earth's atmosphere at high velocity. The Orion module has a diameter of five metres and a total mass of about 9,000kg including the cargo and the crew, which increases or decreases slightly for missions to the International Space Station and the Moon respectively. Unlike the Apollo module, which had a crew capacity of three people, the Orion module can carry between four and six astronauts.

Attached to the crew module is the service module, responsible for propulsion, electrical power, communications and water/air storage. The service module is equipped with a pair of extendable solar panels that are deployed post-launch in addition to batteries to store power for times of darkness. Like the Orion crew module, the service module is also five metres in diameter to provide a clean fit between the two, and has a mass of about 3,700kg in addition to 8,300kg of propellant.

Exerting 33,000 newtons (7,500 pounds) of thrust, the engine of the service module uses hypergolic fuels monomethyl hydrazine and nitrogen tetroxide, which are propellants that ignite on contact with each other and require no ignition source. Another benefit of these propellants is that they do not need to be cooled like other fuels; they can be stored at room temperature. 24 thrusters around the service module will also give it control to change its orientation in all directions, but these are almost 30 times weaker than the main booster.

Upon descent to Earth the Orion crew module will use a combination of parachutes and air bags to allow a cushioned touchdown on land or sea. The service module will detach in space and disintegrate in the atmosphere. The entire Orion crew module will be reusable for at most ten missions except for its ablative heat shield, which burns up on re-entry into Earth's atmosphere to protect the astronauts from the extreme heat. ✦

The first Orion missions will see it dock with the ISS to test its systems

© NASA

The Orion spacecraft will transport a lunar lander to the Moon

5 TOP FACTS
COMMERCIAL SPACE RACE

Orion
1 Although Orion is currently still on schedule, there are several other private companies that are clamouring to provide NASA's transportation to the ISS.

SpaceX Dragon
2 One of the competitors, the Dragon capsule is currently undergoing advanced testing and should be ready to transport crew members to the ISS within a few years.

Boeing CST-100
3 After losing the Orion contract to Lockheed Martin, Boeing's capsule (similar in design to Orion) has been helped by $18m of funding from NASA and could launch by 2015.

Dream Chaser
4 Under development by the Sierra Nevada Corporation, this space plane won $20m from a NASA competition. It could land on almost any runway in the world.

X-37B
5 This US military space plane returned from a seven-month orbit in December 2010 and made the first ever spacecraft landing by autopilot, but its intentions were unknown.

DID YOU KNOW? An Orion test module will use over 150,000 ping-pong balls to stop it sinking after splashing down in the ocean

Launch abort
In a launch pad emergency, this rocket will lift the crew module and allow it to parachute safely to ground

Heat shield
The ablative (burns on re-entry) heat shield protects the crew module as it returns to Earth alone before the parachutes deploy

Airlock
The top of the crew module allows docking with other vehicles such as the ISS and lunar landers

The Launch Abort System will carry the crew module to safety in an emergency

Crew module
Able to accommodate up to six crew members, this module provides a safe habitat for them to stay in during their journey

Service module
This module supports the crew throughout their journey, providing life support and propulsion, before detaching upon Earth re-entry

Cargo
Inside the service module, unpressurised cargo for the ISS and science equipment are stored

Spacecraft adapter
Connects the Orion spacecraft to the launch rocket, and also protects components in the service module

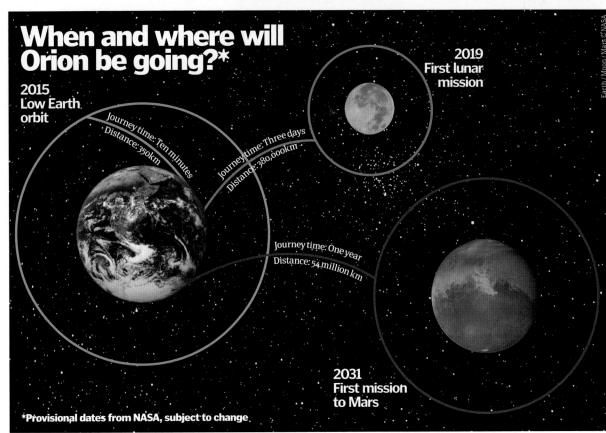

When and where will Orion be going?*

2015
Low Earth orbit

Journey time: Ten minutes
Distance: 350km

Journey time: Three days
Distance: 380,000km

2019
First lunar mission

Journey time: One year
Distance: 54 million km

2031
First mission to Mars

*Provisional dates from NASA, subject to change.

SpaceX Dragon capsule

The first ever commercial spacecraft to leave and return to Earth explained

With the NASA Space Shuttle retired in July 2011, several different companies have been competing to become NASA's choice for cargo and crew transportation to the International Space Station, and possibly beyond. In 2006 and 2009, NASA awarded the SpaceX company two contracts totalling more than $2 billion, and on 10 October 2012 a SpaceX Dragon spacecraft successfully docked with ISS for the second time in a year.

Powered by a combination of solar panels and an advanced lithium battery, the Dragon capsule is large, allowing for the transportation of five to seven crew members or up to ten metric tons of cargo. It uses 18 liquid fuel thrusters equipped with nitrogen tetroxide and monomethyl hydrazine to manoeuvre while in orbit. Like NASA's Orion spacecraft, the conical shape of the Dragon capsule is deemed the best for Earth re-entry, while also allowing for a sizeable interior.

One of its defining features is a variant of NASA's phenolic impregnated carbon ablator (PICA) heatshield. SpaceX's PICA-X heatshield advances on NASA's design in a number of places, notably its significantly reduced cost and added reusability, allowing it to be used hundreds of times, whereas NASA's currently does not survive its flight. This shield protects the capsule as it re-enters Earth's atmosphere

at several thousand degrees centigrade and keeps the interior close to room temperature.

Three oversized parachutes slow its descent to earth, although it can operate on only one if the other two happen to fail. However, while the capsule must land in water for now, SpaceX hopes to eventually develop thrusters that will allow the Dragon capsule to land on the ground as well.

It is hoped the Dragon capsule will soon be given permission to dock with the ISS

© SpaceX

Launch abort
Unlike NASA's Orion spacecraft, which uses a rocket to 'pull' the capsule off in an emergency, the Dragon uses its lower boosters to 'push' the capsule off the launch pad if required

Nosecone
Protects the spacecraft during launch before separating at the separation stage, and also contains the mechanism for docking with the ISS

© SpaceX

Parachutes
Three parachutes, each 35 metres in diameter, deploy at 3,000 metres and slow the spacecraft's descent to about five metres per second

Heat shield
Advancements in technology allow the PICA-X heat shield to be reusable, which provides protection from the heat in the Earth's atmosphere

Service cabin
This unpressurised section contains the thrusters, fuel and parachutes, remaining attached to the spacecraft for the duration of the mission

Inside the Dragon capsule

Trunk
Allows for the storage of unpressurised cargo such as small deployable satellites. Also contains the solar panels, and is jettisoned before Earth re-entry

© SpaceX

Solar panels

Pressurised cabin
Equipped with hatches and windows, this section provides protection against radiation and micrometeorites for crew and cargo

Draco thrusters
These provide precise control of the spacecraft, enabling safe docking with the ISS and a return to Earth within a few hundred metres of its target

Launch vehicles...

	Space Shuttle	Ariane 5	Soyuz	Falcon 9
Origin:	USA	Europe	Russia	Europe
Cargo to ISS:	16.3 tons	7.6 tons	2.6 tons	6 tons

(Metres axis: 0, 30, 60)

5 TOP FACTS
IMPORTANT SPACEMEN

Elon Musk
1 Elon Musk is the CEO of SpaceX and views space exploration as an important step in preserving the human race. He wants to set foot on Mars by 2030.

Gene Kranz
2 NASA's flight director during the Apollo Moon landings, Gene Kranz is best known for managing the successful rescue effort of the famous Apollo 13 crew.

Neil Armstrong
3 His first successful space flight in 1966 performed the first manned docking of two spacecraft, while his second mission in 1969 made him the first man on the Moon.

Carl Sagan
4 Popularised space for the masses in the Eighties with his TV series *Cosmos*, and is famed for his description of the Earth as an insignificant 'pale blue dot' in space.

Wernher von Braun
5 Often cited as the greatest rocket engineer in history, von Braun was the chief architect of the Saturn V rocket that took Americans to the Moon.

The statistics...

© SpaceX

SpaceX Dragon capsule

Height: 5.1m (16.7ft)

Diameter: 3.66m (12ft)

Launch mass: 6,620kg

Re-entry mass: 5,100kg

Top Speed: >17,000mph (>27,300kph)

Flight time: One week to two years

Falcon 9

SpaceX's Falcon 9 rocket is responsible for taking the Dragon capsule into orbit. It has so far completed several successful flights and one unmanned launch, with more launches scheduled for the coming years.

Developed from the ground up by SpaceX for cost-efficient transport into orbit, the Falcon 9 is a two-stage launch vehicle that uses liquid oxygen and rocket-grade kerosene. Its aluminium lithium alloy exterior uses the strongest and most reliable welding techniques available.

The Falcon 9 is powered by nine Merlin engines, which are the highest performing American hydrocarbon rockets ever flown. The engines generate 1 million pounds of thrust in a vacuum, employing the same technology as that used in the Apollo Moon mission.

In line with its goal of reusability, SpaceX plans to make the first stage reusable by its sixth flight. The second stage, which separates from the Dragon capsule and falls to Earth at a much higher altitude, will require significant advances in heat-shield technology to withstand atmospheric temperatures and become reusable.

Elon Musk, founder and CEO of SpaceX, with the impressive Falcon 9

The Falcon 9 rocket is a cheap and efficient solution for space travel

145

Spacecraft re-entry

How do spacecraft survive the journey from space to the ground?

While not all spacecraft are designed to return home after completion of a mission, those that do must overcome intense heat and forces as the spacecraft passes through our atmosphere. Almost all spacecraft undergo a ballistic entry, travelling directly through the atmosphere until parachutes slow their descent. Only a few – NASA's space shuttle and the US Air Force's secretive unmanned space plane X-37B – are capable of performing a glide landing and touch down on a runway like an aeroplane.

The dense gas in our atmosphere is useful for slowing down a spacecraft on re-entry, allowing it to land safely without the need for extra fuel to reduce its velocity when approaching our planet. This is a problem scientists must overcome when a satellite lands on a celestial body with little to no atmosphere, such as Mars or an asteroid. Spacecraft must take care when re-entering the atmosphere of Earth and ensure they approach at a specific angle of entry. Too shallow and they will bounce back off the atmosphere, but too great and they will burn up during re-entry.

Most ballistic re-entry spacecraft return to Earth at approximately 25,000mph (40,000kph), encountering temperatures up to 3,000 °C (5,400 °F). As most metals would melt at this temperature, the base of the spacecraft is made of an ablative material that burns as re-entry occurs and radiates heat away from the spacecraft. These are often made of materials such as phenolic resins and silicone rubbers.

After surviving atmospheric re-entry, spacecraft that cannot glide to the ground use parachutes to slow their descent. Russian Soyuz spacecraft usually perform a soft landing on the ground, but most spacecraft touch down in the sea, where they are recovered. A rare few unmanned spacecraft containing sensitive cargo such as photographic film are recovered in midair by an aircraft.

This photo, taken by the US Air Force, shows Apollo 8's return to Earth in 1968

Heat shield

During re-entry a spacecraft will typically experience a temperature that rises past 3,000°C (5,400°F), which would melt standard metals such as aluminium and steel. To overcome this problem the heat shield was developed, to dissipate heat from the spacecraft by burning on re-entry. Ablative heat shields, such as those that were used on NASA's Apollo and Mercury spacecraft, are normally made of a carbon phenolic resin that completely burns on re-entry, carrying heat away from the spacecraft as it deteriorates and keeping the occupants inside relatively safe from heat outside. This is not re-usable but some spacecraft, such as the space shuttle, use fibreglass tiles capable of absorbing heat, which do not need to be replaced after every flight.

NASA's space shuttle used thermal soak tiles to absorb heat upon re-entry

5 TOP FACTS
RE-ENTRY DISASTERS

Soyuz 1
1 Lone cosmonaut Vladimir Komarov perished in 1967 when the parachutes of Soyuz 1 tangled during re-entry following some problems in orbit.

Soyuz 5
2 In 1969 when a module failed to separate, Boris Volynov's spacecraft re-entered in a ball of fire until it righted itself and crash landed, Volynov suffered only broken teeth.

Soyuz 11
3 In 1971 the Russian Soyuz 11 spacecraft failed to depressurise properly in orbit, killing all three of the crew prior to re-entry, the only astronauts to die in space.

Columbia
4 In 2003 a piece of foam pierced the left wing of the space shuttle Columbia during launch. Atmospheric gases tore it apart during re-entry, killing a crew of seven.

Genesis
5 The sample return capsule of NASA's unmanned Genesis spacecraft failed to deploy its parachutes during re-entry in 2004, and crashed in the Utah desert.

DID YOU KNOW? NASA's Stardust capsule is the fastest man-made object to ever re-enter Earth, at 7.95 miles per sec, in 2006

Overshoot boundary
If a spacecraft approaches the Earth above this boundary, it will fail to be slowed by the drag of the atmosphere

Re-entry corridor
To survive the extremes of an atmospheric re-entry, a spacecraft must be carefully guided to ensure it is within a specific trajectory

Undershoot boundary
A spacecraft outside this boundary will generate intense heat and high g-forces that will disintegrate and burn up the craft

Re-entry corridor

When a spacecraft re-enters Earth's atmosphere it must be between two clearly defined boundaries, to prevent it burning up or missing its chance to re-enter entirely

Deceleration too high
If the angle of entry is too high, the spacecraft will hit the Earth's atmosphere almost head-on and decelerate too fast

Drag too low
A spacecraft without enough drag will follow a trajectory past the surface, and may not have enough fuel for re-entry

Ballistic or glide
Most re-entries are ballistic, where the spacecraft falls directly into the atmosphere, but some – like NASA's space shuttle – perform a glide re-entry at a shallower angle

FANTASY RACE

At top speed, how do these vehicles match up to a spacecraft when travelling from Los Angeles to New York?

Spacecraft re-entry 25,000mph
355 secs

SR-71 Blackbird 2,190mph
67 mins

Veyron 268mph
9 hours

Los Angeles |- - - - - - - - 2,462 miles - - - - - - - - -| **New York**

Design history

Different spacecraft designs have been tested over the years, to provide the ideal method for directing hot atmospheric gases away from the vehicle during re-entry

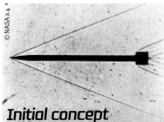

Initial concept 1950

Needle
Early tests focused on needle designs, but these burned up too quickly on re-entry as too much heat was transferred.

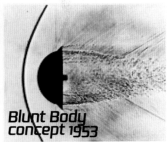

Blunt Body concept 1953

Shockwave
Blunt-body designs allowed heat to be deflected away, increasing its drag and creating a shockwave.

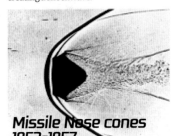

Missile Nose cones 1953-1957

Heat-sink
Early missiles used a blunt-body design with a heat-sink material such as copper to dissipate and absorb heat.

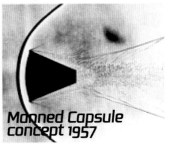

Manned Capsule concept 1957

Ablative
A flattened and ablative (burnable) leading edge, made of a phenolic resin, subjected the spacecraft to even less heat.

"In 2012 the budget for the ESA was just over £4 billion"

Radar dishes at the ESA's ESAC headquarters in Villanueva de la Cañada, Spain

An image of the ESA's headquarters in Paris, France. While centred at the heart of Europe, the ESA has bases all over the world, and co-operates on many missions undertaken by NASA, the FKA and the CNSA

European Space Agency

Europe's gateway to space, the European Space Agency is revealing the wonders of our Earth, solar system and the universe

The purpose of the European Space Agency (ESA) is to develop and advance Europe's space capability, while ensuring such research directly benefits those who fund it – the citizens of Europe. As such, the ESA is an international organisation comprised of 19 member states, which collectively pool their resources, be that financial or intellectual, in order to draw up the European space programme and carry it through – something that would be impossible to achieve if they simply worked as singular nations.

The ESA draws up programmes designed to explore, analyse and actuate information garnered from the Earth's immediate space environment, our solar system and even further a field into distant galaxies, in addition to developing satellite-based technologies and services constructed by European companies and industries. The size and financial/intellectual commitment a member state makes to the ESA is directly proportional to the amount of service contracts for technological construction and mission funding it receives, ensuring that the money spent by the county's government

The average investment per person per annum of an ESA member state is roughly ten pounds, which collectively provides the yearly budget for space expenditure. In 2012 the budget for the ESA was just over £4 billion and it was spent across a wide gamut of missions, divisions and departments, including: the European Astronauts Centre, European Space Astronomy division, European Space Operations Centre, the ESA Centre for Earth Observation, and the European Space Research and Technology Centre.

The majority of space launches occur at the ESA's launch base in French Guiana (a 96,000 hectare base employing 1,500 people), where probes, satellites and rockets carry astronauts and equipment into space either to dock with the International Space Station, orbit the Earth and collect and transmit data, or on a far-off trajectory to monitor distant phenomena. Indeed, the ESA boasts one of the most active and successful mission profiles in the world and is currently embarking on a host of cutting-edge programmes – including the notable launch of CryoSat-2, an orbiting satellite designed to monitor the effects of global warming on

Head to Head SPACE AGENCIES

AMERICA
NASA

EUROPE
esa

CHINA
CNSA

1. NASA
Established: 1958
Budget: £11.4 billion / $17.6 billion
Divisions: 15
Primary spaceport: Kennedy Space Center

2. ESA
Established: 1975
Budget: £3.3 billion / $5.4 billion
Divisions: 5
Primary spaceport: Guiana Space Centre

3. CNSA
Established: 1993
Budget: £850 million / $1.3 billion
Divisions: 4
Primary spaceport: Jiuquan Satellite Launch Center

DID YOU KNOW? ESA's first mission was launched in 1975 and was a space probe designed to monitor gamma-ray emissions

The ESA's primary launch vehicle, the Ariane 5 rocket, blasts off

1. Upper stage
The rocket's payload is housed here, which in the case of most Ariane 5 launches, are satellites

2. Solid rocket boosters
Each of the Ariane 5's rocket boosters deliver 6,470kN of thrust and burn for 129 seconds

3. Cryogenic main stage
This main, first stage delivers 1,114kN of thrust over 589 seconds burning a mixture of liquid hydrogen and oxygen

The Statistics
Ariane 5
Function: Heavy launch vehicle
Height: 46-52m (151-170ft)
Mass: 777,000kg
Stages: 2
Max payload: LEO – 21,000kg / GTO – 10,500kg
Maiden flight: 4 June 1996

Europe's spaceport, the Guiana Space Centre, covers 96,000 hectares and is operated by more than 1,500 personnel

An aerial shot of the sprawling ESTEC division in Noordwijk

ESA budgets
Breakdown of the ESA budgets (using 2009 figures)

- LAUNCHERS – 18.35%, €659m
- NAVIGATION – 10.78%, €387m
- SCIENCE – 12.10%, €434m
- EARTH OBSERVATION – 16.32%, €586m
- TELECOMMUNICATIONS – 8.89%, €319m
- TECHNOLOGY – 3.14%, €112m
- SPACE SITUATIONAL AWARENESS – 0.25%, €9m
- EXPLORATION – 3.22%, €115m
- HUMAN SPACEFLIGHT – 10.77%, €386m
- MICROGRAVITY – 2.61%, €93m
- FINANCED BY THIRD PARTIES – 1.33%, €47m
- ECSA – 0.09%, €3m
- GENERAL BUDGET – 6.67%, €239m
- ASSOCIATED TO GENERAL BUDGET – 5.48%, €196m

Divisions of the ESA

The ESA employs over 2,000 individuals, including scientists, engineers, information technology specialists and administrative personnel, across its five main divisions. These divisions are based all over Europe and are linked by the ESA's headquarters in Paris, France. Two of its larger divisions include ESOC, the European Space Operations Centre in Darmstadt, Germany, which since its creation in 1967 has operated more than 50 satellites, ensured spacecraft meet their objectives and co-ordinated ground-based communications. There's also the ESTEC in Noordwijk, The Netherlands, whose remit includes being the primary test centre for European space activities and all technical preparation and management of ESA space projects (ESTEC is the largest division of the ESA). Other divisions can be found in Frascati, Italy (ESRIN), Villanueva de la Cañada, Spain (ESAC) and Cologne, Germany (EAC).

Member countries
- ESA member countries
- ECS (European Co-operating state)
- Signed Co-operation Agreement countries

©Ssolbergj

1. Site
An Ariane 5 heavy launch vehicle stands on-site

2. Access
The large approach road is necessary considering the size of the equipment being transported

All uncredited images © ESA

Space for Europe

Learn about the three main missions currently being undertaken by the ESA

CryoSat-2

The ESA's most recent launch, CryoSat-2, is imaging and analysing the effects of global warming like never before

The ESA's Earth Explorer CryoSat-2 mission, which was launched on 8 April 2010 on a Dnepr rocket, is concerned with the precise monitoring of the changes in the thickness of marine ice floating in polar oceans and variations in the thickness of Greenland's ice sheets. This is a highly important and timely mission as currently Earth's ice fields are diminishing at an expediential rate.

The CryoSat-2 satellite – which boasts a state-of-the-art SAR/Interferometric Radar Altimeter, which measures ice by sending a series of cloud-piercing radar pulses down to Earth – is orbiting Earth from an altitude of just over 700km and latitudes of up to 88 degrees, a record for this type of platform. It is powered by two angled sheets of solar panels, which each contain hundreds of highly sensitive gallium arsenide solar cells that supply power for the batteries.

The CryoSat-2's technique of transmitting a series of radar pulses works as when they reach Earth they are scattered off the variable slopes of the ice sheet margins and the returned echo comes from the closest surface location with respect to the satellite. These are then received by the CryoSat-2's antennas – which are wrapped in multi-layer insulation – and decoded.

The dedicated control room for CryoSat-2 operations at ESOC, Darmstadt

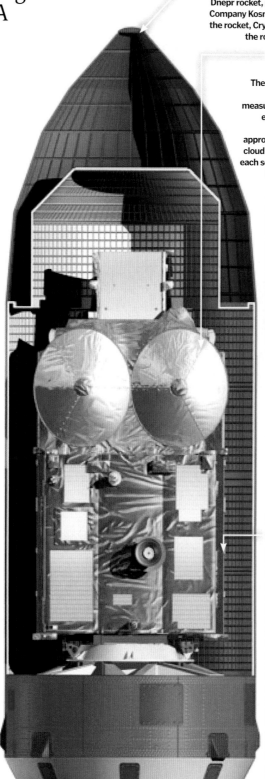

1. Dnepr rocket head
The launch vehicle for the CryoSat-2 satellite was a Dnepr rocket, provided by the International Space Company Kosmotras. Housed in the top section of the rocket, CryoSat-2 separated successfully from the rocket after 17 minutes of vertical lift

2. SAR/Interferometric Radar Altimeter
The primary payload of the CryoSat-2 is designed to meet the nuanced measurement requirements for ice-sheet elevation and sea-ice freeboard data acquisition. This highly advanced approach works by sending thousands of cloud piercing radar pulses to the ground each second and then measuring the time it takes for their echoes to return to CryoSat-2's antennas

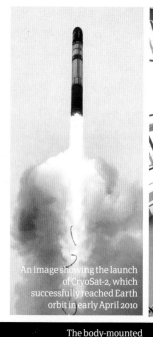
An image showing the launch of CryoSat-2, which successfully reached Earth orbit in early April 2010

The body-mounted solar arrays of the CryoSat-2

The Statistics
CryoSat-2

Operator: ESA
Launch vehicle: Kosmotras Dnepr rocket
Payload: SAR/Interferometric Radar Altimeter
Orbit altitude: 717km (approx)
Mass: 720kg
Power: 2 x GaAs body-mounted solar arrays (1700 W)

3. Solar panels
In order to power the imaging and data recording systems on the CryoSat-2 satellite, it is covered with two large sheets of solar cells, which produce power for the on-board batteries. Unlike many other satellites, these panels are fixed and non-deployable, however they are positioned on optimal angles for the capturing of solar energy throughout an orbit

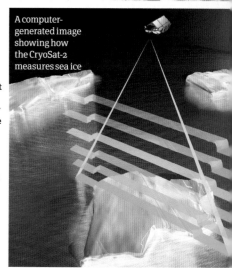
A computer-generated image showing how the CryoSat-2 measures sea ice

5 TOP FACTS
ESA

Jobbing
1 Out of 10,000 people who registered back in 2008 for an ESA astronaut recruitment drive, only six made the cut. That's just a one in 1,666 chance of being successful.

Year-on-year
2 Since 2005 the annual budget of the European Space Agency has grown rapidly from £2.5 billion to the £3.3 billion it currently has at its disposal today.

Canada
3 Since 1 January 1971, Canada has acted as an associate member to the ESA. This means it takes part in the decision-making processes and its programmes.

Corps
4 There are currently 14 astronauts in the European Astronaut Corps, 13 of which are men and only one is a woman. The sole Brit is Timothy Peake.

Spot-on
5 The European Space Agency's spaceport in French Guiana is ideally positioned for space launches due to its proximity to the Earth's equator.

DID YOU KNOW? *The original CryoSat mission failed in 2005. The separation mechanism on its carrying rocket broke at launch*

Mars500
The mission that simulated humanity's journey to Mars

The Mars500 mission was an important study to ascertain the mental and physical strain on humans in closed isolation on a long-haul trip to Mars. The mission was a joint project between the ESA and Russian Institute for Biomedical Problems, beginning on 3 June 2010 and culminating on 4 November 2011. In it, six candidates were sealed in an isolation chamber for 520 days, the approximate journey time for a real mission to and from the Red Planet.

The isolation facility in which they were held was based in Moscow and consisted of five modules: three to replicate the spacecraft (where the volunteers spent the majority of their time), one to replicate the Mars-lander in which the astronauts would travel to the surface and another to simulate the Martian surface, with a total combined area of 550m³ (19,423 ft³).

To accurately simulate a mission to Mars, the volunteers were subjected to the same conditions that would be apparent for astronauts making the trip for real. For example, all communications outside the pod were given a time delay, ranging from 1 minute when near "Earth" to 20 minutes at "Mars", while the crew were also given a diet identical to that of astronauts on board the International Space Station.

The volunteers carried out the same tasks that astronauts would in a real-life Mars trip, including simulating a Martian landing and performing experiments. The participants were able to talk to friends and family via video link at various points in the mission, albeit with the aforementioned time delay.

With the mission finished, future astronauts making the long-haul trip will have useful knowledge of the conditions they might expect when being in isolation for such a long period of time and at such a great distance from home.

An image showing the multiple parts of the Mars500 simulated spacecraft

The members of the 2010 stage of the experiment prepare to go into isolation

Training facilities were included to help keep the astronauts fit and healthy

An artist's impression of the XMM-Newton as it orbits Earth

All uncredited Images © ESA

XMM-Newton
The primary x-ray telescope of the ESA, the XMM-Newton is increasing our knowledge of black holes, the formation of galaxies and the origins of the universe

Launched from the ESA's Guiana spaceport in 1999 on an Ariane 5 rocket, the XMM-Newton is the ESA's largest and most active x-ray observatory and orbiting satellite. It orbits the Earth on a highly eccentric and elliptical orbit of 40 degrees and boasts three x-ray telescopes each containing 58 Wolter-type concentric mirrors. It is powered by twin extendable solar arrays that give the XMM a span of 16 metres. In addition to its three x-ray telescopes, the XMM also includes two reflection-grating spectrometers (used to measure light intensity) and a 12-inch in diameter Ritchey-Chrétien optical/UV telescope (a specialised telescope used to mitigate aberration in images).

The XMM-Newton's name comes from the design of its mirrors, the highly nested x-ray multi-mirrors, and in dedication to the great scientist Sir Isaac Newton. These mirrors are enabling astronomers to discover more x-ray sources than with any of the previous space observatories. In one day, for example, the XMM-Newton sees more sources in one small area than lesser satellites managed in years. Thanks to its orbit, the XMM-Newton has been able to measure the influence of the gravitational field of a neutron star on the light it emits. This was a first in astronomical observation and helped give a valuable insight into these super-dense objects.

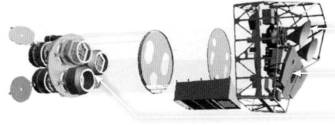
X-ray telescopes

Camera radiators

Telescope tubes

"Japan's Hayabusa probe was the first spacecraft to return a sample from an asteroid"

The development of space technology

SPACE TRAVEL

We take a look at the ten most important space missions of all time

Since Russia's Sputnik 1 satellite entered space on 4 October 1957, thousands of manned and unmanned spacecraft, including Earth satellites and deep-space probes, have launched into the cosmos.

In those five decades, space travel has truly come on leaps and bounds, with the development of liquid and solid fuels, as well as the use of solar panels and radioactive power sources among many of the impressive innovations, allowing space agencies across the planet to undertake evermore ambitious missions that would once have never been thought possible. Here, we've compiled ten of the most successful missions that have advanced the field of space travel to a whole new level. ✿

1969
Apollo 11

Probably the most well-known space mission of all time, Apollo 11 was launched atop the most powerful rocket to date, the Saturn V. The spacecraft was composed of two sections – the Lunar Module and the Command Module – the latter of which remained in orbit around the Moon with Michael Collins on board while the former took astronauts Neil Armstrong and Buzz Aldrin to the surface. Apollo 11 paved the way for a further five successful missions to the Moon, each spending several days on the lunar surface.

◇ **1960s** ● ⋯⋯⋯ ◇ **1970s** ● ◇ **198**

1961
Vostok 1

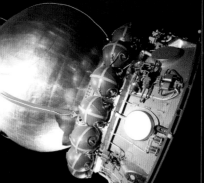

In 1961 Yuri Gagarin became the first man to travel to space, and the spacecraft that took him there for 68 minutes, was a fairly rudimentary sphere known as Vostok 1. As this was the first manned craft to leave Earth orbit, lots of extra precautions were taken, eg Gagarin was not able to freely move around the cabin, nor was he able to manually control the spacecraft. Nonetheless, in the timeline of space exploration, Vostok 1 is without a doubt one of the most important spacecraft of all time.

1977-present
Voyager 1 and 2

The Voyager programme was originally designed to explore Jupiter, Saturn, Uranus and Neptune, but the mission was extended to include the boundary into interstellar space, which they are currently entering. The Voyager probes both receive power from three radioisotope thermoelectric generators, fed by plutonium-238. On board each probe is a variety of sounds and images known as the Golden Record, which also contains instructions on how to find Earth for any passing aliens.

1961-1984
Venera probes

The Venera missions have been Russia's most successful space exploration missions to date. In total, 23 separate probes were launched to the hottest planet in our solar system, Venus, between 1961 and 1984, with ten of these landing on the surface. Each Venera lander was a technical marvel, withstanding incredible temperatures of up to 462 degrees Celsius (864 degrees Fahrenheit) to remain operational for up to two hours. They returned key data about the surface of Venus, including detailed information on the planet's atmospheric structure

1972-2003
Pioneer 10 and 11

The purpose of the Pioneer missions was to learn about the outer reaches of the solar system. These two spacecraft were, at the time of their launch, the most advanced vehicles to venture into space. They contained a number of technical tools never used before, including a charged particle instrument to measure the extent of the Sun's influence. While comms were lost in 1995 (Pioneer 11) and 2003 (Pioneer 10), the probes continue to make their way out of the solar system, with each possessing an on-board plaque detailing their origins.

1981-2011
Space Shuttles

NASA's five cosmos-faring Space Shuttles were the largest spacecraft of all time, and each completed numerous missions that defined them as some of the most important vehicles to enter Earth orbit. Their many accolades include taking the Hubble Space Telescope into orbit (and later repairing it) and launching more than 80 per cent of the modules for the ISS. There were 135 missions in total, but two of these ended in tragedy. The Challenger spacecraft exploded 73 seconds after launch in 1986, while in 2003 the Columbia spacecraft was torn apart on re-entry. While the Shuttles are remembered largely as a success, these two disasters serve as a reminder of just how dangerous space travel is.

2003-2010
Hayabusa

Japan's Hayabusa probe was the first spacecraft to return a sample from an asteroid, but it wasn't without its problems. A fuel leak rendered its chemical engines unusable and, coupled with a variety of mechanical failures, the probe was forced to limp home on its weaker ion engines. It eventually arrived three years behind schedule in 2010, but the mission was still a success. Ion engines on spacecraft have become more and more popular due to their longevity, rather than relying on an initial big 'push'.

> ## 1990s

> ## 2000s

1989-2003
Galileo probe/ spacecraft

NASA's Galileo spacecraft was taken into space in 1989 and went on to study Jupiter after flybys of Venus and Earth. It was the first spacecraft to orbit Jupiter, in addition to performing the first flyby of an asteroid. It also carried the Galileo Space Probe, which it released into Jupiter's atmosphere in 1995, providing unprecedented data about the gas giant. In 2003 the orbiting spacecraft was sent crashing into our solar system's biggest planet to prevent it colliding with a nearby moon and causing contamination.

1997-present
Cassini-Huygens

The Cassini-Huygens probe was a joint mission between NASA, the ESA and ASI (Italian Space Agency) and is often regarded as the most successful deep-space probe of all time. The orbiting component of the probe flew by Jupiter and became the first spacecraft to orbit Saturn. The landing vehicle was the Huygens Probe, which landed on Saturn's moon Titan in 2005, the first and only successful landing in the outer solar system. As with most probes, it is powered by plutonium-238, which has enabled its mission to be extended to 2017.

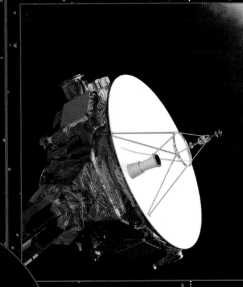

2006-present
New Horizons

NASA's New Horizons spacecraft will become the first probe to fly by Pluto in 2015. While its primary mission is to study the (now) dwarf planet, it has also studied Jupiter and its moons. New Horizons is the fastest probe to have left Earth's orbit. It is currently more than 21 times further from the Sun than Earth; at that distance it takes almost three hours to send or receive a signal.

"They have to be built tougher and more rugged than the hardiest black box recorder"

Unmanned space probes

They have made some of the most fundamental discoveries in modern science, but how do space probes work?

On 4 October 1957 the former Soviet Union launched the world's first successful space probe, Sputnik 1, heralding the start of the space race between Russia and the USA. In the initial ten years the vast majority of man's efforts to conduct scientific experiments in space were failures, and it wasn't until the late Sixties that successes were achieved. While many were chalked up to launch failures, most couldn't weather the harsh realities of space.

Withstanding temperature extremes is a monumental task in itself. Of course, it's not temperatures that pose problems for probes wanting to land in alien environments, they must also be capable of putting up with intense radiation and atmospheric pressures which fluctuate from pure vacuum to 90 times that of Earth's surface pressure and beyond. Russia's 1970 Venera 7 probe successfully landed on the surface of Venus and

managed to send data back for just 23 minutes before being crushed under the immense pressure.

Not only do space probes have to act as highly sensitive scientific instruments, but they have to be built tougher and more rugged than the hardiest black box recorder. As such, the vast majority of a space probe's design is dedicated to sustaining itself and protecting its mission-critical systems. Ultimately their makers consider four fields of science while they're under construction. Engineering (ultimately self sustainability), field and particle sensing (for measuring magnetics among other things), probing (for specific 'hands-on' scientific experiments) and remote sensing, which is usually made up of spectrometers, imaging devices and infrared among other things. ✿

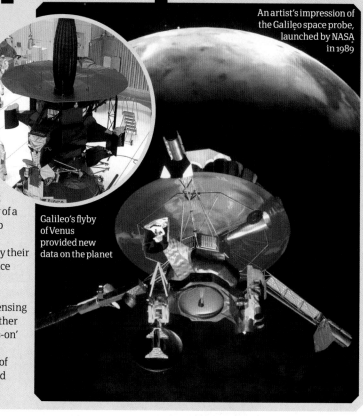

An artist's impression of the Galileo space probe, launched by NASA in 1989

Galileo's flyby of Venus provided new data on the planet

Whether a spacecraft is manned or unmanned will affect how it reaches the Moon's surface

How spacecraft land on the Moon

Unsurprisingly, it's not as easy as Wallace and Gromit made it look

For any spacecraft to land successfully on the Moon many factors need to be considered, however, the most critical of these is deceleration. To carry a spacecraft out of the gravity well of the Earth's atmosphere, massive upward thrust is necessary, a force only currently possible with a rocket. However, when approaching the Moon the massive velocity caused by the rocket (which has by now been detached), as well as the Moon's gravitational attraction, means that the spacecraft's velocity is so high that any sort of safe landing is impossible. Therefore, in order to land, the spacecraft needs to decelerate massively. To achieve this, the spacecraft uses additional braking rockets to change its velocity as it nears the Moon's orbit, slowing its speed of impact in order to land.

Landing even with these velocity-altering rockets is not as straightforward as it may appear. Even with the reduced speed of the

craft, in order to be classed as a successful landing all operational ability needs to be maintained after the impact, both in terms of onboard technology and any astronauts. If the spacecraft is unmanned then the speed of impact can be higher, up to 100 miles per hour, but if there are astronauts on board then that speed needs to be much reduced. If for any reason the spacecraft is not slowed – due mainly to technology malfunction – then it will impact upon the Moon at over 2,500 miles per hour, destroying it completely and killing everyone on board.

Unfortunately, even if the landing is successful there is still then the problem of returning back to Earth after the mission. In order to achieve this yet another transported rocket is needed with enough power to counteract the escape velocity of the Moon and break free, providing enough thrust to match the kinetic energy of the craft to its gravitational potential energy. ✿

DID YOU KNOW? If for any reason the spacecraft is not slowed then it will impact upon the Moon at over 2,500 miles per hour.

Head to Head
The Apollo 11 crew

COMMANDER

1. Neil Armstrong
The first man on the Moon and commander of the Apollo mission. This was his second, and last, space flight.

COMMAND MODULE PILOT

2. Michael Collins
Collins looked after the command modules while Aldrin and Armstrong landed the Eagle on the Moon.

LUNAR MODULE PILOT

3. Buzz Aldrin
The pilot of the Eagle was the second man to ever set to set foot on the Moon, following mission commander Neil Armstrong.

DID YOU KNOW? The Apollo 13 LM helped save the lives of its crew after a systems malfunction

Inside the Apollo Lander

The Apollo Lander was the landing module of the Apollo spacecraft

The Lander, also known as the Lunar Module (LM), was a two-stage craft built to separate from the Apollo Command and Service Module, and then travel to and from the Moon's surface. It first landed on the Moon on 20 July 1969. Generally the descent stage was left on the Moon, while the ascent stage crashed into the Moon's surface once the astronauts returned to the Command Module. Each of the 15 Apollo LMs had unique names. The Apollo 11 LM was named the Eagle, which explains why Neil Armstrong stated that "the Eagle has landed" when it touched down.

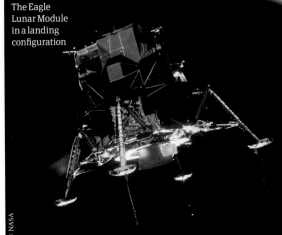

The Eagle Lunar Module in a landing configuration

© NASA

Now boarding for the surface of the Moon

The Apollo Lander was a feat of technological engineering

5. Fuel
The Lander was powered by a rocket fuel called Aerozine 50. It is still used in spacecraft and rockets because it is a highly stable fuel with a low freezing point

7. Landing gear
Initial designs had three legs, which could have resulted in a toppling Lander if one was damaged. Five legs were preferred, but they made the Lander too heavy. Four was an acceptable compromise

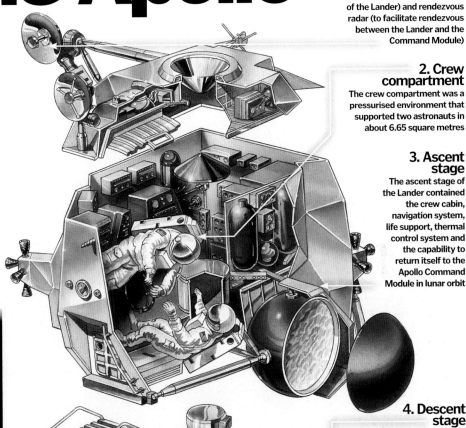

1. Antennas
The Lander had three different types of antenna: VHF (for communication), S-band steerable (to facilitate control of the Lander) and rendezvous radar (to facilitate rendezvous between the Lander and the Command Module)

2. Crew compartment
The crew compartment was a pressurised environment that supported two astronauts in about 6.65 square metres

3. Ascent stage
The ascent stage of the Lander contained the crew cabin, navigation system, life support, thermal control system and the capability to return itself to the Apollo Command Module in lunar orbit

4. Descent stage
The descent stage contained the fuel to land on the Moon, landing gear, a ladder to descent to the surface and materials for experiments and sample collection on the Moon

6. Oxidiser
Aerozine 50 is used in conjunction with a chemical compound called dinitrogen tetroxide, an oxidiser. The Aerozine 50 ignites upon contact with it

© DK Images

"Despite many technical hitches, the Venera spacecraft are regarded as a success"

Venera probes

The highs and the lows of these groundbreaking Russian missions to Venus

Venera 10 returned this image from Venus on 25 October 1975 during its 65 minutes of operation

This 170-degree panoramic image of Venus's surface was taken by Venera 13 on 1 March 1982

The Venera probes were a series of spacecraft designed by the USSR to glean unprecedented data on the hottest planet in our solar system: Venus. Venera 1 was the first to launch in 1961, followed by 15 more missions through to 1984. The spacecraft encountered numerous problems and glitches in almost every launch, but there was more than enough data returned to label the overall mission a success. The spacecraft were launched in batches across the 23-year period, with each group possessing new and upgraded features based on the experiences from the previous missions.

The first two spacecraft – Venera 1 and 2 – were designed as spherical probes intended to merely perform a flyby of the planet and provide information about the density of its atmosphere and temperature. Unfortunately, both probes suffered a communications failure after leaving Earth orbit so couldn't send any data back, although Venera 1 is thought to have come within 100,000 kilometres (62,137 miles) of Venus, thus becoming the first manmade object to pass the planet.

The next four spacecraft – Venera 3 to 6 – employed a similar spherical design but were somewhat heavier, weighing about a ton. Although Venera 3 was unsuccessful, earning itself the unwanted accolade of becoming the first spacecraft to crash-land on another planet on 1 March 1966, Venera 4 finally returned positive results and became the first spacecraft in history to measure the atmosphere of another planet. Each of the spacecraft carried a probe to attempt an atmospheric entry, but the Soviets grossly underestimated Venus's surface pressure, believing it to be just 25 times more than Earth's when in fact it is closer to 100 times, and thus the first two probes were instantly destroyed once they entered the atmosphere. Realising their design error, the USSR's space agency decided to jettison the majority of the instruments on Venera 5 and 6 mid-flight and instead use them solely as atmospheric entry probes; each managed to survive for over 50 minutes in the harsh atmosphere.

The remaining missions were designed to land and operate on the surface of Venus, taking into account the intense pressure measured in previous missions. Venera 7 was the first spacecraft in the programme specifically tailored to survive the intense pressure and heat on Venus's surface (see the 'Landing on Venus' boxout for more detail). It became the first spacecraft to transmit data from the surface of Venus on 15 December 1970 despite a

1. Venera 3
This Russian probe was the first spacecraft to impact another planet – Venus – in 1966. Due to equipment damage, no data was returned.

2. Mars 2
This Soviet-built unmanned probe, with a fairly unoriginal name, crash-landed on Mars in 1971, becoming the first spacecraft to 'touch down' on the Red Planet.

3. Huygens
On 14 January 2005 the Huygens probe performed the first and only landing in the outer solar system, successfully touching down on Saturn's moon Titan.

DID YOU KNOW? Russia and the USA are the only two countries to successfully land spacecraft on another planet

Landing on Venus

How did Venera 7 make it to the surface?

1. Release
The Venera 7 lander was released from the orbiting spacecraft, above the atmosphere

2. Atmosphere
The heat shields were detached after it had cleared the dense atmosphere, so the instruments could take their readings

3. Hadley cell
The winds in the atmosphere of Venus move in a circular motion known as a Hadley cell; this is driven by convection currents

4. Descent
The probe was meant to take 60 minutes to descend, but damage to its parachute meant it reached the surface in just 35 minutes

5. Crash-landing
Venera 7 impacted the surface at 17 metres (56 feet) per second, but it still managed to survive for 23 more minutes

6. Readings
On the surface the lander recorded a temperature of 475°C (887°F) and an atmospheric pressure 90 times greater than that on Earth

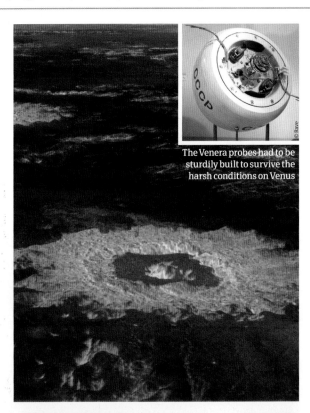

The Venera probes had to be sturdily built to survive the harsh conditions on Venus

parachute failure shortly before landing, which saw it impact the surface at almost 65 kilometres (40 miles) per hour. It survived for 23 minutes, as planned, and despite possessing very few experiments, it was still able to return information on the temperature and pressure, which were calculated at 475 degrees Celsius (887 degrees Fahrenheit) and 90 atmospheres (190,460 pounds per square foot), respectively. Venera 8 was nearly identical to Venera 7 save for a few additional instruments, and it was able to survive on the surface for almost an hour.

Venera 9 to 12 were much larger than their predecessors, weighing close to five tons. They included an orbital craft that relayed data from each spacecraft's landing probe, designed to operate for 30 minutes. For the first time each lander also included two cameras, but unfortunately all of the landers suffered a camera malfunction. Venera 9 and 10 lasted about an hour on the surface and managed to return some images, with the former becoming the first to do so from another planet, but the camera lenses on both Venera 11 and 12 failed.

Venera 13 through to 16 were similar in design but contained more instruments including a drill, compressibility arm (to determine the rigidity of Venus's surface) and a seismometer. They both returned images and data from the planet, but unfortunately for Venera 14 its lens cap was ejected directly beneath its compressibility arm, so it was unable to analyse the surface.

Despite their many technical hitches, the Venera spacecraft are generally regarded as a success for the Soviet space programme, providing a substantial amount of data on Venus. They paved the way for the two Russian Vega spacecraft in 1985, which released atmospheric balloons on Venus that stayed active for two days. ✿

A shot of Venus passing in front of the Sun

VENERA LAUNCHES
A roundup of when all the Veneros took off...

Venera 1:	12 Feb 1961
Venera 2:	12 Nov 1965
Venera 3:	16 Nov 1965
Venera 4:	12 June 1967
Venera 5:	5 Jan 1969
Venera 6:	10 Jan 1969
Venera 7:	17 Aug 1970
Venera 8:	27 Mar 1972
Venera 9:	8 June 1975
Venera 10:	14 June 1975
Venera 11:	9 Sept 1978
Venera 12:	14 Sept 1978
Venera 13:	30 Oct 1981
Venera 14:	14 Nov 1981
Venera 15:	2 June 1983
Venera 16:	7 June 1983

Lander
The upper descent module of this Venera spacecraft contained the lander, which entered the atmosphere of Venus and protected the lander until it reached the surface

Orbiter
The lower section is the orbiting module, which stayed in contact with the landing probe from the orbit of Venus and relayed data back to Earth

157

NASA's Viking programme

The Viking programme of the mid-Seventies was a triumph of space exploration

NASA's Viking programme was the first mission to return numerous images and data from Mars. It comprised two identical spacecraft, Viking 1 and Viking 2, each with an orbiter and a lander.

Both launched using a Titan IIIE/Centaur launch system. Viking 1 launched on 20 August 1975 and reached Mars after a ten-month journey. The orbiter took images and transmitted them back to NASA, who used them to choose a site for the lander. On 20 July, the lander separated from the orbiter and landed in an area called the Golden Plain. For more than six years, the lander took images and collected data from the surface. The orbiter's fuel ran out on 17 August 1980, while the lander shut down on 13 November 1982 when a mistake during a software update caused its antenna to go down permanently.

Viking 2 launched on 9 September 1975, reaching Mars orbit on 7 August 1976. The lander touched down in the Nowhere Plain on 3 September. Viking 2's mission did not last as long as Viking 1; the orbiter shut down after a fuel leak about two years after arrival, while the lander had a battery failure after three and a half years. Together, Viking 1 and Viking 2 provided more than 50,000 photographs. ✿

The Statistics

Viking landers

Launch date:
Viking 1: 20 August 1975
Viking 2: 9 September 1975
Launch site:
Kennedy Space Center
Launch vehicle:
Titan IIIE/Centaur
Mission length:
Viking 1:
4 years, 11 months, 28 days
Viking 2:
1 year, 10 months, 16 days
Lander mass: 883kg
Lander power: 620W

3. Solar panel
Solar panels converted solar energy into about 620 watts of electrical energy for use by the orbiter

1. Attitude control thruster
This thruster on the Viking orbiter was a small rocket engine that steered the orbiter towards Mars

6. Low gain antenna
The low gain antenna was a secondary antenna, to be used if the high gain antenna failed

© DK Images

2. Lander
After circling the planet for landing site selection, the lander detached from the orbiter and landed via parachute on the surface

7. Star tracker
The star tracker pointed the orbiter towards Canopus, a star in the constellation of Carina and Argo Navis

The Viking space probe
A closer look at how the probes worked...

4. High gain antenna
The high gain antenna communicated with ground control on Earth, sending back images and data

5. Thruster engine
This engine burned a liquid bipropellant rocket fuel mixture to propel the orbiter

The Viking landers' discoveries

The Viking programme was the first truly successful mission to Mars, providing NASA with the first real data concerning the existence of water on the planet. Photographs showed large areas of erosion, channels and grooves in rocks, and river valleys. These were likely caused by massive amounts of water. Each Viking lander also carried four different types of experiments to test for signs of life on Mars, which included testing for carbon and gas concentrations in the soil. The results of three of the tests proved negative, while one was ultimately inconclusive.

This panoramic image was taken by Viking 1. It reveals large rocks and sand dunes on the surface of Mars, as well as a layer of clouds below the horizon

Galileo Space Probe

The first man-made object to ever enter Jupiter's atmosphere

NASA launched the Galileo spacecraft, which comprises the Galileo Orbiter and Space Probe, atop a space shuttle in 1989, using a 38-month orbit of Venus and the Earth's gravitational pull to gain the necessary speed to reach Jupiter.

While the Galileo Orbiter was designed to orbit and study Jupiter and its moons, the Galileo Probe was released near Jupiter and was sent into the gas giant itself. It entered the atmosphere of Jupiter at 30 miles per second (47kmps), the highest impact speed ever achieved by a man-made object. Amazingly, Jupiter's gravitational forces slowed the craft to 0.07 miles per second (0.12 kmps) in just four minutes.

The Probe's heat shield, made of carbon phenolic, was able to withstand the 15,500°C ball of plasma caused by this sudden deceleration, producing light brighter than the Sun's surface. It remained active for about 78 minutes as it passed through Jupiter's atmosphere, losing more than half its mass in the process before being crushed by the huge pressure.

Wrapped in black and gold blankets to provide insulations and protect against micrometeorites, the Probe conducted nine experiments that measured Jupiter's atmospheric structure. It discovered the presence of a large amount of argon, krypton and xenon. For these to form Jupiter would need to be at a temperature of -240°C, suggesting it once orbited much further from the Sun.

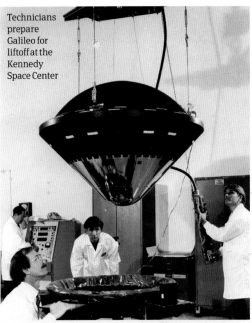

Technicians prepare Galileo for liftoff at the Kennedy Space Center

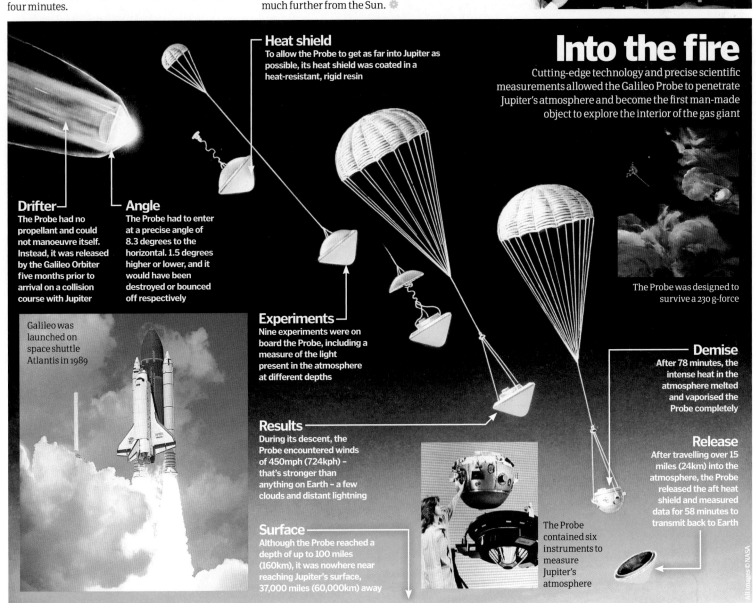

Into the fire

Cutting-edge technology and precise scientific measurements allowed the Galileo Probe to penetrate Jupiter's atmosphere and become the first man-made object to explore the interior of the gas giant

Heat shield
To allow the Probe to get as far into Jupiter as possible, its heat shield was coated in a heat-resistant, rigid resin

Drifter
The Probe had no propellant and could not manoeuvre itself. Instead, it was released by the Galileo Orbiter five months prior to arrival on a collision course with Jupiter

Angle
The Probe had to enter at a precise angle of 8.3 degrees to the horizontal. 1.5 degrees higher or lower, and it would have been destroyed or bounced off respectively

Experiments
Nine experiments were on board the Probe, including a measure of the light present in the atmosphere at different depths

Galileo was launched on space shuttle Atlantis in 1989

The Probe was designed to survive a 230 g-force

Results
During its descent, the Probe encountered winds of 450mph (724kph) – that's stronger than anything on Earth – a few clouds and distant lightning

Surface
Although the Probe reached a depth of up to 100 miles (160km), it was nowhere near reaching Jupiter's surface, 37,000 miles (60,000km) away

The Probe contained six instruments to measure Jupiter's atmosphere

Demise
After 78 minutes, the intense heat in the atmosphere melted and vaporised the Probe completely

Release
After travelling over 15 miles (24km) into the atmosphere, the Probe released the aft heat shield and measured data for 58 minutes to transmit back to Earth

All images © NASA

"The probes have studied all the major planets of the solar system past Mars"

PLUTO (DWARF PLANET)

Voyager spacecraft

How the furthest man-made objects from Earth work

Distance from Earth today: 14 billion

NEPTUNE

Date reached: 25/8/89

On 20 August 1977 Voyager 2 launched from Cape Canaveral in Florida aboard a Titan-Centaur rocket, heralding the start of one of the most ambitious deep space exploration missions of all time. Two weeks later Voyager 1 was sent up in an identical launch, although its greater speed meant that it eventually overtook Voyager 2. The list of accomplishments by the two probes is astounding. Between them they have studied all of the major planets of the solar system past Mars, in addition to some moons of Jupiter and Saturn, making countless new discoveries in the process. Now, as the furthest man-made objects from Earth, they are on their way out of the solar system.

The launch of the mission coincided with a favourable alignment of the planets in the Seventies that would allow Voyager 2 to visit Jupiter, Saturn, Uranus and Neptune. The list of achievements by the two Voyager spacecraft is extensive. The Voyager mission was only the second – after Pioneer 10 and 11 in 1974 and 1975, respectively – to visit Jupiter and then Saturn, but it also discovered the existence of rings around Jupiter, while Voyager 2 was the first mission to visit Uranus and Neptune.

The primary objective of the mission was to study Jupiter and Saturn, but once it became apparent that the spacecraft could continue working, the mission was extended to include Neptune and Uranus for Voyager 2. Voyager 1 could have travelled to Pluto, but NASA decided to extend its mission to Saturn and its moon Titan, leaving the dwarf planet Pluto one of the largest bodies in the solar system yet to be explored.

The Voyager probes obtain power from their radioactive generators, which have kept them running even at such a great distance from Earth and will continue to do so until about 2020, when they will no longer be able to power their instruments. Voyager 1 is roughly now over 17 billion kilometres (10.6 billion miles) from the Sun, while Voyager 2 is at a distance of over 14 billion kilometres (8.5 billion miles).

After making so many groundbreaking discoveries, both spacecraft are now on their way out of the solar system. They are both expected to pass out of the Sun's influence and into interstellar space in the coming years, although it is not entirely clear when this will happen as no machine has yet experienced the conditions that the Voyager probes are about to endure.

In 40,000 years, Voyager 1 should be within 1.6 light years (9.4 trillion miles) of a star in the constellation of Camelopardalis thought to harbour a planetary system. 256,000 years later, Voyager 2 will be 4.3 light years (25 trillion miles) from Sirius, which is the brightest star other than the Sun in our night sky. ✱

Voyager 2 launched atop a Titan III-Centaur rocket on 20 August 1977

Data
A single 8-track digital tape recorder (DTR) and Flight Data Subsystem (FDS) handle data and calibrate instruments too

Golden Record
The Golden Record is a collection of sounds and imagery from Earth, intended to provide any passing extraterrestrial race with information about our home planet

Thrust
The probes manoeuvre via Hydrazine thrusters, although since leaving the planets they have stopped doing so

Power up
Three radioisotope thermoelectric generators (RTGs) supply electrical power, which will eventually diminish but currently supply about 315 watts

Instruments
On board both probes is a science payload with ten instruments, including those to measure solar wind and those that can detect low-energy particles

Antenna
The high-gain antenna (HGA) transmits data to Earth

Power down
To conserve energy as the probes continue their journeys, many instruments deemed unnecessary have or will be switched off

Magnetometer
This instrument enables the probes to measure nearby magnetic field intensities, which was used to study the magnetospheres of the outer planets

Inside Voyager
What's going on inside the long-distance probes?

Communication
It takes 16 hours for a message from the Voyager probes to reach Earth. However, they're not in constant communication, and only periodically send data back to our planet

Phone home
Each of the identical spacecraft use celestial or gyroscopic attitude control to ensure that their high-gain antennas are constantly pointed towards Earth for communication

Weight
Each Voyager probe weighs 773kg (1,704lbs), with the science payload making up about 105kg (231lbs) of this

TOP FACTS
VOYAGER DISCOVERIES

Moons

1 Around the outer planets the Voyager probes discovered 23 new moons, including five around Saturn and 11 around Uranus, in addition to imaging our own.

Interstellar medium

2 Both of the Voyager probes are now in a region where the Sun's influence is increasingly waning, and soon they will enter the interstellar medium.

Atmospheres

3 Voyager probes 1 and 2 both provided unprecedented information about the atmospheres of the following planets: Jupiter, Saturn, Uranus and Neptune.

Jupiter

4 The probes discovered for the first time a ring system encircling Jupiter, and they also observed hurricane-like storms in the planet's atmosphere.

Io

5 Voyager 1 discovered the only known body in the solar system other than Earth to be volcanically active: Jupiter's moon Io. This moon also affects the surrounding Jovian system.

DID YOU KNOW? *Voyager 1 is now travelling at 38,000mph, while Voyager 2 is slightly slower at 35,000mph*

The journey so far...

What path have the Voyager probes taken through the solar system, and where are they now?

Distance from Earth today: 17 billion km

URANUS

Date reached: 12/11/80

Date reached: 5/3/79

JUPITER

SATURN

VOYAGER 1 launch: 5/9/77

EARTH

Date reached: 24/1/86

Date reached: 25/8/81

Heliopause
This is where the Sun's influence is almost non-existent and the Voyager probes will enter the interstellar medium, the matter between stars in our galaxy. No one is sure how far the probes are from this point

Termination shock
At the edge of the heliosheath, the Sun's influence in the form of solar wind slows dramatically and heats up at an area known as the termination shock, which Voyager 1 passed in 2004

Voyager 1

VOYAGER 2 launch: 20/8/77

Date reached: 9/7/79

Bow shock

On 16 November 1980, Voyager 1 looked back at Saturn and snapped this picture four days after it had passed the planet

Heliosphere
Our solar system is contained within an area of space where the Sun exerts an influence, known as the heliosphere

Voyager 2

What lies ahead...

All images © NASA

The Herschel crater

Mimas, Saturn's closest moon, looks like the Death Star with its massive impact crater

Of Saturn's major moons, Mimas is the closest to the planet at 185,520 kilometres away. The moon is believed to have created the Cassini Division, a ,800-kilometre gap between Saturn's A and B rings. Mimas has an average diameter of 396 kilometres, with an ovoid shape. This is due to its ow surface gravity – about one 25th that of Earth's moon – as well as the strong gravitational pull from Saturn. The same side of Mimas always faces Saturn, and it has an asynchronous rotation meaning that it takes the same amount of time to both orbit and rotate on its axis) of 22.5 hours.

Mimas has a very low density, about 1.17 times that of water, so astronomers believe that it probably comprises a small rocky core with an outer layer of ice. It appears to be solidly frozen at about 64 Kelvin. The moon's main geological features are chasms and impact craters. Mimas is best known for its massive Herschel crater, however. This crater has a diameter of 130 kilometres, about a third of the moon's own diameter. Its walls are about five kilometres high, and it has areas that are 10 kilometres deep. If a crater of the same scale were found on Earth, it would be wider than the entire country of Canada. ✿

The Herschel crater mystery

Mimas's most distinguishing feature is also something of a mystery. Astronomers cannot figure out why the force necessary to create such a wide, deep crater didn't destroy the moon completely. The massive impact appears to have left fissures on the opposite side of the moon, although these may also be the result of cracking in its icy surface. If Mimas had been destroyed, its remaining pieces might have become other Saturnian moons or even formed another ring around the planet. It is not known exactly what caused the crater, which has an unusual, hexagonal shape. It could have been a massive meteor, or rubble that broke away during the formation of Saturn's moons.

Ellipsoid moon
Due to the forces acting upon it, Mimas is not perfectly spherical. Its longest axis is about ten per cent longer than the shortest

Exploration
Mimas has been imaged several time by the Cassini orbiter. The closest flyb occurred on 13 February 2010, when Cassini passed by Mimas at 9,500km

Saturn's major icy moons

Although Saturn has more than 60 named moons, the majority of them are very small satellites. Mimas is one of the seven major icy moons in Saturn's orbit. It is in resonance with two of its neighbours, Dione and Enceladus. The orbits of these three moons speed up when they get closer to each other and slow down as they separate.

Mimas
Diameter: 396 kilometres
Orbital period: 22.5 hours
Distance from Saturn: 185,520 kilometres
Fact: Mimas is best known for its massive, Death Star-like impact crater

Enceladus
Diameter: 505 kilometres
Orbital period: 1.37 days
Distance from Saturn: 238,020 kilometres
Fact: Enceladus is a bright white moon with widely varying terrain

Tethys
Diameter: 1,066 kilometres
Orbital period: 1.9 days
Distance from Saturn: 294,660 kilometres
Fact: The terrain on Tethys is dominated by both a massive crater and a wide, deep valley

Dione
Diameter: 1,123 kilometres
Orbital period: 2.7 days
Distance from Saturn: 377,400 kilometres
Fact: Dione orbits Saturn at about the same distance that our moon orbits Earth

Rhea
Diameter: 1,528 kilometres
Orbital period: 4.5 days
Distance from Saturn: 527, 040 kilometres
Fact: Has a region of craters larger than 40km and another with smaller craters

Cassini-Huygens

The mission launched in 1997 to explore Saturn and its many moons

Cassini-Huygens is an orbiting spacecraft resulting from collaboration among NASA, the European Space Agency and the Italian Space Agency (ASI). The spacecraft comprises two parts: the Cassini orbiter and the Huygens probe.

This spacecraft is the biggest and most elaborate interplanetary space probe ever built – partly due to the extensive technology needed to conduct more than 25 planned investigations during the mission. Cassini also had to be able to make the long, difficult journey to Saturn. It took over six years for Cassini to enter the planet's orbit. On the way to Saturn, Cassini conducted fly-bys of Earth's moon, the asteroid 2685 Masursky, Venus, as well as several of Jupiter's moons.

The Huygens probe landed on Titan and began transmitting data on 14 January 2005 while the Cassini orbiter continued on. The mission objectives included conducting studies of Saturn's atmosphere, magnetosphere and rings. The Cassini-Huygens mission was also intended to learn more about some of Saturn's satellites. This included studies of the atmosphere and surface of Titan and of the surface of Iapetus, Saturn's third-largest moon. While the original mission ended on 30 July 2008, NASA has extended it because the Cassini orbiter is still functioning and in good condition. Now renamed Cassini Equinox (which will change to Cassini Solstice), the mission is planned to continue until 2017. ✿

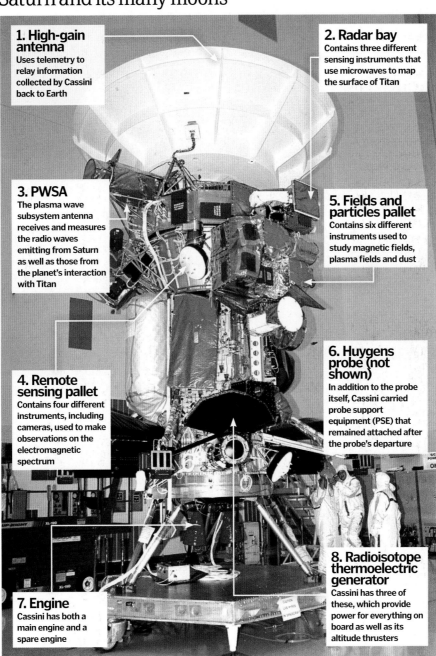

1. High-gain antenna
Uses telemetry to relay information collected by Cassini back to Earth

2. Radar bay
Contains three different sensing instruments that use microwaves to map the surface of Titan

3. PWSA
The plasma wave subsystem antenna receives and measures the radio waves emitting from Saturn as well as those from the planet's interaction with Titan

4. Remote sensing pallet
Contains four different instruments, including cameras, used to make observations on the electromagnetic spectrum

5. Fields and particles pallet
Contains six different instruments used to study magnetic fields, plasma fields and dust

6. Huygens probe (not shown)
In addition to the probe itself, Cassini carried probe support equipment (PSE) that remained attached after the probe's departure

7. Engine
Cassini has both a main engine and a spare engine

8. Radioisotope thermoelectric generator
Cassini has three of these, which provide power for everything on board as well as its altitude thrusters

The Statistics
Cassini-Huygens

Cassini orbiter weight: 2,125kg
Huygens probe weight: 320kg
Total dimensions: Seven metres high x four metres wide
Power: 885 watts
Launch: 15 October 1997
Cost: $3.27 billion

The complex Cassini

At nearly 6,000 kilograms at launch, the Cassini is the second-heaviest exploratory spacecraft built to date. It contains a massive number of components, housing more than 1,500 electronic parts and over 14km of cable. The Cassini also houses 12 different instruments, while the Hugyens probe housed six.

Learn more

For the latest info on the Cassini Equinox mission, check out the NASA website **saturn.jpl.nasa. gov.** NASA also has a DVD about the Cassini-Huygens mission called *Ring World*. A free podcast download is available at **http:// tinyurl.com/36rjwf2.**

The Huygens probe

After separating from the Cassini orbiter, the Huygens probe descended via parachute and landed on the surface of Titan in what appears to be a floodplain covered with small chunks of ice. The main portion of the probe's mission was the descent itself, which took about three hours. As the probe passed down through the hazy atmosphere, it transmitted radio data to Cassini (which in turn relayed it to Earth) as well as nearly 300 images.

This mission revealed that Titan has a dense atmosphere comprising nearly 98 per cent nitrogen gas, with hazy clouds made of methane and ethane that rain down onto the surface. This atmosphere reflects back what little sunlight reaches the moon, contributing to its low average surface temperature of -179°C. The surface of Titan is covered with dunes along its equator, and both rough and smooth areas elsewhere. These were likely formed by lakes and rivers of liquid methane and ethane.

This image of Jupiter taken by Cassini in 2000 is the most detailed ever seen

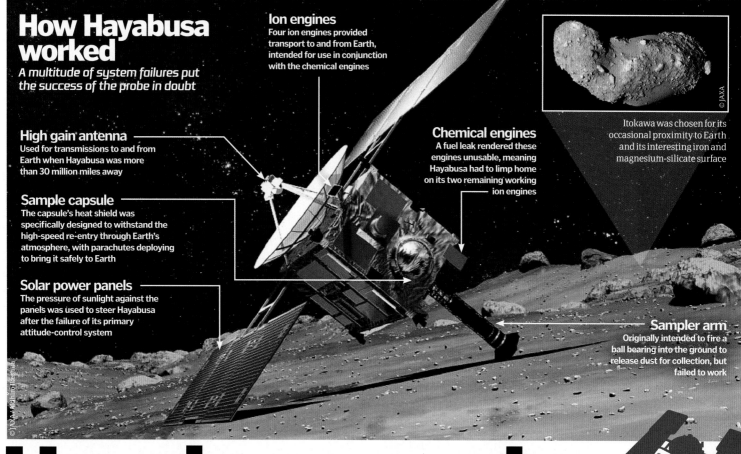

How Hayabusa worked
A multitude of system failures put the success of the probe in doubt

Ion engines
Four ion engines provided transport to and from Earth, intended for use in conjunction with the chemical engines

High gain antenna
Used for transmissions to and from Earth when Hayabusa was more than 30 million miles away

Sample capsule
The capsule's heat shield was specifically designed to withstand the high-speed re-entry through Earth's atmosphere, with parachutes deploying to bring it safely to Earth

Solar power panels
The pressure of sunlight against the panels was used to steer Hayabusa after the failure of its primary attitude-control system

Chemical engines
A fuel leak rendered these engines unusable, meaning Hayabusa had to limp home on its two remaining working ion engines

Itokawa was chosen for its occasional proximity to Earth and its interesting iron and magnesium-silicate surface

Sampler arm
Originally intended to fire a ball bearing into the ground to release dust for collection, but failed to work

Scale of probe to average human

Hayabusa probe

How the mission that seemed certain to fail returned the first asteroid samples to Earth

The Hayabusa probe, built by the Japanese Aerospace Exploration Agency (JAXA), was launched on a Japanese M-V rocket on 9 May 2003 from the Uchinoura Space Centre in Japan. Its mission was to become the first man-made object to return samples from an asteroid – in this case, Itokawa. To obtain the necessary speed to reach Itokawa 186 million miles (300 million km) away, Hayabusa used its ion engines to orbit the sun for more than a year. This provided continual acceleration, and when it finally approached Earth again it performed a swing-by to propel itself towards the Itokawa asteroid.

Communication to and from Hayabusa at the asteroid took 40 minutes, so it had to finish most of its mission alone. Upon its approach it dropped a 10cm-wide sphere with a reflective surface onto Itokawa. By shining light onto the sphere, Hayabusa could calculate its distance to the ground. When a lander intended to retrieve samples failed, Hayabusa was instructed to hover close to the ground to kick up dust into its collector via its engines.

Upon leaving the asteroid it lost all propulsion, barring two ion engines in addition to a communication failure with mission controllers. It eventually limped home three years behind schedule, with the probe burning up as planned in the atmosphere. The capsule containing the collected samples landed safely in Australia on 13 June 2010.

While the probe burned up in the atmosphere, the capsule returned safely to Earth

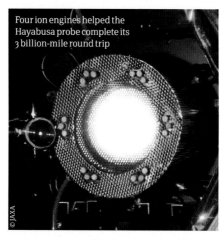
Four ion engines helped the Hayabusa probe complete its 3 billion-mile round trip

The capsule was recovered from the Australian desert

The Lunar Reconnaissance Orbiter

The LRO is the first step in NASA's new programme to return to the Moon and extend man's presence in the solar system

The Lunar Reconnaissance Orbiter (LRO) follows in the hallowed footsteps of the Ranger, Lunar Orbiter and Surveyor missions that preceded the Apollo missions, leading to man's first steps on the Moon. Like LRO these missions were designed to allow NASA to test new technologies and closely survey the Moon's surface on the lookout for

suitable landing sites and areas of outstanding scientific interest. Since the LRO signals the start of a new stage in NASA's programme to create a lunar outpost and then take man to Mars, the science and technology required to achieve these goals is light years ahead of those famous missions of the Sixties and Seventies. Here's a breakdown of exactly how the LRO works. ✸

4. Lunar Exploration Neutron Detector (LEND)
LEND will create a map of hydrogen deposits and gather data on the neutron ctomponent of the lunar environment to help find water-ice near the surface

1. Cosmic Ray Telescope for the Effects of Radiation (CRaTER)
CRaTER will test the potential biological impacts of putting man on the Moon for extended periods. This will help NASA create protective technologies to keep the crew safe

5. Lunar Orbiter Laser Altimeter (LOLA)
LOLA will create a 3D map of the Moon to allow NASA to measure and analyse the lunar topography, measure slopes on potential landing sites and determine surface roughness

7. Mini-RF Technology Demonstration (Mini-RF)
The Miniature Radio Frequency Technology Demonstration is an advanced synthetic aperture radar that images the polar regions on the lookout for water ice and demonstrates the ability to communicate with Earth-based stations

6. Lunar Reconnaissance Orbiter Camera (LROC)
LROC is designed to make hi-res images of the Moon. Though these images are black and white and will only shoot around ten per cent of the lunar surface, details just 3.3 feet across will be discernable

3. Lyman-Alpha Mapping Project (LAMP)
An exciting experiment, LAMP will map the entire lunar surface in the ultraviolet spectrum. It'll be central to finding permanently shadowed regions that could contain permafrost

2. Diviner Lunar Radiometer Experiment (DLRE)
LDRE will capture data on the surface (and subsurface) temperatures. As well as discovering ice deposits and potential cold traps it will also be able to spot dangers like rough terrain

Telstar 1

How the world's first active communications satellite worked

Telstar 1 was a collaboration between NASA and American Telephone & Telegraph (AT&T), launched atop a Delta rocket on 10 July 1962. For the first time ever, it provided audio communication and simultaneous video between the USA, Europe and Japan, becoming the first active communications satellite capable of transmitting a signal.

The first passive communications satellite was NASA's 1960 Echo 1 balloon, which bounced signals off its Mylar structure that could be received around the world. Telstar 1 completed one orbit of the Earth in two and a half hours, which meant that it could only

relay signals between two places for up to 40 minutes during each orbit when it was in line with more than one ground station.

Telstar 1 relayed its first public pictures on 23 July 1962, broadcasting images of the Statue of Liberty and the Eiffel Tower. It eventually went out of service on 21 February 1963. The cause of its demise was a series of nuclear bomb tests by the USA and USSR at the height of the Cold War, with the radiation from several explosions energising the Earth's Van Allen Belt and overwhelming Telstar 1's fragile transistors. However, today Telstar 1 remains in orbit around the Earth, the longest orbiting manmade satellite. ✸

Engineers attach a fairing to Telstar 1 to protect it during launch

Ion engines

Positioned at the meeting point of science fiction and reality, ion drives are propelling humanity to the furthest outskirts of the universe

Ion engines generate thrust by forming and then accelerating ions at high speed. This is achieved in a two-stage process, firstly by electron bombardment – enforcing controlled collisions of negatively charged electrons with neutrally charged propellant atoms to form ions – and secondly by accelerating formed ions massively through a multi-aperture grid system out into space.

Ions are atoms or molecules that are electrically charged. Ionisation – the process all ion engines undertake – is the process of electrically charging an atom or molecule by adding or removing electrons. Ions themselves, therefore, can be positive or negative and any gas is considered ionised only when some or all of its atoms or molecules are converted into ions.

In a conventional ion engine – in the example detailed here, a gridded electrostatic ion thruster – propellant fuel (xenon, for example) is injected into the thruster's discharge chamber from its downstream end and then bombarded with electrons flowing from a hollow cathode at its upstream end. The electrons from the cathode are attracted to the discharge chamber's walls, which themselves are lined with high-strength magnets that are charged to a high positive potential by the engine's power supply. These positively charged magnets cause the electrons to be redirected back into the discharge chamber by a high magnetic field, forcing them to collide with the atoms of the propellent and maximising ionisation efficiency.

Xenon atoms

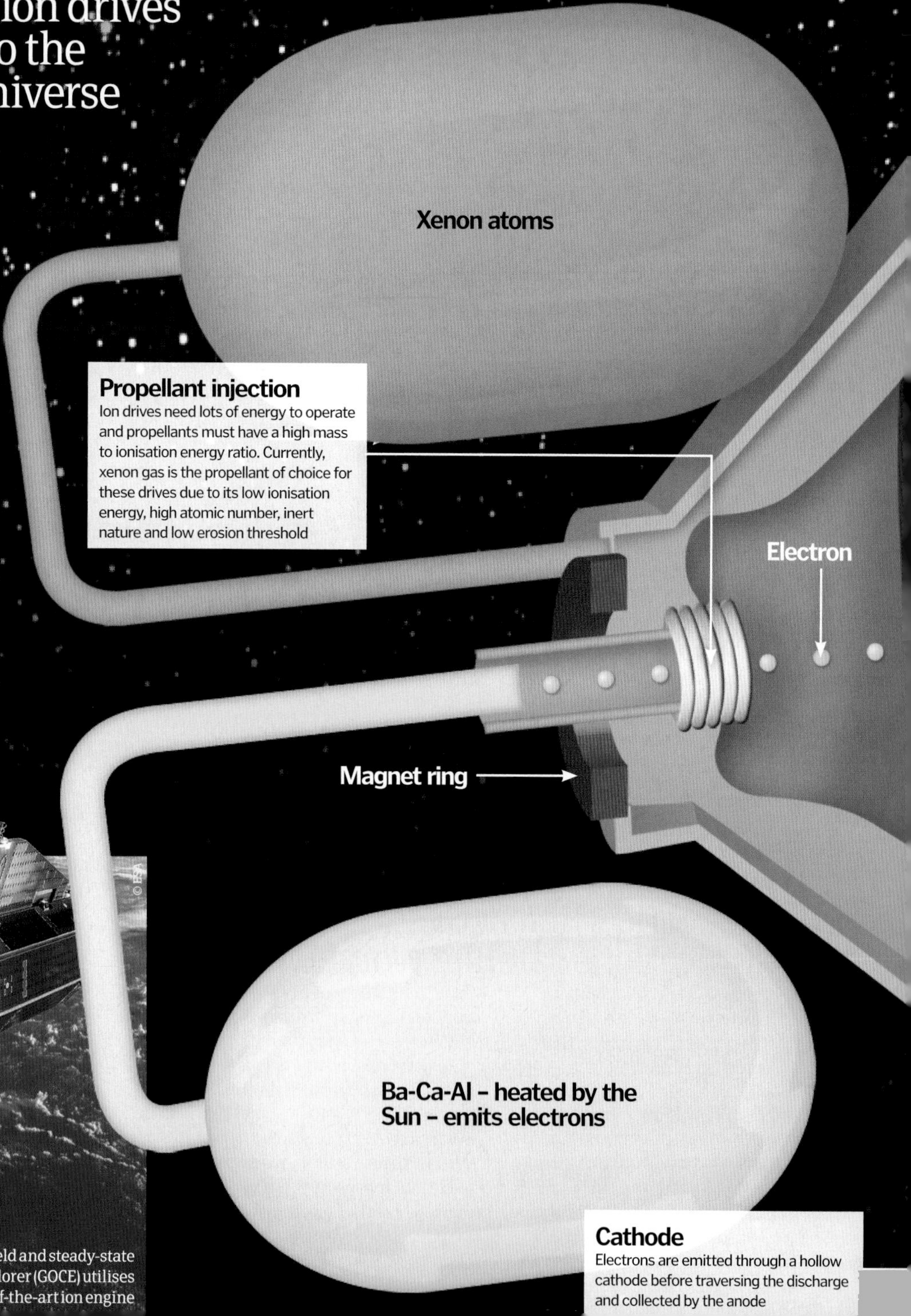

Propellant injection
Ion drives need lots of energy to operate and propellants must have a high mass to ionisation energy ratio. Currently, xenon gas is the propellant of choice for these drives due to its low ionisation energy, high atomic number, inert nature and low erosion threshold

Electron

Magnet ring →

Ba-Ca-Al – heated by the Sun – emits electrons

Cathode
Electrons are emitted through a hollow cathode before traversing the discharge and collected by the anode

The ESA's Gravity field and steady-state Ocean Circulation Explorer (GOCE) utilises a state-of-the-art ion engine

5 TOP FACTS
ION DRIVES

Potential
1 The lowest energy state required to detach an electron from an atom is called its ionisation potential, and can also be known as its ionisation energy.

Thirsty
2 GOCE, the European Space Agency's Earth-orbiting satellite, will consume 40 kilograms of xenon over 20 months simply to power its ion drive.

Pioneer
3 Dr Robert H Goddard, an American physicist and inventor, was the first person to postulate on the possibility of an ion drive all the way back in 1906.

Sci-fi
4 A large number of space crafts in science fiction are powered by ion drives, including the instantly recognisable SS Enterprise of *Star Trek* fame.

Noble
5 Xenon, the primary gas used to power current ion engines, is referred to as a 'noble gas' as it is odourless, colourless and has a very low chemical reactivity.

DID YOU KNOW? An ion is simply an atom or molecule that is electrically charged

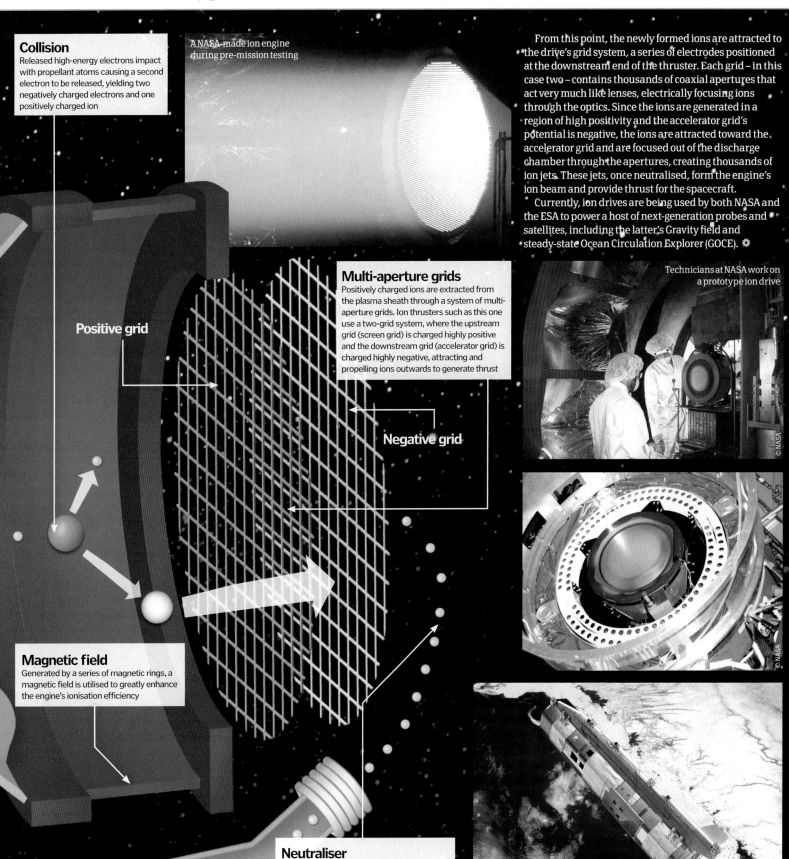

Collision
Released high-energy electrons impact with propellant atoms causing a second electron to be released, yielding two negatively charged electrons and one positively charged ion

A NASA-made ion engine during pre-mission testing

From this point, the newly formed ions are attracted to the drive's grid system, a series of electrodes positioned at the downstream end of the thruster. Each grid – in this case two – contains thousands of coaxial apertures that act very much like lenses, electrically focusing ions through the optics. Since the ions are generated in a region of high positivity and the accelerator grid's potential is negative, the ions are attracted toward the accelerator grid and are focused out of the discharge chamber through the apertures, creating thousands of ion jets. These jets, once neutralised, form the engine's ion beam and provide thrust for the spacecraft.

Currently, ion drives are being used by both NASA and the ESA to power a host of next-generation probes and satellites, including the latter's Gravity field and steady-state Ocean Circulation Explorer (GOCE). ✿

Positive grid

Multi-aperture grids
Positively charged ions are extracted from the plasma sheath through a system of multi-aperture grids. Ion thrusters such as this one use a two-grid system, where the upstream grid (screen grid) is charged highly positive and the downstream grid (accelerator grid) is charged highly negative, attracting and propelling ions outwards to generate thrust

Negative grid

Technicians at NASA work on a prototype ion drive

Magnetic field
Generated by a series of magnetic rings, a magnetic field is utilised to greatly enhance the engine's ionisation efficiency

Neutraliser
Another hollow cathode outside of the main engine injects negatively charged electrons into the positively charged ion beam to ensure neutralisation of the beam, spacecraft and surrounding void

The GOCE's ion drive ejects xenon ions at velocities exceeding 40,000m/s

"The challenge will be keeping the solar sail flat"

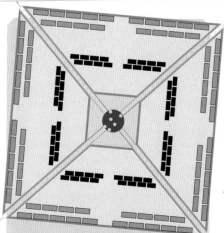

IKAROS solar sail

IKAROS is the first space mission to be propelled by sunlight alone

On 21 May 2010, the Japan Aerospace Exploration Agency (JAXA) launched a new kind of spacecraft. Named IKAROS, short for Interplanetary Kite-craft Accelerated by Radiation of the Sun, this square-shaped craft is propelled through space by using the Sun's energy in two different ways. It is embedded with thin solar cells that store sunlight as electricity, and it also reflects light particles from the Sun. As the light particles bounce off the sail, they should provide the bulk of the momentum that is needed to propel the craft.

IKAROS was launched on an H-IIA rocket from the Tanegashima Space Center on Tanegashima Island in

Japan. The rocket also carried an unmanned Venus probe called Akatsuki and some small satellites. IKAROS will take the same trajectory as Akatsuki, but will pass by Venus and keep going on its way to the Sun.

The solar sail weighs about 315 kilograms in total and cost around £11 million to build and launch. A previous Japanese space organisation, the Institute of Space and Astronautical Science, demonstrated successful deployment of prototype solar sails in 2004, but the propulsion system remains unproven. However, JAXA is confident that IKAROS will reach its ultimate destination. The challenge will be keeping the solar sail flat, stable and orientated correctly to take in enough sunlight. ✿

The IKAROS membrane

The sail is made of four trapezoid-shaped panels of polyimide, a lightweight material about 32 micrometres thick. It is about 20 metres on the diagonal. One side of the sail has an aluminium layer, which reflects sunlight and provides thrust. The sail is embedded with several different components. Silicon solar cells about 25 micrometres thick are attached at points around the centre perimeter of the sail. LCD panels are also arrayed around the sail, which are used to control its attitude, or steer. Dust collectors will take samples of the debris encountered by the sail and relay it to a dust counter on the main body.

© Artists rendition of LightSail-1 by Rick Sternbach. Credit: Planetary Society

IKAROS's competition

An independent non-profit organisation called the Planetary Society has had its own solar sail project in the works. LightSail-1 is based on the NanoSail-D, a former NASA project. The Planetary Society planned to launch LightSail-1 by October 2011, but the launch was dependent on funding and whether rockets were available. Its membranes are made of Mylar and its body comprises several tiny satellites called CubeSats.

© JAXA

5 TOP FACTS
JAXA PROJECTS

Hayabusa
1 Hayabusa was a probe sent to gather samples from asteroid 25143 Itokawa. After numerous glitches, the probe returned to Earth; scientists have not yet opened the sample container.

SELENE
2 The largest lunar mission since NASA's Apollo, SELENE orbited the moon for 20 months. It provided data used to improve topographical and gravity maps.

Akari
3 In 2006, JAXA launched Akari, an infrared astronomy satellite. Its mission is to survey the entire sky in infrared. On 26 August 2007 it had surveyed 94 per cent.

OICETS
4 This experimental satellite was designed to demonstrate optical communications between distant satellites. Launched in 2005, it was retired in 2009.

Yohkoh
5 Launched in 1991, Yohkoh orbited the Sun for over a decade. It made observations via x-ray telescope and provided insight into the behaviour of the Sun's corona.

DID YOU KNOW? *The name is similar to Icarus, a figure in Greek mythology who melted his wings flying too close to the Sun*

IKAROS deployment

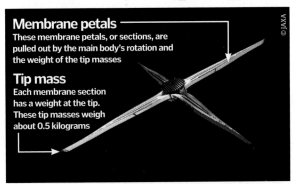

Membrane petals
These membrane petals, or sections, are pulled out by the main body's rotation and the weight of the tip masses

Tip mass
Each membrane section has a weight at the tip. These tip masses weigh about 0.5 kilograms

FIRST STAGE: In this first stage of deployment, actuators in the main body release tip masses. As the sail continues to rotate, the membrane petals emerge and form a cross shape about two and a half minutes after the initial launch.

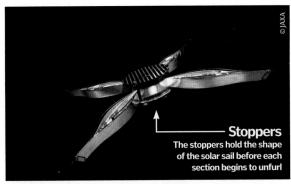

Stoppers
The stoppers hold the shape of the solar sail before each section begins to unfurl

SECOND STAGE: Next, the motor drivers turn to orient stoppers into alignment, and spring hinges release the stoppers to maintain tension and keep the shape of the solar sail. The membrane sections begin to unfurl.

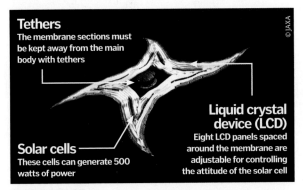

Tethers
The membrane sections must be kept away from the main body with tethers

Liquid crystal device (LCD)
Eight LCD panels spaced around the membrane are adjustable for controlling the attitude of the solar cell

Solar cells
These cells can generate 500 watts of power

THIRD STAGE: The solar sail continues to spin at 25rpm as each membrane section is deployed. The rotation helps to keep the membranes flat.

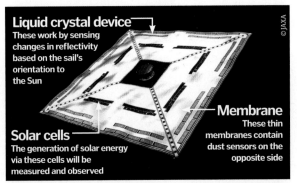

Liquid crystal device
These work by sensing changes in reflectivity based on the sail's orientation to the Sun

Solar cells
The generation of solar energy via these cells will be measured and observed

Membrane
These thin membranes contain dust sensors on the opposite side

DEPLOYMENT COMPLETION: With the membranes fully deployed, the sail spins down to just a few rpms. The sail should now begin generating enough solar power to accelerate.

Central hub

This image focuses on the central hub, or main body of the solar sail. Upon separating from the H-IIA launch rocket, the main body began to spin at about 5rpms, facing the Sun. As it continued on its trajectory, the hub reached 20rpms and communicated with mission control.

Upper deck
The upper deck of the main body contains instrumentation such as the low- and high-gain antennas for communication via X-band and a dust counter

Middle deck
This centre component consists of a drum around which the membrane and all of its components are wound.

Lower deck
The lower deck contains any additional mission instrumentation, including the motor and actuator drivers that power the drum and the two tiny cameras

IKAROS missions and objectives

JAXA hopes IKAROS will deploy and show that power and thrust can be generated using its solar cells. On 10 June 2010 JAXA confirmed the membrane had deployed. IKAROS took a picture of itself and relayed it back to mission control. The solar cells are also generating some power.

Long term, IKAROS will spend six months travelling to Venus, then three years to the far side of the Sun. Spacecraft may one day use solar power for propulsion, cutting down on expensive fuel and allowing for exploration. JAXA hopes to send a larger sail to Jupiter by 2020. IKAROS will investigate and measure space phenomena and gather data on its way past Venus.

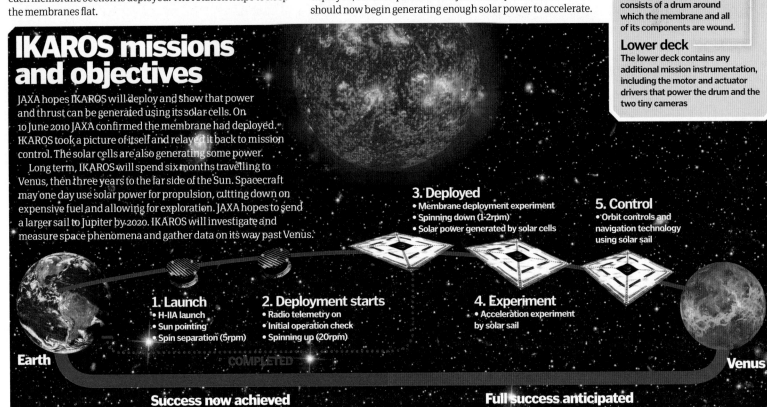

1. Launch
• H-IIA launch
• Sun pointing
• Spin separation (5rpm)

2. Deployment starts
• Radio telemetry on
• Initial operation check
• Spinning up (20rpm)

3. Deployed
• Membrane deployment experiment
• Spinning down (1-2rpm)
• Solar power generated by solar cells

4. Experiment
• Acceleration experiment by solar sail

5. Control
• Orbit controls and navigation technology using solar sail

Earth

COMPLETED

Venus

Success now achieved

Full success anticipated

169

Hundreds of miles above us, an intricate system of machines is hard at work to ensure our everyday lives tick along, from sending us TV shows to providing untold scientific data on the Earth and the universe...

SATELLITES & SPACE JUNK

5 TOP FACTS
HISTORY OF SATELLITES

Sputnik I
1 Russia stunned the world in October 1957 when it announced it had placed the first man-made object in orbit around the Earth, the basketball-sized Sputnik I.

Explorer I
2 America replicated the success of Russia three months later when it launched its first satellite, Explorer I, which discovered the belts of radiation around Earth.

Echo 1
3 NASA launched this giant balloon, 30 metres in diameter, in 1960. It reflected incoming signals and was the world's first rudimentary communications satellite.

Satcom 1
4 Developed by RCA Americom, Satcom 1 (launched 1975) pioneered US cable TV broadcasts with high-profile networks and spurned the age of satellite TV.

ISS
5 Construction of the world's largest man-made satellite began with the launch of the Zarya module in 1998, and is scheduled for completion in mid-2012.

DID YOU KNOW? There are 100 trillion man-made bits and pieces (such as glass shards) in Earth orbit

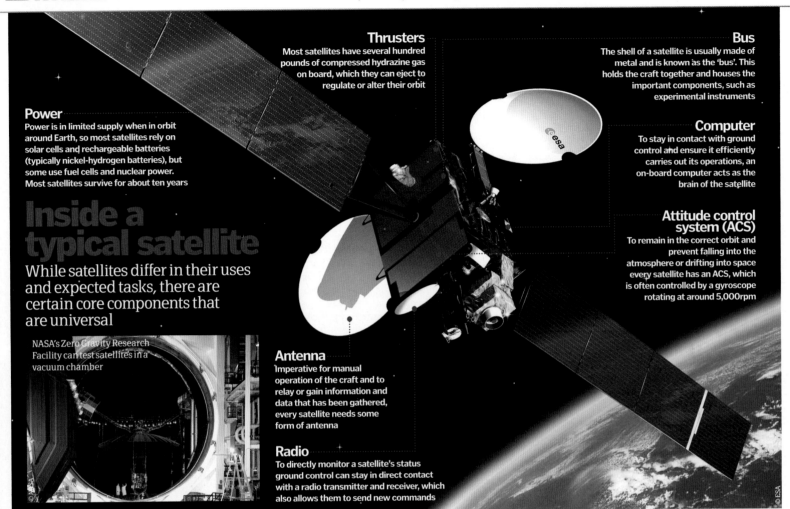

Thrusters
Most satellites have several hundred pounds of compressed hydrazine gas on board, which they can eject to regulate or alter their orbit

Bus
The shell of a satellite is usually made of metal and is known as the 'bus'. This holds the craft together and houses the important components, such as experimental instruments

Power
Power is in limited supply when in orbit around Earth, so most satellites rely on solar cells and rechargeable batteries (typically nickel-hydrogen batteries), but some use fuel cells and nuclear power. Most satellites survive for about ten years

Computer
To stay in contact with ground control and ensure it efficiently carries out its operations, an on-board computer acts as the brain of the satellite

Inside a typical satellite

While satellites differ in their uses and expected tasks, there are certain core components that are universal

NASA's Zero Gravity Research Facility can test satellites in a vacuum chamber

Attitude control system (ACS)
To remain in the correct orbit and prevent falling into the atmosphere or drifting into space every satellite has an ACS, which is often controlled by a gyroscope rotating at around 5,000rpm

Antenna
Imperative for manual operation of the craft and to relay or gain information and data that has been gathered, every satellite needs some form of antenna

Radio
To directly monitor a satellite's status ground control can stay in direct contact with a radio transmitter and receiver, which also allows them to send new commands

Since the launch of the first artificial satellite back in 1957, the Soviet Union's Sputnik I, satellites have really come on in huge leaps and bounds. We use them to call friends, watch television, surf the web and much, much more besides. Today, about 8,500 man-made satellites, both defunct and operational, are in orbit around the Earth. Advances in technology alongside new methods of propulsion have allowed us to study our own world and the universe like never before, and it's all thanks to this extensive network of flying machines.

Isaac Newton first presented the theoretical idea of a satellite orbiting the Earth way back in the 18th Century. He suggested that if a cannonball was fired from a very great height and with a high enough velocity, the ball would fall towards Earth. However, its speed would mean that the ground beneath would continually fall away, leaving the cannonball

encircling the entire planet. This is basically how a satellite operates today.

Typically, satellites orbit the Earth at a speed of between 7,000 and 17,000mph (11,300 to 27,400kph) and are constantly falling towards the ground, but their sideways motion keeps them in orbit above the planet. Often a satellite is pulled towards the planet as a result of other forces, such as atmospheric drag and the gravity of the Moon and the Sun, so it is either left to burn up in the atmosphere or propelled higher with a thruster. In the case of the International Space Station, a spacecraft attaches to the giant satellite and pushes it into a higher orbit, so that it doesn't fall into the atmosphere and burn up. Satellites began use to provide a better service than ground-based facilities. A satellite is visible from large sections of the Earth, thus sending and receiving signals is possible across great distances and at a quicker speed. Observational satellites also have a much clearer view of space,

thanks to the lack of obscurity from clouds and atmospheric particles.

While in orbit, not all satellites follow a circular path; some have erratically elliptical (egg-shaped) motions that enable them to make specific observations of the Earth and surrounding space. The farthest point a satellite is from the Earth is known as the 'apogee', and the nearest point the 'perigee'. Some satellites get as close as just 80 miles from the surface, while some extend as far out as 24,000 miles in their orbit. Typically, reconnaissance and imaging satellites orbit just a few hundred miles from the surface, while some (such as navigation satellites) are thousands of miles away. Some other man-made satellites orbit at the 'Lagrangian L2 point', 1 million miles (1.6 million km) from Earth, but at this distance they are said to orbit the Sun instead.

The closer a satellite is to the Earth, the faster its orbital velocity must be. A satellite at a distance of

Orbital altitudes of major satellites

SPUTNIK-1 215km/133.6mi
ISS 340km/211.3mi
HUBBLE SPACE TELESCOPE 595km/369.7mi
POLAR ORBITING SATELLITES 700-1,700km/435-1,056mi

GPS SATELLITES
20,350km/12,645mi
These are on a semi-synchronous orbit, meaning they orbit the earth every 12 hours

GEO (GEOSYNCHRONOUS) AND GSO (GEOSTATIONARY) SATELLITES 35,786km/22,238mi
These satellites orbit at the same rate as the Earth, remaining stationary over a single line of longitude. They are fixed over a location on the surface, making it easy to target with a dish

LEO zone
Low Earth orbit

MEO zone
Medium Earth orbit

HEO zone →
High Earth orbit

"A satellite gets into orbit by hitching a ride on a rocket"

124 miles (200 km) from the surface must travel at 17,000mph (27,400kph), but for a satellite further away at 22,223 miles (35,786km), such as a geostationary satellite, the speed is much slower at 7,000mph (11,300kph). The higher a satellite is in orbit the longer it can survive, as it is less affected by atmospheric drag from the Earth.

Timing is important when launching a satellite; it needs to be placed in the correct orbit to carry out its intended operations. If it is sent up at the wrong time, it could end up in the wrong orbital path. Therefore, satellites have a specific launch window in which they are able to get into orbit around Earth.

Despite global use by millions of people, the satellite global positioning system (GPS) is serviced by just 24 satellites in orbit around Earth, placed there and run by the US government. This is the minimum number needed to provide the GPS service but, as some of the satellites deteriorate over time, more are added to keep it running. However, there are rival GPS systems in (or soon to be in) operation, such as Russia's GLONASS system (launched in 2007) and the EU's planned Galileo positioning system.

A satellite gets into orbit by hitching a ride on a rocket. Often, one rocket will take multiple satellites into orbit and, once above Earth, each will move into their allocated orbit. Most satellite orbits start out elliptical but, by firing thrusters as the satellite reaches its furthest point from Earth, the orbit can be squashed until it is circular. Despite 8,500 man-made objects orbiting the Earth, there is only one recorded collision in the history of space exploration, when two American and Russian communications satellites collided in 2009. It's possible to obtain this statistic because we know the orbital path of each satellite. When a new satellite is launched, it is placed within a particular orbital band at a given point and at a certain speed to ensure it doesn't come

In this annotated Google Earth map, active satellites are in green and defunct ones in grey

into contact with another man-made object. For example, geostationary satellites orbit in a circular band at 22,223 miles (35,800km) above the surface, with many in a 'satellite parking strip' over the equator. However, the orbit of a satellite isn't perfect, and forces such as the Moon's gravity and the Sun can alter its path. A Tracking Telemetry & Control link (TT&C) allows ground controllers to monitor the status of a satellite and, if it has its own propulsion (often compressed hydrazine), they can change its orbit to prevent a collision. The other factor is how much space there is around the Earth. Satellites orbit in a range of just 100 to over 24,000 miles, while the circumference of their path is thousands of miles. While there are thousands of satellites in orbit, they only make up an incredibly tiny proportion of space.

Once a satellite has exhausted all its fuel (usually after ten years), it is given one last push into either the atmosphere or interstellar space to burn up or drift away from the Earth respectively. Canadian firm MacDonald, Dettwiler and Associates Ltd plans to launch the first space gas station in 2015 that will refuel satellites and prolong their lifetime. ✹

By the numbers

Many countries have sent satellites into orbit around the Earth, but there is a huge amount of space junk consisting mostly of defunct machines. NASA and Russia lead the way considerably in satellite launches, but as the technology becomes cheaper and more private companies become involved, that is sure to change in the future.

United Sta
453 | 683 | 3

Some satellites like the ISS can be repaired on spacewalks

TYPES OF ORBIT

There are three main orbital bands into which a satellite may be placed, but satellites also orbit at varying heights for a variety of purposes

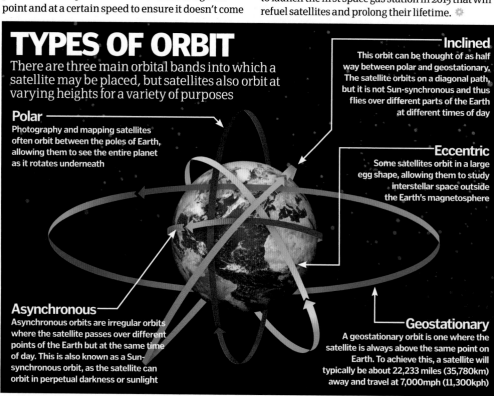

Polar
Photography and mapping satellites often orbit between the poles of Earth, allowing them to see the entire planet as it rotates underneath

Inclined
This orbit can be thought of as half way between polar and geostationary. The satellite orbits on a diagonal path, but it is not Sun-synchronous and thus flies over different parts of the Earth at different times of day

Eccentric
Some satellites orbit in a large egg shape, allowing them to study interstellar space outside the Earth's magnetosphere

Asynchronous
Asynchronous orbits are irregular orbits where the satellite passes over different points of the Earth but at the same time of day. This is also known as a Sun-synchronous orbit, as the satellite can orbit in perpetual darkness or sunlight

Geostationary
A geostationary orbit is one where the satellite is always above the same point on Earth. To achieve this, a satellite will typically be about 22,233 miles (35,780km) away and travel at 7,000mph (11,300kph)

Satellite television

It's something we all take for granted, but how do ou favourite TV shows get beamed to our living room?

Studio/transmitter
Audio and video signals are sent from a TV station to a transmitter, to be relayed up to a satellite orbiting Earth in geostationary orbit

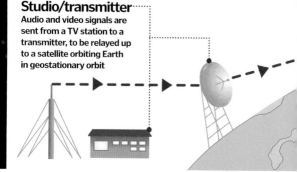

Head to Head
OLDEST SATELLITES

OLD

1. Intelsat 1
Nicknamed 'Early Bird', the first communications satellite to be placed in geostationary orbit has been in orbit since 1965, but is now defunct.

OLDER

2. Telstar 1
Now retired at a ripe old 49 years of age, this satellite relayed the first television pictures through space after its launch in 1962.

OLDEST

3. Vanguard I
In orbit since 17 March 1958, the USA's Vanguard 1 satellite has orbited the Earth over 200,000 times, but is also no longer operational.

DID YOU KNOW? *Geostationary satellites orbit within the Clarke Belt, named after sci-fi writer Arthur C. Clarke*

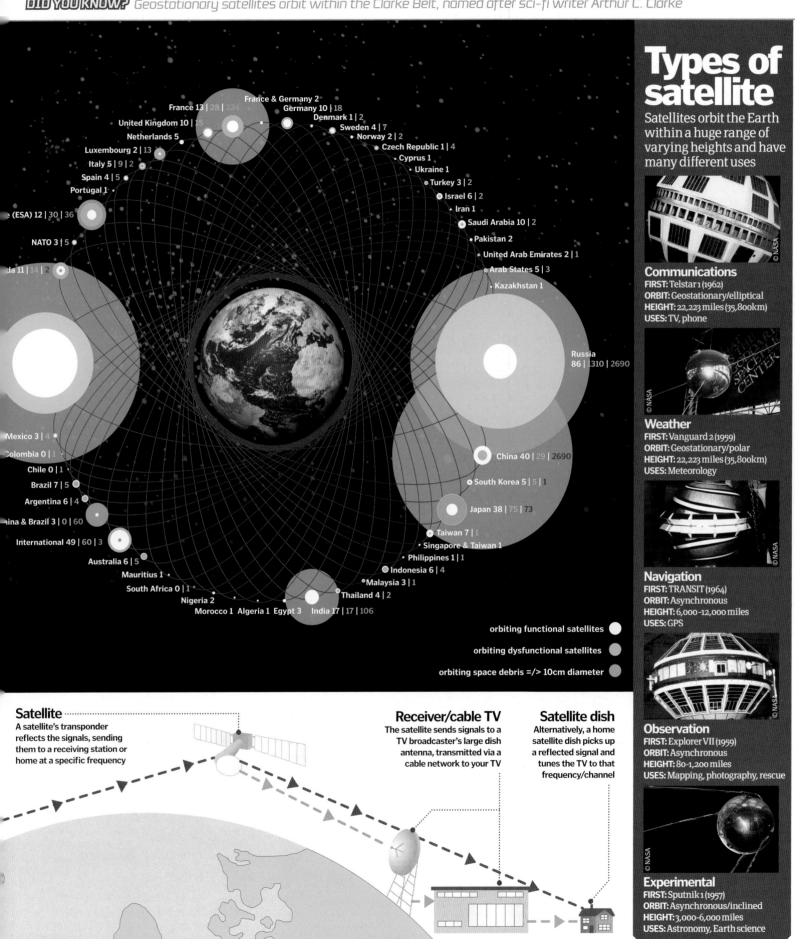

France & Germany 2
France 13 | 28 | 324
Germany 10 | 18
United Kingdom 10 | 15
Denmark 1 | 2
Netherlands 5
Sweden 4 | 7
Luxembourg 2 | 13
Norway 2 | 2
Italy 5 | 9 | 2
Czech Republic 1 | 4
Spain 4 | 5
Cyprus 1
Portugal 1
Ukraine 1
Turkey 3 | 2
e (ESA) 12 | 30 | 36
Israel 6 | 2
Iran 1
NATO 3 | 5
Saudi Arabia 10 | 2
Pakistan 2
United Arab Emirates 2 | 1
da 11 | 14 | 2
Arab States 5 | 3
Kazakhstan 1

Russia
86 | 1310 | 2690

Mexico 3 | 4
Colombia 0 | 1
Chile 0 | 1
China 40 | 29 | 2690
Brazil 7 | 5
South Korea 5 | 5 | 1
Argentina 6 | 4
Japan 38 | 75 | 73
ina & Brazil 3 | 0 | 60
International 49 | 60 | 3
Taiwan 7 | 1
Singapore & Taiwan 1
Australia 6 | 5
Philippines 1 | 1
Mauritius 1
Indonesia 6 | 4
South Africa 0 | 1
Malaysia 3 | 1
Nigeria 2
Thailand 4 | 2
Morocco 1 Algeria 1 Egypt 3 India 17 | 17 | 106

● orbiting functional satellites
● orbiting dysfunctional satellites
● orbiting space debris =/> 10cm diameter

Types of satellite
Satellites orbit the Earth within a huge range of varying heights and have many different uses

Communications
FIRST: Telstar 1 (1962)
ORBIT: Geostationary/elliptical
HEIGHT: 22,223 miles (35,800km)
USES: TV, phone

Weather
FIRST: Vanguard 2 (1959)
ORBIT: Geostationary/polar
HEIGHT: 22,223 miles (35,800km)
USES: Meteorology

Navigation
FIRST: TRANSIT (1964)
ORBIT: Asynchronous
HEIGHT: 6,000-12,000 miles
USES: GPS

Observation
FIRST: Explorer VII (1959)
ORBIT: Asynchronous
HEIGHT: 80-1,200 miles
USES: Mapping, photography, rescue

Experimental
FIRST: Sputnik 1 (1957)
ORBIT: Asynchronous/inclined
HEIGHT: 3,000-6,000 miles
USES: Astronomy, Earth science

Satellite
A satellite's transponder reflects the signals, sending them to a receiving station or home at a specific frequency

Receiver/cable TV
The satellite sends signals to a TV broadcaster's large dish antenna, transmitted via a cable network to your TV

Satellite dish
Alternatively, a home satellite dish picks up a reflected signal and tunes the TV to that frequency/channel

UNIVERSE

188 Planets

186 White dwarf

192
Search for a new Earth

197
Brown dwarf

203
The Milky Way

184
A star is born

10 SPACE MYTHS BUSTED

Sifting the cosmic facts from the cosmic fiction

 What we know about space is analogous to the farthest reaches of the universe any manmade object has probed. In other words, it's an infinitesimally tiny drop of information in a vast ocean of potential knowledge that we'll only ever know – for certain – a tiny fraction of. Luckily, we can fill in all sorts of blanks thanks to theoretical physics and join the dots between what we do know to come up with a likely conclusion. The problem with that is, as it's filtered down from the astrophysicists to those not so clued-in to the cutting-edge discoveries in astronomy, the truth – whether it's an established fact or a theory grounded in scientific evidence – tends to get distorted. That and the fact that Hollywood has never let reality get in the way of a spectacular special effect has done nothing to dispel the galaxy of half-truths and outright fiction dressed up as truth that's been perpetuated ever since man first looked up at the sky. So here are ten of our favourite space myths that we'd like to shed some light on… ✦

TOP FACTS
BLACK HOLES

Sagittarius A*
1 The supermassive black hole at the centre of our galaxy is, for now, only scientific theory, but several celestial bodies in the centre are orbiting nothing – apparently – at thousands of miles per second.

The numbers game
2 Strictly speaking, there are currently 14 confirmed black holes, the closest being Cygnus X-1 which is around 8,000 light years from Earth.

Compression
3 Theoretically, anything can become a black hole as long as it is compressed to zero volume and yield infinite density (known as the Schwarzschild radius).

Dog eat dog
4 What happens when two black holes collide? Most believe that the one with the bigger gravitational force will suck up the other, creating an even bigger black hole.

In the middle
5 At the centre of a black hole reality becomes warped as matter is crushed to infinite density, so essentially space and time as we know them cease to exist.

DID YOU KNOW? *Jim LeBlanc survived a space-like vacuum when a 1965 NASA test went wrong*

I know I won't explode, but I'm still not getting out of this suit...

1 People explode in space

Space is a terrible, empty nothingness that's out to explode our fragile bodies. It's common knowledge that, when exposed to the vacuum of space, our blood will boil and our precious, pressurised internals will seek an exit from the nearest orifice.

THE REALITY

The vacuum of space is deadly, there's no doubt about that. But, actually, your connective tissues do an excellent job of holding everything in place and, thanks to your skin, neither will your blood boil; think about it – if that were the case then no one would be able to climb Everest or sky-dive and survive. You won't immediately freeze either because although the coldest parts of space are just above absolute zero (-273 degrees Celsius/-460 degrees Fahrenheit), there's little matter to transfer your body heat away. So the most immediate problem you will have is breathing: holding your breath prior to entering a vacuum can injure your lungs and, without oxygen, you will quickly black out. Exposure to intense UV radiation will cause serious sunburn too and without sufficient insulation, you will eventually succumb to the cold. Still, it's nice to know that if someone does accidentally eject you from the airlock, you won't pop like a balloon.

4 The Sun is yellow

You have eyes: look up into the daytime sky – though don't look directly at the Sun because it will damage your retinas. You can see it's yellow. Not only that, you know the star at the heart of our solar system is classified a yellow dwarf, so it must be yellow, mustn't it?

THE REALITY

By that same logic then, space must be blue... at least, during the day, until it burnishes an angry red in the evening and then turns black. But it's not and the Sun's natural colour isn't yellow either – it just appears that way because we're seeing it through the filter of the Earth's atmosphere, which absorbs some wavelengths of the Sun's rays. In fact, much like anything that burns at nearly 6,000 degrees Celsius (10,832 degrees Fahrenheit) at its surface, the Sun is white to the human eye and, if we were to look at it through the relative vacuum of space with no filter obscuring it, we'd see its true colour.

Of course the Sun's yellow... or is it?

2 SETI is part of NASA

The National Aeronautics and Space Administration (NASA) sends people to the Moon in rockets, probes the solar system and beyond for its hidden mysteries and has SETI (the Search for Extraterrestrial Intelligence) as a subsidiary institution, constantly scanning the sky for signs of intelligent alien communication.

THE REALITY

While SETI has an agenda that seems to align with some of NASA's goals, they're two completely independent organisations. NASA was formed in 1958 as a response to Russia's launch of the world's first artificial satellite, Sputnik I. NASA is government funded and is typically allocated around one per cent of the annual US federal budget. The SETI Institute, on the other hand, was formed in 1984 and is dedicated to the search for and research of possible intelligent life in the universe. It's financed entirely by private contributions although some of these funds do come from NASA, as the two organisations have a history of collaborating on various projects.

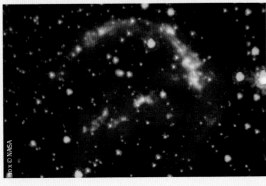

© NASA

If we have to point out the Great Wall in this photo, imagine what it's like from the Moon!

3 The Great Wall is visible from orbit

It's a quiz-master's favourite: which is the only manmade object visible from orbit/space/the Moon? To which we all know the answer: the Great Wall of China. That makes sense too, because it's huge, right?

THE REALITY

The dull reality is that whether the Great Wall of China is visible or not depends on the distance you're viewing from, the atmospheric conditions, whether you're viewing with the naked eye and, of course, if you're orbiting the right part of the world at the time! It's actually only visible with the naked eye in clear daylight, from a maximum low Earth orbit of around 2,000 kilometres (1,240 miles). And as the wall is crumbling in parts and is a similar colour to the land, it's quite hard to pick out. It's certainly not visible with the naked eye from the Moon, as confirmed by Neil Armstrong, who could see continents and lakes during his 1969 lunar walk but no manmade structures.

"Quantum singularities are indeed powerful entities... but they still have to play by the rules of physics"

5 There is a dark side of the Moon

The Moon rotates on its axis proportionally with the rotation of the Earth, so we only ever see one side of it and the far side is in perpetual darkness.

THE REALITY

In fact, that's mostly true. The Moon does indeed spin in proportion with our planet so that we can only ever see exactly the same side of it from Earth. The Sun, however, lights up the bit we can't see as often as the near side of the Moon. During a solar eclipse in particular, the far side gets completely illuminated while the near side to Earth is plunged into darkness. The inset image (right) is of a 68-kilometre (42-mile)-wide crater called Poinsot on the far side of the Moon, clearly lit up by sunlight, taken by the MoonKAM system on the Ebb spacecraft on 15 March 2012. One of the reasons why the 'dark side' myth has been perpetuated may be Pink Floyd's famous album entitled *The Dark Side Of The Moon* released in 1973.

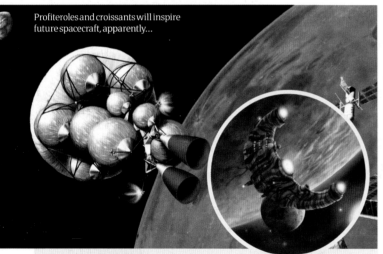

Profiteroles and croissants will inspire future spacecraft, apparently...

7 Space travel will mirror the movies

In the future, we'll walk in spaceships like on Earth, using artificial gravity. We'll view the vastness of space through shielded windows, point the bow to our next star system and brace ourselves for light speed.

THE REALITY

We're busting several space myths for the price of one here, though they're all straight out of television programmes like *Star Trek* and its science-fiction kin. For a start, there's no way of creating Earth-like gravity without something that has the mass of Earth. We can approximate it using centrifugal force, but gravity and mass are strictly proportional. For the same reason, travelling really fast in space will have no g-force effect beyond the rate of your spacecraft's acceleration. Windows are pointless; they're structurally weak compared with a solid bit of hull between you and the void, and it makes no difference what shape the ship is because, for you, up will always be the direction that the ship is thrusting in while it's accelerating. And what about light speed? Well, until we can figure out how to bend the rules governing Einstein's General Theory of Relativity, that will never be possible.

6 Black holes are inescapable

Black holes are the universe's Dysons, vacuuming up everything within an enormous radius and packing it into their mysterious epicentres with a force that even light cannot escape.

THE REALITY

Quantum singularities, the more scientific name by which black holes are known, are indeed powerful entities that help to shape the universe. But they still have to play by the rules of physics, which means that the farther you move away from the event horizon – the critical threshold at which light gets sucked into oblivion – the less force you need to escape the black hole's gravity. Which brings us to our second point: that although black holes appear to break the rules, they can still be explained by physics. So a black hole with the same mass as our Sun will have the same gravitational force as our Sun, otherwise, by now, we may have succumbed to the awesome power of Sagittarius A*, the suspected supermassive black hole at the centre of the Milky Way.

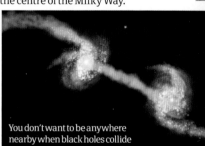

You don't want to be anywhere nearby when black holes collide

Sagittarius A* isn't gradually sucking the Milky Way in, or it would have happened by now

<1/3 OF THE SUN

SMALLEST SINGULARITY
The suspected smallest black hole is less than three times the mass of our Sun and resides in a binary star system (IGR J17091-3624) in the Milky Way.

DID YOU KNOW? Earth was 'seeded' with asteroids bearing life-supporting minerals over 3 billion years ago

8 Asteroid belts are deadly

Asteroid belts, like the one located between Mars and Jupiter, are a near-impenetrable obstacle course of fist-sized to kilometre-wide rocks hurtling chaotically at thousands of miles an hour – a potential minefield for anything traversing them.

THE REALITY

If any one of the probes that NASA has sent to Jupiter and beyond got hit by one of the rocks in the asteroid belt, it would certainly be damaged, if not destroyed. But the myth that's been perpetuated by the likes of *Star Wars* is that this area is jam-packed with asteroids, with scant few metres between them. In reality, though there are millions of hazardous rocks in the main asteroid belt, they have an unbelievable expanse to cross with around 1-3 million kilometres (621,000 to 1.86 million miles) between them. NASA estimated that the odds of a probe passing through the belt accidentally hitting an asteroid was one in a billion, meaning a space probe would have to be extremely unlucky for its trajectory to put it on a collision course.

7x © NASA

9 Auroras are only visible at the poles

Due to the way particles, excited by solar winds, are guided around Earth's magnetic field and focused at the poles, we only ever see auroras at our planet's north and south extremes.

THE REALITY

It's true that auroras are concentrated at the north and south end of a planet, but you won't always be looking north to see the aurora borealis and south to see the aurora australis. They're actually quite uncommon at the geomagnetic poles themselves where only unusual circumstances like a solar storm can cause the aurora to flare. Instead, they occur geographically at 60 and 70 degrees latitude where, in the north, they cut a west-east path across Canada through to Greenland, Scandinavia and Russia. In fact, from northern Alaska, under normal circumstances, you'll have to look south to see the aurora borealis.

Space may look empty, but looks can be deceptive...

10 Space is a vacuum

It's common knowledge that between the planets and gases there's nothing but dead pockets of empty space. No doubt this is at least partly the reason why we suffer explosive decompression when exposed to this 'vacuum of space' (also see space myth number 1).

THE REALITY

Actually, there is something in that space: plasma. Plasma is ionised gas, usually charged by heating or applying a strong magnetic field. It has some similar properties as gas, as with no distinct shape or volume it takes on the form of any container it's in. But unlike gas, it can form structures under the influence of a magnetic field. Because of this, it's considered the fourth state of matter – after solid, liquid and gas – and it actually makes up a massive 99 per cent of the known universe. There's not much of it on Earth, although you can see it in the flame of a candle, in fluorescent lighting and in those funky plasma lamps you can buy. In space though, the plasma is spread so thinly that, on the face of it, it appears to be a vacuum.

> "The bubble, many times smaller than a single proton, contained all matter and radiation in our current universe"

As an elegant explanation of the origins of both atoms and galaxies, the big bang is the ultimate theory of everything

The big bang theory begins with a simple assumption: if the universe is expanding and cooling – something Edwin Hubble and company proved at the beginning of the 20th Century – then it must have once been very small and very hot. From then on, the simple becomes infinitely complex. Big bang theory is nothing less than the summation of everything we've learned about the very big (astrophysics) and the very small (quantum physics) in the history of human thought.

Cosmologists – people who study the origin and evolution of the universe – theorise that 13.7 billion years ago, a bubble formed out of the void. The bubble, many times smaller than a single proton, contained all matter and radiation in our current universe. Propelled by a mysterious outward force, the bubble instantaneously expanded (it didn't explode) by a factor of 1,027, triggering a cosmic domino effect that created the stars, the galaxies and life as we know it. ✿

The Planck era
Time: Zero to 10^{-43} seconds

The Planck era describes the impossibly short passage of time between the absolute beginning of the universe (zero) and 10-43 seconds (10 trillionths of a yoctosecond, if you're counting). In this fraction of an instant, the universe went from infinite density to something called Planck density ($1093g/cm3$), the equivalent of 100 billion galaxies squeezed into the nucleus of an atom. Beyond the Planck density, rules of General Relativity don't apply, so the very dawn of time is still a complete and utter mystery.

ERA

TIME

Inflation era
In the Eighties, cosmologists theorised a period of spontaneous expansion in the very early moments of time. Instantaneously, every point in the universe expanded by a factor of

10^{-36} to 10^{-32} after big bang

1,027. The universe didn't get bigger, it just was bigger. Because the universe got so big, so fast, its naturally spherical shape appeared flat to objects on the surface, solving one of the early problems with big bang theory.

Quark era
After the explosive inflation period, the universe was a dense cauldron of pure energy. Under these conditions, gamma rays of energy collided to briefly form quarks and anti-quarks, the fundamental building blocks of matter. Just as quickly, though, the quarks and anti-quarks collided in a process called annihilation, converting their mass back to pure energy.

10^{-32} to 10^{-12}

Quark

Antiquark

Quark - antiquark pair

X-boson

The big bang

Particle soup
If you turn the heat up high enough, everything melts. When the universe was 10-32 seconds old, it burned at a magnificent 1,000 trillion trillion degrees Celsius. At this remarkable temperature, the tiniest building blocks of matter – quarks and anti-quarks, leptons and anti-leptons – swirled freely in a particle soup called the quark-gluon plasma. Gluon is the invisible 'glue' that carries the strong force, binding quarks into protons and neutrons.

3 TOP FACTS
EVIDENCE FOR THE BIG BANG

Background radiation

1 Cosmic microwave background radiation (CMB) – which fills the universe uniformly – is well explained as the super-cooled afterglow from the original big bang.

Expanding universe

2 Galaxies outside of the Milky Way move away from us at a rate that is proportional to their distance from us, pointing to a continual expansion from a single source.

Big bang nucleosynthesis

3 Big bang theory predicts that the earliest atoms to emerge from the dense particle soup were hydrogen and helium in a 3:1 ratio. Using powerful telescopes and spectrometers, cosmologists confirm that the observed universe is 74 per cent hydrogen, 25 per cent helium and one per cent heavier elements.

DID YOU KNOW? *None of the essential elements of human life (carbon and oxygen) were created during the big bang*

Let there be light

The primordial soup of the early universe was composed of pairs of particles and anti-particles (mostly quarks, anti-quarks, leptons and anti-leptons). Picture this ultra-hot, supercharged environment as the original super collider. Particles and anti-particles smashed together in a process called annihilation, producing beams of photons (light radiation). As more particles collided, more light was generated. Some of those photons reformed into particles, but when the universe finally cooled enough to form stable atoms, the spare photons were set free. The net result: the (observable) universe contains a billion times more light than it does matter.

X-bosons

A funny thing happened at 10-39 second after the beginning of time. The universe produced huge particles called X-bosons (1,015 times more massive than protons). X-bosons are neither matter nor anti-matter and exist only to carry the Grand Unified Force, a combination of the electromagnetic, weak and strong forces that exist today.

The Grand Unified Force drove the early expansion of the universe, but rapid cooling caused X-bosons to decay into protons and anti-protons. For reasons that aren't clear, a billion and one protons were created for every billion anti-protons, creating a tiny net gain of matter. This imbalance, forged during a short blip in time, is the reason for our matter-dominated universe.

Recreating the big bang

CERN's Large Hadron Collider (LHC) is the world's largest particle accelerator. At full power, trillions of protons will travel at near light speed through super-cooled vacuum tubes buried 100 metres below the surface. As the protons smash into each other – at a rate of 600 million collisions per second – they will generate energy 100,000 times hotter than the Sun, a faithful recreation of the cosmic conditions milliseconds after the big bang. Using ultra-sensitive detectors, scientists will scour the debris trails for traces of quarks, leptons and even the Higgs boson, a highly theoretical particle believed to give mass to matter.

A computer simulation of the decay path of a Higgs boson after two protons collide in the LHC

Separation of the Electroweak force

During the Planck era, the four forces of nature were briefly unified: gravity, the strong force, electromagnetism and the weak force. As the Planck era ended as the universe cooled, gravity separated out, then the strong force separated during the inflation. But it wasn't until the end of the Quark era that the universe was cool enough to separate the electromagnetic and weak forces, establishing the physical laws we follow today.

110^{-9} to 10^{-62}

iggs boson (hypothetical)

Photon

Quark-aniquark forming and annihilating

W-boson

ton (hetical)

Decaying X-boson

X-boson decay products (particles and antiparticles)

Antiquark pair

Antineutrino

"72 per cent is dark energy, a bizarre form of matter that works in opposition to gravity"

The origins of matter

Everything in the universe – the galaxies, the stars, the planets, even your big toe – is made of matter. In the beginning (roughly 13.7 billion years ago), matter and radiation were bound together in a superheated, super-dense fog. As the universe cooled and expanded, the first elemental particles emerged: quarks and anti-quarks. As things cooled further, the strong force separated, pulling together clumps of quarks into protons and neutrons, building the first atomic nuclei. Half a million years later, conditions were finally cool enough for nuclei to pull in free electrons, forming the first stable atoms. Small fluctuations in the density of matter distribution led to clusters and clouds of matter that coalesced, over hundreds of millions of years, into the stars and galaxies we explore today.

Dark forces

So what is the universe made of? Well, there is more to the universe than meets the eye. Cosmologists have proven that the visible or 'luminous' portions of the cosmos – the stars, galaxies, quasars and planets – are only a small fraction of the total mass and composition of the universe. Using super-accurate measurements of cosmic microwave background radiation fluctuations, scientists estimate that only 4.6 per cent of the universe is composed of atoms (baryonic matter), 23 per cent is dark matter (invisible and undetectable, but with a gravitational effect on baryonic matter), and 72 per cent is dark energy, a bizarre form of matter that works in opposition to gravity. Many cosmologists believe that dark energy is responsible for the accelerating expansion of the universe, which should be contracting under its own gravitational pull.

Hadron era

When the expanding universe cooled to 1,013K (ten quadrillion degrees Celsius), quarks became stable enough to bond together through the strong force. When three quarks clump together in the right formation, they form hadrons, a type of particle that includes protons and neutrons. Miraculously, every single proton and neutron in the known universe was created during this millisecond of time.

Lepton era

During this comparatively 'long' era, the rapidly expanding universe cools to 109K, allowing for the formation of a new kind of particle called a lepton. Leptons, like quarks, are the near mass-less building blocks of matter. Electrons are a 'flavour' of lepton, as are neutrinos.

Nucleosynthesis era

For 17 glorious minutes, the universe reached the ideal temperature to support nuclear fusion, the process by which protons and neutrons bond together to form atomic nuclei. Only the lightest elements have time to form – 75 per cent hydrogen, 25 per cent helium – before fusion winds down.

10^{-6} to 1 second

1 second to 3 minutes

3 minutes to 20 minutes

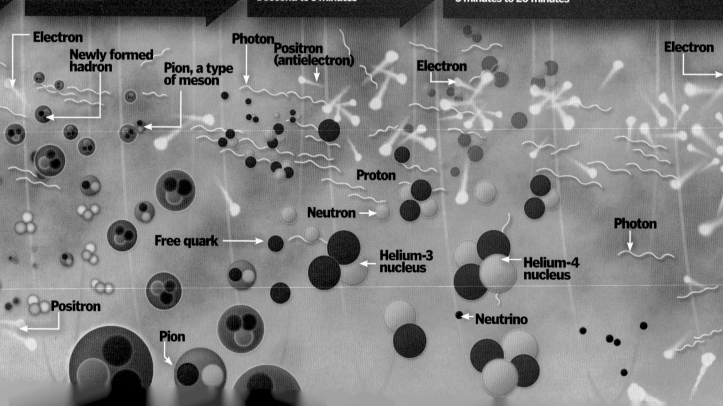

Electron

Newly formed hadron

Pion, a type of meson

Photon

Positron (antielectron)

Electron

Electron

Proton

Neutron

Free quark

Helium-3 nucleus

Helium-4 nucleus

Photon

Positron

Neutrino

Pion

Head to Head Scientists

MOST FAMOUS

1. Albert Einstein
Albert Einstein's revolutionary Theory of General Relativity paved the way for the idea that all matter in the universe was uniformly distributed from a common source.

LESS FAMOUS

2. Edwin Hubble
Edwin Hubble calculated that galaxies moved away from one another at a rate relative to the distance between them, first proving that the universe was expanding.

LEAST FAMOUS

3. Gamow, Alpher & Herman
In the Forties, these three analysed the creation of elements from the big bang's fallout, discovering that only hydrogen and helium could've been produced in large quantities.

DID YOU KNOW? If there were more matter in the universe, its mass would be too great and it would collapse on itself

Cosmic microwave background radiation

The residual heat from the big bang can give us a clue to the origin of the universe

As the universe expands, it also cools. The inconceivable heat released during the big bang has been slowly dissipating as the universe continues its 14 billion-year expansion. Using sensitive satellite equipment, cosmologists can measure the residual heat from the big bang, which exists as cosmic microwave background radiation (CMBR). CMBR is everywhere in the known universe and its temperature is nearly constant (a nippy 2.725K over absolute zero), further proof that the radiation emanated from a single, ancient source.

Minute differences in microwave background radiation levels (+/- 0.0002K) reveal fluctuations in the density of matter in the primitive universe

Opaque era

These are the 'dark ages' of the universe, when light and matter were intertwined in a dense cosmic fog. Photons of light collided constantly with free protons (hydrogen ions), neutrons, electrons and helium nuclei, trapping the light in a thick plasma of particles. It is impossible for cosmologists to 'see' beyond this era, since there is no visible light.

Balance of elements

When the temperature dropped to 10,000K, electrons slowed down enough to be pulled into orbit around atomic nuclei, forming the first stable, neutral atoms of hydrogen, helium and other trace elements. As atoms started to form, photons were freed from the cosmic fog, creating a transparent universe. All cosmic background radiation originated with this 'last scattering' of photons.

Matter era

During the Opaque era, matter and light were stuck together as plasma. Photons of light applied radiation pressure on matter, preventing it from bonding together to form atoms and larger particles. When light and matter 'decoupled', the radiation pressure was released as light, freeing matter to clump and collect in the first clouds of interstellar gas. From there, the first stars were born around 400 million years after the big bang.

20 minutes to 377,000 years

500,000 to the present

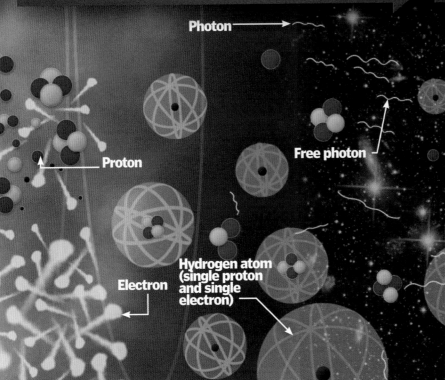

Photon

Helium atom (two protons and two electrons)

Free photon

Proton

Hydrogen atom (single proton and single electron)

Electron

The 'God' particle

We take for granted the idea that if something is made of protons, neutrons and electrons, then it inherently has mass. But cosmologists now believe that no particle has mass simply by merit of its existence. Instead, mass is bestowed on particles as they pass through a Higgs field, a theoretical quantum field named after British physicist Peter Higgs. Imagine the Higgs field as a bowl of honey and quantum particles as a string of pearls. As you drag the pearls through the honey, they are imbued with mass. Every quantum field has a fundamental particle, and the particle associated with Higgs field is the Higgs boson. One of the goals of the Large Hadron Collider at CERN is to prove the existence of the elusive

"The Sun, a type G yellow-white star with a radius of 700,000 kilometres and a temperature of 6,000 kelvin"

A star is b

There may be as many as 10 billion trillion stars in the 100 billion galaxies throughout the universe, but "only" about 100 billion in our galaxy, the Milky Way. Most stars comprise plasma, helium and hydrogen. They form when giant molecular clouds (GMCs), also known as star nurseries, experience a gravitational collapse. This increase in pressure and temperature forces fragments into a body known as a protostar. Over the course of its life, a typical star goes through continuous nuclear fusion in its core. The energy released by this fusion makes the star glow.

Stars are classified according to the Hertzsprung-Russell Diagram, which lists their colour, temperature, mass, radius, luminosity and spectra (which elements they absorb). There are three main types of star: those above, below and on the main sequence. Within these types, there are seven different classifications. We're most familiar with the main sequence star that we call the Sun, a type G yellow-white star with a radius of 700,000 kilometres and a temperature of 6,000 kelvin. However, some stars above the main sequence are more than a thousand times larger than the Sun, while those below the main sequence can have a radius of just a few kilometres. ✿

LOW-MASS STARS

Red dwarf

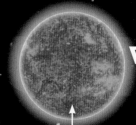

The cool star
Red dwarfs are small and relatively cool stars, which while being large in number tend to have a mass of less than one-half that of our Sun. The heat generated by a red dwarf occurs at a slow rate through the nuclear fusion of hydrogen into helium within its core, before being transported via convection to its surface. In addition, due to their low mass red dwarfs tend to have elongated life spans, exceeding that of stars like our Sun by billions of years.

Giant molecular cloud

Proto-stars

SUN-LIKE STARS

Red giant

A star explodes
If a star has enough mass to become a supergiant, it will supernova instead of becoming a white dwarf. As nuclear fusion ends in the core of a supergiant, the loss of energy can trigger a sudden gravitational collapse. Dust and gas from the star's outer layers hurtle through space at up to 30,000 kilometres per second.

Almost a star
A protostar is a ball-shaped mass in the early stages of becoming a star. It's irregularly shaped and contains dust as well as gas, formed during the collapse of a giant molecular cloud. The protostar stage in a star's life cycle can last for a hundred thousand years as it continues to heat and become denser.

Brown dwarf

HIGH-MASS STARS

Star or planet?
A brown dwarf is sometimes not even considered a star at all, but instead a sub-stellar body. They are incredibly small in relation to other types of stars, and never attained a high enough temperature, mass or enough pressure at its core for nuclear fusion to actually occur. It is below the main sequence on the Hertzsprung-Russell Diagram. Brown dwarfs have a radius about the size of Jupiter, and are sometimes difficult to distinguish from gaseous planets because of their size and make-up (helium and hydrogen).

The rarest star
Supergiants are among the rarest types of stars, and can be as large as our entire solar system. Supergiants can also be tens of thousands of times brighter than the Sun and have radii of up to a thousand times that of the Sun. Supergiants are above the main sequence on the Hertzsprung-Russell Diagram, occurring when the hydrogen of main sequence stars like the Sun has been depleted.

Head to Head
TYPES OF STAR

NEAREST

1. Proxima Centauri
Other than our Sun, the closest star to Earth is Proxima Centauri. It is about four light-years from the Sun.

LARGEST
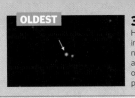
2. VY Canis Majoris
The largest known star, VY Canis Majoris, has a radius of between 1,800 and 2,100 times that of the Sun.

OLDEST
3. HE0107-5240
HE0107-5240, a giant star in the Milky Way, may be nearly as old as our universe at about 13.2 billion years old. It could've once been part of a binary star system.

DID YOU KNOW? A star may have a life cycle of millions to trillions of years. The larger the star is, the shorter its life cycle

om

Compared to other stars, the Sun is in the middle of the pack when it comes to size and temperature

Only gas pressure counter-balances gravity

Star starts to collapse as hydrogen is used up

Star continues to collapse as no helium burning occurs

Small, dim star gradually fades

Black dwarf

Catch a dying star
White dwarfs are considered the final phase in a star's life cycle unless it attained enough mass to supernova (and more than 95 percent of stars don't). The cores of white dwarfs typically comprise carbon and oxygen, left over after the gas is used up during nuclear fusion and occurring after a main sequence star has gone through its giant phase. A white dwarf is small, with a volume comparable to that of Earth's, but incredibly dense, with a mass about that of the Sun's. With no energy left, a white dwarf is dim and cool in comparison to larger types of stars.

The stellar remnant
Black dwarfs are the hypothetical next stage of star degeneration after the white dwarf stage, when they become sufficiently cool to no longer emit any heat or light. Because the time required for a white dwarf to reach this state is postulated to be longer than the current age of the universe, none are expected to exist yet. If one were to exist it would be, by its own definition, difficult to locate and image due to the lack of emitted radiation.

White dwarf

Black dwarf

Beyond the supernova
A hypernova is a supernova taken to an even larger degree. Supergiant stars with masses that are more than 100 times that of the Sun are thought to have these massive explosions. If a supergiant were close to Earth and exploded into a hypernova, the resulting radiation could lead to a mass extinction.

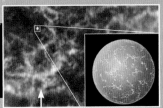

Neutron star

All Images © NASA

Super giant

Super-novae

The neutron dance
Neutron stars are a potential next stage in the life cycle of a star. If the mass that remains after a supernova is up to three times that of the Sun, it becomes a neutron star. This means that the star only consists of neutrons, particles that don't carry an electrical charge.

The absence of light
Stellar black holes are thought to be the end of the life cycle for supergiant stars with masses more than three times that of our Sun. After supernova, some of these stars leave remnants so heavy that they continue to remain gravitationally unstable.

Hypernovae

Black hole

All images courtesy of NASA

A composite shot of a Type Ia supernova, formed when a white dwarf accretes mass from neighbouring stars and explodes

A shot of white dwarf Sirius B from NASA's Hubble Space Telescope

White dwarfs

With a mass comparable to the Sun, white dwarfs are an intriguing space phenomenon

White dwarfs are small stars in the last throes of their life span, degenerate plasma centres of matter that are no longer creating energy through nuclear fusion. To understand how a star enters its white dwarf state, it is best to chart its progress from birth.

Stars are formed when clouds of space dust build in knots under internal turbulence to the point in which they collapse under their own gravitational attraction. As the cloud collapses a dense, hot core is formed which continues to collect dust and gas before turning into the heart of a protostar. Over millions of years this star continues to gather material and mass before entering its main sequencing stage where it fuels its expansion by the nuclear fusion of hydrogen into helium within its core. This is the main stage of any star (the stage our Sun is presently in) and is when the star is most stable, fusing hydrogen into helium while transferring heat outwards via radiation.

After billions of years hydrogen reserves within the core run out, slowing fusion and causing a massive reduction in energy. This lack of energy stops the star from pushing its multiple layers outwards and, under the force of gravity, slowly starts to collapse upon itself. Under this increased pressure the central temperature of the star rises to a critical point where helium, stored internally from the hydrogen fusion, starts to fuse together in the core, creating carbon and oxygen. Due to this increased core temperature the force of expelled radiation becomes so great that it forces the star's photosphere outward by a colossal distance, turning it into a red giant, and then due to the now weak gravitational pull on the outer layers, causes colossal mass loss to stellar winds.

After the star has exhausted its helium supplies and lost its outer layers, it enters the white dwarf stage. With no fuel left to burn in its core and the pressure of outbound radiation reducing, the star is compressed by gravity continuously, becoming denser and denser to the point where its very electrons become smashed together. Finally, the compression of these electrons cause every energy level available within the individual atoms to be filled and are left with nowhere else to go, stabilising the newly formed white dwarf. The dwarf is now comparable to Earth in volume and our Sun in density, with only two courses of action left – slowly dissipate any remaining energy until all that remains is an inert lump of astronomically dense matter, or continue to collect mass from a companion star pushing itself over critical mass and explode in a Type Ia supernova. ✿

Image courtesy of NASA

WASP-12b is a super-hot, super-fast planet

Is this the hottest planet in space?

WASP-12b is one of the fastest orbiting, hottest planets we've found

Of all the strange anomalies we have discovered in the known universe, one of the strangest is the planet WASP-12b. Orbiting just .002 astronomical units from its sun (one astronomical unit is the distance between our Sun and the Earth), the aptly named WASP-12b (and the very recently discovered WASP-18b) is so large, moving so fast, and is so hot – at about 2,250°C – that it should probably be a star, says Patricia Reiff, the director of the Rice Space Institute in Houston. Most 'hot Jupiter' planets that mimic the gaseous giant in our solar system are much farther out in the solar system. WASP-12b is located about 800 light years from Earth, so we can only get a faint picture of why it has not turned into a small rock by now.

Interestingly, most planets this hot and this fast do become stars even while in orbit or just boil off into nothing. ✿

Light years

The distance light travels in a year

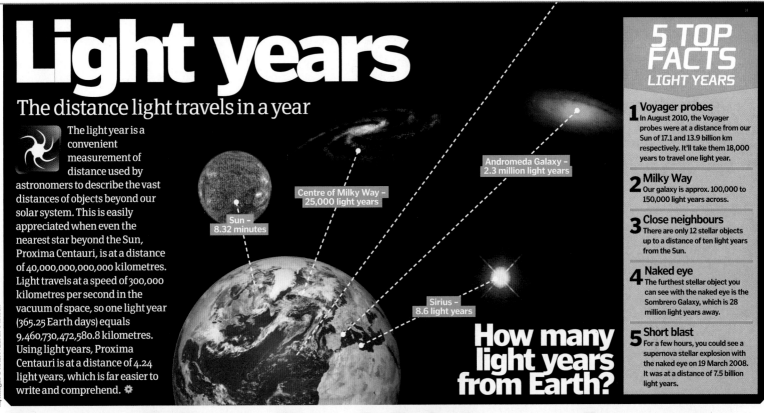

The light year is a convenient measurement of distance used by astronomers to describe the vast distances of objects beyond our solar system. This is easily appreciated when even the nearest star beyond the Sun, Proxima Centauri, is at a distance of 40,000,000,000,000 kilometres. Light travels at a speed of 300,000 kilometres per second in the vacuum of space, so one light year (365.25 Earth days) equals 9,460,730,472,580.8 kilometres. Using light years, Proxima Centauri is at a distance of 4.24 light years, which is far easier to write and comprehend. ✿

Sun – 8.32 minutes

Centre of Milky Way – 25,000 light years

Andromeda Galaxy – 2.3 million light years

Sirius – 8.6 light years

How many light years from Earth?

5 TOP FACTS LIGHT YEARS

1 **Voyager probes**
In August 2010, the Voyager probes were at a distance from our Sun of 17.1 and 13.9 billion km respectively. It'll take them 18,000 years to travel one light year.

2 **Milky Way**
Our galaxy is approx. 100,000 to 150,000 light years across.

3 **Close neighbours**
There are only 12 stellar objects up to a distance of ten light years from the Sun.

4 **Naked eye**
The furthest stellar object you can see with the naked eye is the Sombrero Galaxy, which is 28 million light years away.

5 **Short blast**
For a few hours, you could see a supernova stellar explosion with the naked eye on 19 March 2008. It was at a distance of 7.5 billion light years.

Searching for hidden planets

How bending light can reveal hidden worlds

It's been over 80 years since Einstein first published his general theory of relativity and he's still making headlines. Astronomers are now using a central tenet of Einstein's revolutionary theory – that massive objects like stars and galaxies can bend the fabric of space-time – to create celestial magnifying glasses called gravitational lenses.

Here's how it works. Using Einstein's theory, scientists proved that light travelling toward Earth from a distant star bends slightly as it passes by the Sun. The bending effect is almost imperceptible

because the Sun doesn't contain tremendous amounts of mass.

But imagine if an entire galaxy sat between the Earth and a far-off star. The mass of the galaxy cluster would act like a thick lens, bending and warping the light as it passed. To someone on Earth, the effect would be multiple images of the star, or in some cases, a glowing halo called an 'Einstein ring'.

To discover one of farthest 'extrasolar' planets – a planet 15,000 light years from our solar system – astronomers have used a version of a gravitational lens. In this case, astronomers used a nearby star as a

'lensing star' to bend the light of a distant source star. They chose the lensing star because of its size and its likelihood to have orbiting planets.

What they observed was remarkable. When the source star aligned behind the lensing star, the astronomers observed a double image of the source star. Then they witnessed two sudden spikes in the brightness of the double images. The spikes, they deduced, were caused by the gravitational pull of an unseen planet orbiting the lensing star. Powerful gravitational lenses also act as magnifying glasses, detecting faint light from distant sources. ✿

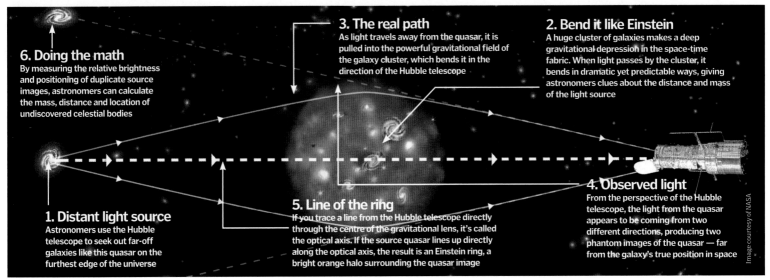

6. Doing the math
By measuring the relative brightness and positioning of duplicate source images, astronomers can calculate the mass, distance and location of undiscovered celestial bodies

3. The real path
As light travels away from the quasar, it is pulled into the powerful gravitational field of the galaxy cluster, which bends it in the direction of the Hubble telescope

2. Bend it like Einstein
A huge cluster of galaxies makes a deep gravitational depression in the space-time fabric. When light passes by the cluster, it bends in dramatic yet predictable ways, giving astronomers clues about the distance and mass of the light source

1. Distant light source
Astronomers use the Hubble telescope to seek out far-off galaxies like this quasar on the furthest edge of the universe

5. Line of the ring
If you trace a line from the Hubble telescope directly through the centre of the gravitational lens, it's called the optical axis. If the source quasar lines up directly along the optical axis, the result is an Einstein ring, a bright orange halo surrounding the quasar image

4. Observed light
From the perspective of the Hubble telescope, the light from the quasar appears to be coming from two different directions, producing two phantom images of the quasar — far from the galaxy's true position in space

Planets

Today, we know of several hundred planets throughout the universe, from fiery rocky worlds to gas giants bigger than Jupiter, but there are many billions more just waiting to be discovered. What do we know so far, and what might we find in the future? Read on to find out

 The definition and classification of planets has been the cause of debate for many years. You may recall one controversy in 2006 when Pluto, previously the ninth planet of the solar system, was stripped of its 'true' planet status, and demoted to a dwarf planet, sending the astronomical and scientific communities into an uproar. But just why was this reclassification necessary, and what exactly is a planet? You're about to find out.

The word 'planet' derives from the Greek word 'planetes', or 'wanderer', named because of their apparent motion across the sky relative to the stars. A planet is a celestial body that orbits a parent star, and is larger than an asteroid but smaller than a star. Planets are differentiated from stars by not being able to radiate energy through nuclear fusion, instead 'powered' by a core composed of metal and other elements.

There are a number of boxes a body must tick in order to be classified as a planet. For starters, its mass and gravity must be large enough to have squashed it into a sphere through its own rotation and interaction with other bodies. Asteroids and comets do not possess enough mass for this to occur, and thus they are often seen to have irregular shapes, while planets are almost spherical in appearance, with a slight bulge around their equator due to their rotation. It is loosely agreed that for this to occur, a planet must be bigger than the largest known asteroid, Ceres, which is

USA

1. Kepler
NASA's Kepler telescope, which is in orbit around Earth, has found over 1,200 planetary candidates to date since its launch in 2009.

FRANCE

2. COROT
The French Space Agency's COROT mission has confirmed the discovery of dozens of planets, and found hundreds more candidates since the mission began in 2007.

CANADA

3. MOST
Canada's only space telescope, MOST is the first spacecraft to deal in asteroseismology, observing variations in stars to find planets.

DID YOU KNOW? As of September 2011, over 600 celestial bodies have been found, classed and verified as planets

1. Nebula
A spinning solar nebula many times larger than the final planetary system forms, with a temperature of about -230°C (-382°F)

2. Condensed
Gravitational forces condense the nebula into a region called a protosun, with a diffuse outside region called the 'protoplanetary disc' forming

3. Spin
The continued spin of this dense protosun forces the dust and gas to flatten into a disc. The spin speed increases, eventually giving the planets their orbital periods, but also causing collisions

4. Rings
The disc is not uniform, and thus regions of different density arise, ultimately forming rings

5. Planetesimals
The accretion of dust and gas within the dense rings causes planetesimals – small clumps of rock and/or ice – to form. They are several kilometres in diameter, and have enough mass to attract more and more material in a runaway process. Many planetesimals progress to a protoplanet phase, where they become moon-sized bodies that experience dramatic collisions with other cosmic bodies

9. Hot
Hot planets such as Venus formed in a molten state because they experienced so many high-energy collisions, but they later cooled and solidified

8. Terrestrial
Near the protostar it is very hot. Thus, only rock and metal can survive, leading to the formation of terrestrial (rocky) planets with a metal core

7. Star
The central region's protostar forms into an actual star around the same time as the formation of the gas giants

11. Blown away
The now-active star blows away the remaining dust and gas from the planetary system with its radiation. The only remaining objects other than the planets are asteroids (rocks) and comets (rock/ice) that failed to form planets

10. Gas giants
In the outer rings where it is cooler, the ice survives, and the planets form from rock and ice. They attract gas from the edges of the disc, which surrounds their cores with a dense atmosphere, and then form into gas giants

Planet formation
The nebular hypothesis, explained here, is currently the preferred idea as to how the planets formed. Most planetary systems discovered so far appear to have undergone this process, including our own solar system

6. Planets
The planetesimals accrete matter in their vicinity, including each other, for tens of millions of years, and eventually form planets orbiting in the now-cleared rings around the protosun

All Images © NASA

measured at roughly 1,000 kilometres (600 miles) across (although Ceres has been reclassified as a dwarf planet).

Next, a body must be in orbit around a parent star to be considered a planet, and must itself not be a satellite of another planet. For example, while the Moon can be said to be in orbit around both the Sun and the Earth, its motion is largely determined and regulated by the latter. Thus, it is not a planet. Similarly, Pluto was found to be directly under the influence of Neptune. In fact, Neptune accounts for more than two thirds of Pluto's motion, orbit and rotation.

Finally, a planet must have cleared or accumulated all debris in its vicinity, either causing it to form a moon through its gravitational forces, or adding it to its own structure. In other words, the planet must 'dominate' its orbital zone. For example, Jupiter has its own Jovian system, consisting of moons and asteroids in its orbital band around the Sun. Its mass is many thousand times more than that of nearby celestial bodies, and it has accumulated debris in the form of rings encircling the planet.

It is on this characteristic that Pluto predominantly failed. It orbits in and around the Kuiper asteroid belt, but has not cleared or accumulated debris in its vicinity, namely other asteroids.

Thus, it is now classed as a dwarf planet, or 'plutoid', with the latter term denoting a dwarf planet that is beyond the orbit of Neptune.

Another reason for the reclassification of Pluto was that many bodies of a similar size were found in the solar system, but they had not been considered planets. One such body that would prove to be a game changer was Xena, later to be known as Eris. It was larger than Pluto, and was briefly regarded as the

"To be a dwarf planet, an object must meet two of three conditions of being a planet"

tenth planet of the solar system before the International Astronomical Union (IAU) changed its classification of a planet in 2006 to include a new category: dwarf planets.

To be a dwarf planet, an object must meet two of the three conditions of being a regular planet. It must be in orbit around a star and it must be spherical in shape. However, a dwarf planet has not cleared its neighbourhood, and it also cannot be the moon of another planet. For example, Charon, which has a body more than half the size of Pluto, would be classified as a dwarf planet if it were not in orbit of Pluto, and thus is regarded as a moon. So far, no dwarf planets have been found outside the solar system, as they are too small for modern telescopes to find. The smallest extrasolar planet discovered to date, Kepler -10 b, is roughly 1.4 times the size of Earth.

Finding planets outside the solar system is no easy feat. Indeed, the first was not discovered until the Nineties. Extrasolar planets, as they are known, are too distant to be directly observed by telescopes on Earth or in space, so instead the relative luminosity of a star is measured to determine if another body, such as a planet, is in orbit. If the observed luminosity of a distant star regularly dims, then the motion of a planet across its plane can be measured. In addition, noting the gravitational effects a planet has on its host star can also enable astronomers to determine many of the planet's characteristics, including its rotation, composition, temperature and orbital distance.

Planet hunting is a very new area of astronomy that is still in its infancy. There are billions of worlds just waiting to be found, and it's likely that some will be unlike anything we've seen before, such as the planet found 4,000 light years away in August 2011 composed entirely of carbon, resembling a giant diamond. As Earth and space telescopes get more and more powerful, it's likely that we'll find other fascinating planets like this that break our preconceptions about the structure, size and appearance of planets. ❁

Amazing planets

Hottest, coldest, largest, oldest... We take a look at the greatest planets of the universe discovered so far

Most Earth-like
Gliese 581 g

Informally known as Zarmina, Gliese 581 g has three to four times the mass of Earth, is no more than 1.4 times the size, and orbits its host red dwarf star, Gliese 581, in just under 37 days. It is located 20 light years from Earth in the Libra constellation. The honour of most Earth-like planet was previously held by Gliese 581 d, located in the same planetary system as Gliese 581 g, until the latter was discovered in 2010. Observations indicate that Zarmina is a rocky planet with enough mass to hold on to an atmosphere, in addition to possessing a solid surface. It is located within the habitable zone of its host star – the region around any star where a planet could possess liquid water, and possibly life.

Locked
Gliese 581 g is tidally locked to its host star, meaning that one side always faces towards it, much like the same side of the Moon always faces Earth

Hot and cold
Due to the tidal locking, one side of the planet is scorching hot, while the other is freezing cold. The average temperature at the boundary of hot and cold is somewhere in the region of -20°C (-4°F)

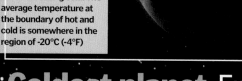

Coldest planet Eris

The coldest planet that we currently know of in the universe is the dwarf planet Eris (known as Xena until September 2006), located in the Kuiper asteroid belt on the outer edges of our solar system. Eris is roughly 27 per cent bigger than Pluto, and is the farthest planet found to be orbiting the Sun, three times further than Pluto at a distance of 16 billion kilometres (10 billion miles). However, in its 560-year orbit, it moves between 38 and 97 AU, which directly affects its surface temperature. Eris is currently at its furthest distance from the Sun, and thus also its coldest temperature – as low as -250°C (-418°F). At this temperature, its atmosphere is frozen solid.

In 280 years, Eris will be at its closest point to the Sun, when its temperature will rise to a 'mild' -218°C (-360°F).

While Eris is the coldest known planet, it's likely that there are colder planets elsewhere in the universe. Some scientists predict that there are rogue planets unattached to stars wandering through the universe. If this is true, then these could be similar in temperature to the universe itself; about -270°C (2.7 Kelvin).

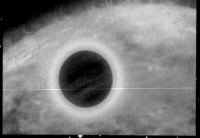

Hottest planet
WASP-33 b

This planet, 1.4 times the size of Jupiter and almost 4.5 times its mass, is located 380 light years from Earth in the Andromeda constellation. It is 35 times closer to its parent star than the Earth is to the Sun, or in other terms it orbits at a distance just seven per cent that of our solar system's innermost planet, Mercury, and completes one orbit every 29 hours. While the Sun has a surface temperature of 5,600°C, WASP-33 b's parent star is a scorching 7,160°C, giving the planet a blistering temperature of 3,200°C. That's seven times hotter than the warmest planet in our solar system, Venus.

Gliese 581

© National Science Foundation

Earth

DID YOU KNOW? One AU (astronomical unit) is the distance from the Sun to the Earth; roughly 150 million kilometres

Oldest planet PSR B1620-26 b

You might want to remember this ancient planet by one of its unofficial names, either Methuselah or the Genesis planet. At 12.7 billion years old, nearly three times the age of Earth, Methuselah is the oldest planet yet discovered in the universe, and suggests that planets formed very soon after the Big Bang 13.7 billion years ago. This bodes well for planet hunters, as if planets formed this early then there could be millions or even billions more spread throughout the universe. Methuselah orbits two stars, one a pulsar and the other a white dwarf, known as a circumbinary orbit. It's 12,400 light years from Earth in the Scorpius constellation and has a mass 2.5 times that of Jupiter.

Orbit
Methuselah orbits a white dwarf, as well as a pulsar that rotates at 100 times per second

Biggest planet WASP-17 b

Located in the Scorpius constellation 1,000 light years from Earth, WASP-17 b is the largest planet discovered in the universe thus far. It's twice the size of Jupiter, but only half its mass, making it 'fluffy' in appearance and structure. Currently, it is believed that the larger a planet is above the size of Jupiter, the lower its mass will become. This is because a planet with both a mass and size greater than Jupiter would not be able to support itself. If both were significantly greater – by around 15 times – the body would likely form a star instead of a planet.

Two American astronomers, John Matese and Daniel Whitmire of the University of Louisiana at Lafayette, assert that there is a planet hidden in the Oort Cloud of our solar system that is four times the mass of Jupiter, provisionally named Tyche. Although it has not been observed, Matese and Whitmire point to the highly elliptical orbits of comets that suggest they are influenced by another body in the solar system, namely the hidden theoretical gas giant Tyche. Many astronomers remain sceptical of this view, however.

Size comparison
WASP-17 b is twice the size of Jupiter, but only half its mass

TYPES OF PLANET

The study of extrasolar planets is a very new area of astronomy, one that is barely 20 years old. As such, the classification of planets is still in its early stages, and for now, extrasolar planets are categorised in a similar manner to the planets of our own solar system; namely, they are defined as either terrestrial or gas giant planets, while dwarf planets are limited to our own solar system. It is likely that future planetary discoveries may require further reclassification of the planets into more clearly defined categories, such as mostly silicon, carbon or water worlds.

Although a dwarf planet is not technically a planet, we include them here as their formation and structure are largely similar to 'true' planets.

Terrestrial

Terrestrial planets like Earth, Mars and Gliese 581 g are rocky planets with metal cores and high densities. They have solid surfaces and can vary in temperature, although they tend to be warmer than gas giants. They are smaller than gas giants due to their high densities, and have slower rotation periods. In addition, their smaller size means they are less likely to have moons than gas giants. Indeed, in our solar system, only Earth (one) and Mars (two) have moons; Venus and Mercury have more.

Example: Earth

Gas giant

These large, gaseous planets form further out from their parent stars than terrestrial planets. At a further distance from their orbiting star, they are able to accrete more matter in their formation, giving them a large size and mass. For example, Jupiter is 11 times larger than Earth, and has a volume 1,000 times greater. They have a low density, but high speed of rotation, and are often encircled by rings because they have gathered a lot of material.

Example: Jupiter

Dwarf planet

These are larger than asteroids but smaller than 'true' planets. The difference between an asteroid and a dwarf planet comes down to its shape. Bodies smaller than a few kilometres – like asteroids and comets – do not have sufficient mass to pull themselves into a spherical shape, instead forming irregular 'potato' shapes. To be a dwarf planet, a body must have sufficient mass to achieve hydrostatic equilibrium, when it will become spherical.

Example: Ceres

"The answer will have huge implications for humanity"

The search for a new Earth

Discover how new advances in technology are revealing hundreds of extrasolar planets across our galaxy

Since Galileo pointed a telescope at the heavens 400 years ago, the discovery of exoplanets beyond our own solar system is a goal astronomers have long cherished. Allied to this is the greater hope of finding Earth-like planets capable of supporting life. If it is proved we are alone in this

universe, or share it with other life forms, the answer will have huge implications for humanity.

Earth-based techniques introduced in the Nineties, using interferometry and coronagraphy, finally proved that other star systems do have giant extrasolar planetary bodies orbiting them. The race to

discover life-supporting Earth-sized planets, that are light years away, needs far greater precision and accuracy. To meet this challenge observatories throughout the world are constantly upgrading their technology, but the biggest hopes are pinned on telescopes launched into outer space.

Hunting ground
Most of the new planets found have been within about 300 light years from our Sun

DISCOVERED FIRST

1. 51 Pegasi b
This extrasolar planet was detected in 1995 and named Bellerophon. It is a hot Jupiter-type planet, 50.1 light years away from us, in the Pegasus constellation.

BIGGEST

2. WASP-17 b
Discovered by the UK's super WASP (Wide Area Search for Planets), in August 2009. This exoplanet is a gas giant twice the size of Jupiter.

TRIPLE SYSTEM

3. HD 188753 Ab
This hot Jupiter was the first to be discovered in a system with three suns. It is 149 light years away and was discovered by the Keck observatory back in 2005.

DID YOU KNOW? *The search for exoplanets requires measurements that are fractions of an arcsecond*

How are we looking?

Extrasolar planets are small, distant and hidden in the glare of their parent stars, unable to be seen directly by telescope. Astronomers use four main methods to infer their existence...

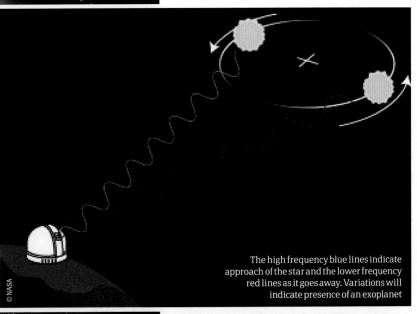

The high frequency blue lines indicate approach of the star and the lower frequency red lines as it goes away. Variations will indicate presence of an exoplanet

Doppler shift

This is based on analysing the spectrum of the light from a star. The spectrum of a star is as individual to it as a fingerprint. When light is refracted through a prism, it creates a spectrum of violet, indigo, blue, green, yellow, orange and red light. A rainbow naturally produces this effect. The invisible electromagnetic radiation at either end of the spectrum, like x-rays and infrared, can also be analysed by astronomers.

As a star moves towards us its light waves shift towards the higher-frequency blue end of the spectrum, and when it moves away they go to the lower frequency red end of the spectrum. This phenomenon is known as Doppler shift.

If a star has a nearby large planet, the two will orbit around a common centre of mass. The star will move faster around this centre of mass the bigger and closer the planet. This radial velocity can be measured, as the spectrum of the star will show correspondingly bigger colour shifts.

Transit method

As a planet passes (transits) in front of its parent star, it will cause the apparent brightness of the star to be reduced. During the transit, the spectrum of the light from the planet's atmosphere can be detected and analysed. Furthermore, when the Sun transits the planet the photometric intensity of the star can be compared with the data gathered during the planet's transit, enabling astronomers to calculate the temperature of the planet.

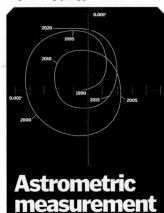

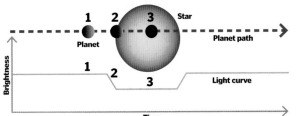

Where are we looking?

The search for exoplanets is presently restricted to our own Milky Way spiral galaxy, which has a diameter of about 100,000 light years. This is mainly due to the various limitations on the technology and techniques used to seek them out.

Using astrometric and Doppler shift methods, the area of search is a range of from 100 to 300 light years. This can be extended by the transit method to 6,000 light years and using chronometry, as proposed for the TPF-C spacecraft, to 12,000 light years. Gravitational lensing can find extrasolar planets 25,000 light years away. As these techniques are refined, the search range is constantly being extended.

One theory is that the galaxy itself has a Goldilocks Zone, so that star systems in the spiral arms or too close to the centre of the galaxy would be too inhospitable for life-supporting planets. If this is true then Earth-like life-supporting exoplanets will be rarer to find.

Milky Way and Sun © NASA

Gravitational microlensing

This technique uses the lensing effect produced when one star is in alignment with another star. The gravitational field of the star nearest the observer magnifies the light from the star behind it, and if the foreground star has a planet, it will cause detectable variations in this lensing effect. Huge numbers of stars have to be monitored to discover these alignments that last only a few days or weeks.

Observer **Planet** **Source star** **Lens star**

Astrometric measurement

The precise position of the star is recorded and plotted by telescope to detect the slight wobble of a star caused by radial velocity, implying the effects of a nearby planet. Astrometry is the earliest method of searching for exoplanets that dates back to the use of hand-plotted stars in the 18th Century.

Zone conditions

The Goldilocks Zone explains why the Earth's position is perfect for us to survive

The term 'Goldilocks Zone' comes from the 'Goldilocks and the Three Bears' story. Goldilocks tested bowls of porridge to find out which one was not too hot or too cold. Earth is inside the Goldilocks Zone that is just right for habitation. If Earth was closer to the Sun, like Mercury and Venus, conditions are too hot for us. If we were further away, like Mars and beyond, conditions are too cold and arid.

Our Sun is a G-dwarf type star, for larger stars like A-dwarfs the habitable zone is further away, and for cooler stars like M-dwarfs the habitable zone is closer. Life is also dependent on the rotation, axial tilt and orbit of Earth that gives us our regular procession of days, seasons and years. If these factors were too extreme or irregular, the variations in temperature and effects on our climate and ecosystem would not be suitable for us.

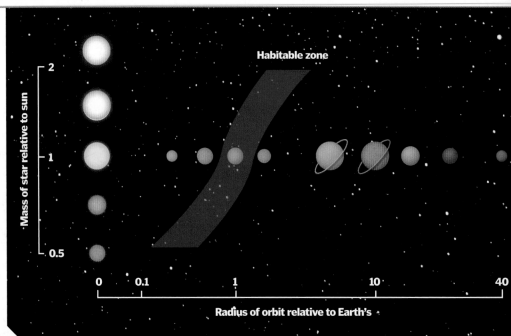

Habitable zone

Mass of star relative to sun

2

1

0.5

0 0.1 1 10 40

Radius of orbit relative to Earth's

What has been found?

Up to October 2012, over 840 extrasolar planets have been discovered. Only one Earth-sized planet has been found (orbiting the Alpha Centauri solar system); the majority are hot Jupiters or gas giants. Hot Jupiters have a mass between 110 to 430 times that of Earth. They are created beyond their parent star before forming a close orbit around it. Other types include super Earths, which have a mass between that of Earth and Jupiter. So far hundreds of super Earth candidates have been detected. A good example is COROT-7 b, which was discovered in 2009 by the European COROT (Convection Rotation and planetary Transits) spacecraft. It resides 500 light years away in the Unicorn constellation, and orbits a Sun-like G-class star. Unfortunately, it orbits very close to its parent star and its surface could be as hot as 2,600°C. In addition, it orbits its star at the rate of 466,030mph; making Earth's 67,000mph look sluggish.

COROT found its 23rd confirmed exoplanet in 2011, Named COROT-23b, it has a stead but rapid orbit around its parent star of just 3.6 days. It is positioned in the Serpens constellation and, at 2.8 Jupiter masses, is likely to be yet another hot gas giant.

In March 2010, HAT-P-14b was discovered 670 light years away in the Hercules constellation, and 235 light years away in the Andromeda constellation HAT-P-16b was reported too. These are also hot Jupiter exoplanets but there is the possibility of a smaller exoplanet existing near HAT-P-14b.

NASA's Kepler space telescope analysed 150,000 stars to detect any exoplanets using the transit method when it started operating in May 2009. This early data revealed five exoplanets, named Kepler 4b, 5b, 6b, 7b and 8b that were confirmed by ground-based observatories. All of them are in the Cygnus constellation and are hot Jupiter-type exoplanets. It has since obtained data from thousands more stars that revealed hundreds of potential candidate planets, many of which were confirmed as exoplanets throughout 2011.

An artist's impression of the COROT spacecraft

© NASA

Head to Head
EXOPLANET-FINDING TELESCOPES

BIGGEST TWIN

1. W. M. Keck Observatory
The Keck's twin 10m primary mirrors weigh 300 tons each. It is located on the top of an extinct volcano on Hawai'i Island.

NEW CONTENDER

2. Large Binocular Telescope (LBT)
Located on Mount Graham, Arizona, USA, it has twin 8.4-metre (27.6-foot) primary mirrors.

A FUTURE GIANT

© Swinburne Astronomy Productions/ European Southern Observatory, 2010

3. European Extremely Large Telescope (E-ELT)
This will have a 42 metre mirror and is planned to search for Earth-like exoplanets in the Goldilocks Zone in 2022.

DID YOU KNOW? *COROT-7 b orbits its star at a speed of 466,030mph*

Future planet-finding missions

Space agencies have proposed the following spacecraft missions to study extrasolar planets

NASA's Terrestrial Planet Finder (TPF) Project

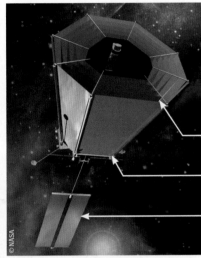

TPF Coronagraph

Solar coronagraphs were originally used with telescopes to block out the disc of the Sun to study its corona – this is hot plasma emitted by stellar bodies that travels millions of miles beyond its surface. Applied to the search for extrasolar planets the problem of blocking out the direct light of a star poses a much bigger problem. By isolating and studying the stellar corona, any planet within this area should be detected by the TPF-C spacecraft's telescope combined with coronagraph detection equipment.

Sunshade
The conical v-grooved sunshade fans out to insulate the telescope from the changing position of the Sun

Primary mirror
Located at the base of the sunshade, the mirror is set at an angle to deflect its light to the top of the secondary mirror

Secondary mirror tower
The smaller secondary mirror is mounted on top of this tower. The light from this and the primary mirror is reflected down the tower to the coronagraph assembly

TPF Interferometer

This TPF-I mission would employ a formation of five spacecraft. Four would each be equipped with a four-metre infrared telescope, and one spacecraft would receive the data from them and combine it. The interaction of the light waves from the telescopes produces interference that can be used to eliminate the glare of a star by a factor of 1 million. This so-called nulling technique allows the detection of any infrared emissions from planets near its parent star. The term interferometer is explained by the fact that it can also be used to measure the distance and angles of celestial objects.

Combiner spacecraft
It receives the light from the collector craft and analyses it in a 'nulling beam combiner'

Stray light baffles
Beams of light from the collector spacecraft telescopes travel along these 35-metre-long baffles to the combiner spacecraft

Collector spacecraft
Each has a four-metre diameter telescope mirror shielded and cooled by a five-layer sunshade

SIM Lite

The SIM Lite spacecraft will take five and a half years to reach an orbit around the Sun at a distance of 82 million km from the Earth. Here it will search the Goldilocks Zones of 60 stars for Earth-sized planets at a distance of up to 33 light years away. To achieve this it employs sensitive interferometer equipment that can detect a star's wobble to an accuracy of 20 millionths of an arcsecond. These are incredibly small measurements; an arcsecond is 1/60th of an arcminute, which in turn is 1/60th of a degree. A star-tracking telescope is also carried by the craft to carry out astrometric calculations to compare and use with the inferometric data.

Collecting apertures
The twin mirrors of a six-metre baseline 'science' telescope have 50cm apertures at either end of the craft, and a 'guide' telescope with a 4.2 metre baseline has twin 30cm apertures

Communications antenna
Once a week the craft will transmit the data it has collected back to Earth

Inside spacecraft
The images from the science and guide telescopes inside the spacecraft are sent to central beam combiners and analysed by inferometric equipment

Interview

Wesley Traub

Chief scientist, NASA Navigator Program

We caught up with Wesly Traub, the chief scientist for NASA's Exoplanet Exploration Program, and the project scientist for the Terrestrial Planet Finder Coronagraph (TPF-C)

Q: What type of outer space missions are needed to find exoplanets?
Wesley Traub: An astrometric mission is needed to discover planets around our nearest neighbour stars. This mission could determine the orbital parameters of each planet and accurately measure its mass.
This is important because we need a list of planets that are close enough to Earth that we can measure their properties; nearest-neighbour planets are bright enough for us to measure, but more distant ones are not.

Q: Will you be able to find evidence of Earth-type and even life on these planets?
WT: A visible spectroscopy mission is needed to look for biomarkers in the visible wavelength range. For an Earth-like planet these biomarkers include oxygen, ozone, water, an atmosphere at least as thick as the Earth's (via the blue colour of a blue sky, like ours), and possibly the enhanced reflection of red light from vegetation (grass, trees and plants, all of which look green to us but also reflect red light that we cannot see).
For a planet like the early Earth, you could see methane and carbon dioxide, in addition to the blue-sky effect. An infrared spectroscopy mission is needed to look for different biomarkers like carbon dioxide, ozone, and water. This mission could also measure the temperature of the planet, and its size. We need to look

for these biomarkers in both wavelength ranges because together they give us a more complete picture than either one alone. For example, we can measure oxygen only in the visible spectrum, and temperature only in the infrared.

Q: What is the most important objective for these missions?
WT: I think the most important thing would be to answer the question of whether there's life on other planets. I guess at heart I believe there are planets with life on them. I don't know about intelligent life. The usual argument is that there are billions of stars out there, and today we think the chances of planets being around each one of them are pretty high, which we didn't used to think. And we think that life formed very quickly, as soon as it was possible on Earth. But out of the billions of stars in our galaxy, we only have a chance of looking at about 200 stars that are nearby. The chances of intelligent life being there on one of those, right now, are pretty small.

Q: Will TPF-I, TPF-C or SIM Lite go ahead?
WT: None of these missions have started development yet. Once the current suite of missions in development is completed, then an exoplanet mission may begin development. The earliest a mission of this type can be flown is towards the end of this decade.

Where on an Earth?

Exoplanet study has only been conducted over the past 15 years, and has already revealed completely different planetary bodies from those in our own solar system. Due to the limitations of our current technology, we have so far only found giant exoplanets. In future, we might discover rogue planets that do not orbit a parent star and exoplanets that are dominated by oceans, fields of ice, or boiling hot volcanic crusts like COROT-7b. None of these are likely to sustain life, as we know it, so the Holy Grail of this work is to find life-supporting Earth-type planets.

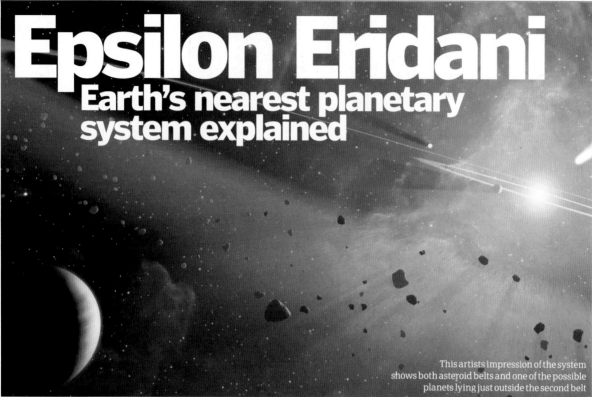

Epsilon Eridani
Earth's nearest planetary system explained

This artists impression of the system shows both asteroid belts and one of the possible planets lying just outside the second belt

Spotting extrasolar planets

Finding planets around other stars is very difficult. Scientists use sophisticated ways to calculate their presence. So far the most common of these methods is to measure the source star's radial velocity, and this is how Epsilon Eridani was found to be a system. Radial velocity measures the Doppler-style shift of the star as the planet(s) around it pull it off its centre of gravity making it 'wobble'. Scientists then measure the speed at which the star wobbles to infer details about the planet itself.

At only 10.5 light years away, Epsilon Eridani is the nearest star with an orbiting planet, find out more...

Epsilon Eridani is a surprisingly important star as far as your average fiery ball of plasma goes. For starters, it's the third nearest star that can be observed from Earth with the naked eye, lying just ten light years away in the Constellation Eridanus (otherwise known as the River). In astronomical terms we're pretty much as good as roommates.

It's also of quite similar composition to our very own Sun, which wouldn't be all that exciting were it not for its close proximity and tender age making it of great interest to those scientists who are interested in the birth and development of our own Sun. At just 800 million years of age Epsilon is still a very young star and a whole 3.7 billion years our Sun's junior. Given the absence of a working time machine, it's probably one of our best bets for studying its birth and development. It's also the unsuspecting next-door neighbour to *Star Trek*'s very own Mr Spock. His famous home world Vulcan orbits 40 Eridani A – which is just six light years farther away than Epsilon from home.

The question as to whether there's life – and if it's as we know it – isn't quite as daft as it might seem though. You see, while all these facts make this young, energetic star of familiar breed and bearing of great interest to the scientific community, its biggest claim to fame makes the rest pale in comparison; it harbours planets, extrasolar planetary bodies – perhaps as many as three. Extrasolar planets are very hard to detect and almost impossible to see, but by measuring the source star's radial velocity, one of a growing number of extrasolar detection methods, scientists can indirectly detect the presence of these planets and – hopefully in time – a dusty ball of rock, not entirely unlike our own. ✿

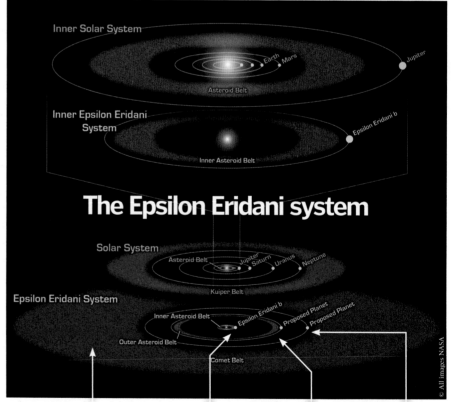

Inner Solar System

Earth · Mars · Jupiter

Asteroid Belt

Inner Epsilon Eridani System

Epsilon Eridani b

Inner Asteroid Belt

The Epsilon Eridani system

Solar System

Asteroid Belt · Jupiter · Saturn · Uranus · Neptune

Kuiper Belt

Epsilon Eridani System

Inner Asteroid Belt · Epsilon Eridani b · Proposed Planet · Proposed Planet

Outer Asteroid Belt

Comet Belt

Does size really matter?
While Epsilon Eridani is actually smaller than our own, the system itself is quite noticably wider – this blown up view only shows the inner part of the very much larger system

Jupiter-class planet
Epsilon Eridani B, which actually orbits the star at around three and a half times the Earth's distance from the Sun, is thought to be a gas giant not entirely different from Jupiter

The bigger picture
There are clues to this system's size. A second uniform asteroid belt between the inner one indicates the presence of a further planet and the icy comet belt further out suggests another

Historical centrepiece
Epsilon Eridani itself is younger than our Sun, so any planets orbiting it will be in an early state of development. Its age also means it's a virile sun – giving off plenty of radiation

What is a brown dwarf?

These so-called 'sub-stellar' objects are barely bigger than planets, so what makes these failed stars stellar at all?

It's a conundrum that's racked the field of astronomy for the last 30 years – is a brown dwarf star really a star at all? Since they don't have the mass to initiate nuclear fusion like a normal star during its formation, they're often referred to as 'failed stars'. With masses that range from just a few times larger than our solar system's gas giant Jupiter, to around 75 times its size, brown dwarfs are often considered to be the missing link between gas giant planets and red dwarf stars – the smallest known 'true stars'.

Measuring or even discovering the presence of a brown dwarf star is notoriously difficult because they're so cool and small, so scientists use the presence of lithium as a determining factor. The presence of lithium is actually common in all young stars, but is usually burnt up in the first 100 million years of its life. Since the core of a brown dwarf isn't hot enough to get rid of the lithium it's a very useful indicator in labelling low-mass stellar objects 'brown dwarf stars'. ✿

Size difference
Though an entirely hypothetical scenario, this artist's conception demonstrates the relative size difference between our own solar system and that of a particularly small brown dwarf system

Not quite a star...
Brown dwarfs are also considered stars since they're born in exactly the same way – from the collapsing of a cloud of gas and dust. Sadly, the birth of a brown dwarf doesn't go to plan and the star doesn't gain enough mass for a hydrogen fusion engine in its core to ignite. In this respect, brown dwarfs are effectively stillborn stars

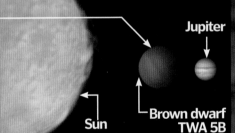

Jupiter

Sun

Brown dwarf TWA 5B

All images © NASA

Goldilocks Zone fully explained

Life-sustaining planets require such exacting standards that scientists call the area they occupy 'the Goldilocks Zone'

The Goldilocks Zone is an area 'just right' for a life-sustaining planet – the perfect distance from a star with a surface neither too hot nor too cold. It is an intersection of life-sustaining regions within both a solar system and a galaxy. Astronomers believe that the Goldilocks Zone ranges from 0.725 to three astronomical units (each about 150 million kilometres, or the mean distance between the Earth and the Sun).

Recently some planetary bodies have come close to fitting the bill. The April 2007 discovery of Gliese 581c in the Libra constellation, for example, seemed promising until further research proved it was too hot. However, a nearby planet, Gliese 581d, may turn out to be just right. At the same time, the definition of the Goldilocks Zone is expanding as scientists discover life on Earth in places previously thought too extreme to sustain it. ✿

HOTTER STARS

SUN-LIKE STARS

COOLER STARS

Solar systems must be in the right place in the galaxy to sustain the formation of terrestrial planets, but not receive high doses of radiation

If the Earth had formed just a few percentage points closer or further from the Sun, it would be either covered in ice or have no oceans

The Goldilocks Zone is also known as the Solar Habitable or Circumstellar Habitable Zone

197

Different types of galaxies explained

They might be grouped like a galactic tuning fork, but galaxy types don't always sing from the same hymn sheet

There are several different galaxy classification systems, but the most widely used is the Hubble Sequence, devised by the great Edwin Hubble in 1926 and later expanded upon by Allan Sandage among others. It's more commonly known as the Hubble tuning fork due to the shape the system represents in diagrammatic form.

Hubble's system was designed to demonstrate the various classifications of three main classes of galaxy broken down into elliptical, spiral and lenticular shapes. The latter is essentially an intermediate of the other two types. The tuning fork was erroneously thought that each galaxy type represented snapshots of the entire life span of galaxies, but it has since been demonstrated that this is not the case.

The most recent version of Hubble's tuning fork comes courtesy of the Spitzer Space Telescope's infrared galaxy survey made up of 75 colour images of different galaxies and includes a new sub-section of irregular galaxy types. You can find a full resolution image of this remarkable accomplishment at http://sings.stsci.edu/Publications/sings_poster.html. Thanks to the internet, anyone can try their hand at galaxy classification and further the science – simply go to www.galaxyzoo.org and join in alongside 150,000 other volunteers. ✿

Edwin Hubble's classification scheme

Ellipticals

E0 E3 E5 E7 S0

Spirals

Sa Sb Sc

SBa SBb SBc

Edwin Hubble Pioneer to the stars

No person in history has had a greater impact in determining the extent of our universe than Edwin Hubble. From proving that other galaxies existed to giving evidence that galaxies move apart from one another, Hubble's work defined our place in the cosmos. Shown above posing with the 48-inch telescope on Palomar Mountain, the Orbiting Space Telescope was named in memory of his great work.

Today a great controversy rages on about the rate of the universe's expansion, parameterised by a quantity known as Hubble's constant.

Types of galaxies

Galaxies can be categorised into these types…

Elliptical galaxies
On the far left of the Hubble Sequence lies the elliptical galaxy types. They show no defined features like the intricate dust lanes seen in classic spiral galaxy types, besides a bright core. Ellipticals are represented by the letter E, followed by a number that represents the ellipticity of its shape

Spiral types
Appearing flatter on the sky than an elliptical galaxy, spiral galaxies feature two or more spiral 'arms' that wrap around the galaxy core and are made up of vast lanes of stars. The upper half is populated with the standard spiral type, while the lower half contains 'bar' spirals. The twist of the spiral begins at the end of an extended bar

Lenticular galaxies
Where the handle of the tuning fork and the two spiral arms meet lie the lenticular galaxies. These galaxies feature aspects of both spiral and elliptical galaxies and didn't actually feature on Hubble's original sequence. They have a bright central bulge like an elliptical galaxy, but are surrounded by a structure not unlike a disc

Head to Head
SUPER STARBURST

RAPID

1. Supernova
A chain reaction of shockwaves emanates throughout a starburst galaxy as supernova after supernova explodes in close proximity.

HOT

2. Superbubble
Supernovae are so common in starburst galaxies that they produce rapidly expanding bubbles of gas millions of degrees in temperature.

FAR

3. Superwind
The heavy elements and energetic radiation dispersed by supernovae are carried between galaxies on waves known as superwinds.

DID YOU KNOW? There are ten known galactic recurrent novae, which have erupted 37 times since 1866

What is a nova?

It might not be super, but it's still very impressive

Novae are not to be confused with their more explosive supernovae brothers. The latter are the result of red supergiants (very large stars) collapsing, or most of the mass of a white dwarf exploding. A supernova will typically eject more than 1.38 solar masses (the mass of our Sun) of material. A nova, by comparison, ejects just 1/10,000th of a solar mass.

Novae occur in binary systems where two stars are orbiting one another. One of these will typically be a small, white dwarf star and the other a red giant. As the red giant expands, it moves into the gravitational influence of its small companion. A white dwarf has a very strong gravitational field and therefore rips matter from the red giant. Once the white dwarf has absorbed so much matter that it can no longer support itself, it suddenly explodes as a nova and ejects its hot surface gas. However, the central white dwarf star survives, unlike in a type 1 supernova where the majority of the white dwarf's mass explodes. It then immediately begins consuming matter from the red giant again and the nova process will repeat within a period of 100,000 years.

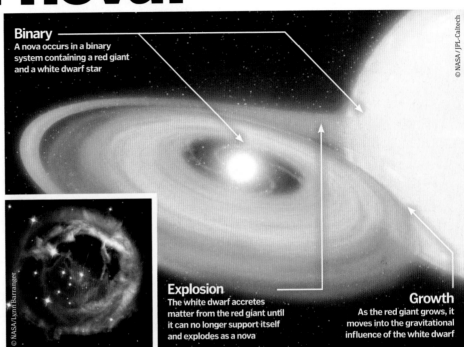

Binary
A nova occurs in a binary system containing a red giant and a white dwarf star

Explosion
The white dwarf accretes matter from the red giant until it can no longer support itself and explodes as a nova

Growth
As the red giant grows, it moves into the gravitational influence of the white dwarf

Starburst galaxies

These galaxies produce stars much faster than anywhere else in the universe

This composite image of the Messier 82 starburst galaxy in the Ursa Major constellation was taken by the Spitzer Space Telescope

A galaxy experiencing an unusually high level of star formation is known as a starburst galaxy. This increased activity is so intense that stars only form for a period of approximately 10 million years, a very tiny amount of time compared to the life of a 10 billion year old galaxy. With production at up to 100 times faster than a regular galaxy, the resultant stars are typically very massive and very luminous.

These events usually occur when two galaxies collide, sending shockwaves through the clouds of dust and gas within each galaxy and crushing them together to begin the process of star formation. The stars produced are often so massive that they use up their fuel quickly, becoming supernovae and sending more shockwaves throughout the galaxy. This creates a chain reaction of events until the available material in the galaxy is used up and the starburst comes to an end.

The Cigar Galaxy, 11 million light years away, is the nearest starburst galaxy to Earth

Explore the miracle of

OUR GALAXY

It's one of about 100 billion other galaxies in the universe, but it's our home – join us as we explore the Milky Way

DID YOU KNOW? *According to Greek mythology, the Milky Way was formed when Hera spilt milk while breastfeeding Heracles*

The Milky Way is our galaxy, home to our solar system. It formed a little more than 13 billion years ago, just a few billion years after the Big Bang. The galaxy is estimated to be about 100,000 light years in diameter and 1,000 light years thick. It is part of a system of 50 galaxies known as the Local Group, which is part of the Virgo Supercluster. Containing as many as 50 billion planets and 400 billion stars, the Milky Way is a spiral galaxy. It has a centre known as a 'bulge', surrounded by a flat disk comprising several loose arms that contain stars and their orbiting bodies, as well as gases and dust. The centre contains a massive black hole and a complex radio source known as 'Sagittarius A'. Around the outside of the Milky Way there is a halo containing dark matter and a very small percentage of the galaxy's total number of stars. Some astronomers believe that the Milky Way is actually a special type of spiral galaxy called a barred spiral, meaning that it has a bar-shaped distribution of stars running across its centre.

Aristotle first wrote of the Milky Way in the mid-300s BCE. He broke with other Greek philosophers, who believed that the milky streak in the sky might be stars. Aristotle thought that it was a sort of fiery emission coming from a cluster of very large stars, and that it resided in the Earth's atmosphere. Astronomers continued to speculate about the true nature of the Milky Way, until Galileo determined in 1610 that it comprised a massive number of stars. In 1755 Immanuel Kant realised that the Milky Way rotated and was held together by gravity. 30 years later, William Herschel attempted to depict the shape of the Milky Way and the Sun's location in it by counting and recording the position of visible stars. Finally Edwin Hubble determined in the Twenties that there were nebulae beyond the Milky Way, proving

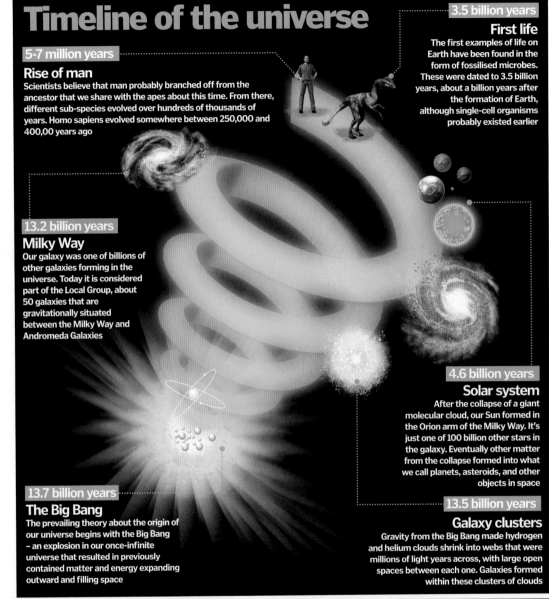

Timeline of the universe

5-7 million years

Rise of man
Scientists believe that man probably branched off from the ancestor that we share with the apes about this time. From there, different sub-species evolved over hundreds of thousands of years. Homo sapiens evolved somewhere between 250,000 and 400,00 years ago

13.2 billion years

Milky Way
Our galaxy was one of billions of other galaxies forming in the universe. Today it is considered part of the Local Group, about 50 galaxies that are gravitationally situated between the Milky Way and Andromeda Galaxies

13.7 billion years

The Big Bang
The prevailing theory about the origin of our universe begins with the Big Bang – an explosion in our once-infinite universe that resulted in previously contained matter and energy expanding outward and filling space

3.5 billion years

First life
The first examples of life on Earth have been found in the form of fossilised microbes. These were dated to 3.5 billion years, about a billion years after the formation of Earth, although single-cell organisms probably existed earlier

4.6 billion years

Solar system
After the collapse of a giant molecular cloud, our Sun formed in the Orion arm of the Milky Way. It's just one of 100 billion other stars in the galaxy. Eventually other matter from the collapse formed into what we call planets, asteroids, and other objects in space

13.5 billion years

Galaxy clusters
Gravity from the Big Bang made hydrogen and helium clouds shrink into webs that were millions of light years across, with large open spaces between each one. Galaxies formed within these clusters of clouds

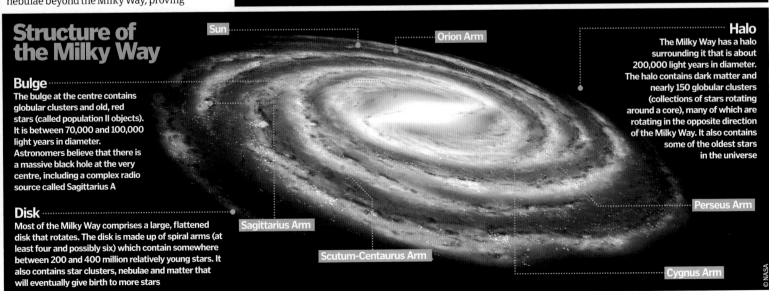

Structure of the Milky Way

Sun · **Orion Arm** · **Halo**

Bulge
The bulge at the centre contains globular clusters and old, red stars (called population II objects). It is between 70,000 and 100,000 light years in diameter. Astronomers believe that there is a massive black hole at the very centre, including a complex radio source called Sagittarius A

Disk
Most of the Milky Way comprises a large, flattened disk that rotates. The disk is made up of spiral arms (at least four and possibly six) which contain somewhere between 200 and 400 million relatively young stars. It also contains star clusters, nebulae and matter that will eventually give birth to more stars

Halo
The Milky Way has a halo surrounding it that is about 200,000 light years in diameter. The halo contains dark matter and nearly 150 globular clusters (collections of stars rotating around a core), many of which are rotating in the opposite direction of the Milky Way. It also contains some of the oldest stars in the universe

Sagittarius Arm

Scutum-Centaurus Arm

Perseus Arm

Cygnus Arm

© NASA

"For all our observations, the Milky Way is still mysterious"

that there were other galaxies in the universe. Hubble is also responsible for coming up with the classification system for galaxies that we use today, which includes spiral, elliptical and irregular galaxies.

For all our observations, the Milky Way is still mysterious. Determining its actual size and our location in it has been difficult; Herschel and astronomers before him believed that our solar system was in its centre because of the apparently equal distribution of stars in our sky, for example. Several different indirect methods have been used to calculate the actual size of the Milky Way. This includes using the period-luminosity relation of certain stars. The luminosity, or brightness, of some stars pulse in a predictable pattern, which can be measured along with its apparent magnitude to estimate distance. In the early-20th Century, an astronomer named Harlow Shapley used some of these measurements to extrapolate the distances of globular clusters outside the Milky Way. This showed that the Sun was not at the centre of the galaxy and provided a rough (although inaccurate) estimate of the Milky Way's diameter. Today we can map the galaxy using telescopes that pick up light and radio waves emitted by gases and molecules that are floating in space.

The Milky Way isn't a static object – the arms rotate about the centre, and it is also moving in the direction of a large gravitational anomaly known as the Great Attractor. Our galaxy also has its own orbiting galaxies. The two largest of these galaxies, the Small Magellanic Cloud and the Large Magellanic Cloud, create a vibrational warp in the Milky Way's disk as they orbit, due to the invisible presence of dark matter.

Because of light and other types of atmospheric pollution, it's difficult to view the Milky Way from Earth with the naked eye; it's best viewed in very rural areas under clear skies, and looks like a faint milky band of clouds stretching across the night sky. Light pollution maps are available online, and local astronomy clubs can help locate the best place to go.

Trip through the Milky Way

A trip from Earth out beyond the edge of the Milky Way would mean travelling a distance of thousands of light years

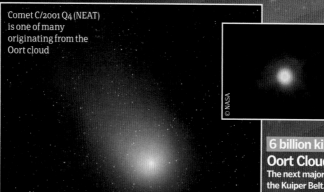

Comet C/2001 Q4 (NEAT) is one of many originating from the Oort cloud

4.22 light years
Nearest stars
Aside from the Sun, the nearest star to Earth is the red dwarf Proxima Centauri. Part of the three-star Alpha Centauri system, it's slightly closer to Earth than the more visible Alpha Centauri A and B. Sirius, the brightest star in the night sky, is 8.6 light years

6 billion kilometres
Oort Cloud and Kuiper Belt
The next major objects are the Oort Cloud and the Kuiper Belt. The Oort Cloud is a cloud of comets believed to be the source of many of the comets in our solar system. The Kuiper Belt is an area of the solar system containing dwarf planets and other small astral bodies

40 million kilometres
Other planets and Sun
We'll have to travel tens of millions of kilometres before coming upon the other planets that share our solar system. At nearly 40 million kilometres away at the closest point in its orbit, Venus is our nearest neighbour. Once we reach the furthest planet from Earth, Neptune, we're about 4.4 billion kilometres away

643,737 kilometres
Near-Earth asteroids
Our first stop past the Moon would be a visit to our near-Earth asteroids. There are at least 7,000 of these small rocky, metallic objects. They can be up to 32 kilometres in diameter. Compared to the lifetime of other objects in the galaxy, these asteroids have life spans of just a few million years

A digital composite of the Milky Way's disk over Tenerife

BIG

1. Irregular galaxies
The smallest types of galaxies are irregular, including compact dwarf irregulars that are as small as 200 light years across.

© NASA

BIGGER

2. Spiral galaxies
Our Milky Way is an average-sized spiral, but others such as UGC 2885 can be more than 800,000 light years across.

© NASA

BIGGEST

3. Elliptical galaxies
The biggest galaxies, ellipticals can be up to 100 kiloparsecs across and may form when two smaller galaxies collide.

© NASA

DID YOU KNOW? The name 'Milky Way' comes from Latin and Greek astronomers, who observed the stars' milky appearance

GALACTIC OBJECTS

DISTANCE

300 light years
Neighbour stars
Once we get 100 light years away from the Earth, we're nearing the outer edges of the Milky Way. Some of the better-known stars past this distance include Canopus at more than 300 light years away and Betelgeuse at about 640 light years away

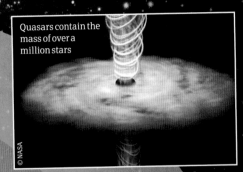
Quasars contain the mass of over a million stars

© NASA

3 billion light years
Distant quasars and galaxies
Quasars are the most distant visible objects in the universe; the closest one is about 3 billion light years away and the furthest is nearly 13 billion light years away. That means that on Earth we see this distant quasar, named CFHQS J2329-0301, less than 1 billion years after the Big Bang

300 million light years
Galaxy groups and galaxy clusters
The further we get, the greater the leaps in distance. Now we encounter groups of galaxies and other massive structures. The Great, or Coma Wall, is a super-structure filling large spatial voids in the universe. It contains superclusters of galaxies and has dimensions of more than 500 million light years long and 300 million light years wide

© NASA

25,000 light years
Nearby galaxies
Now we're beyond the Milky Way, visiting other galaxies. There's a dwarf galaxy known as Canis Major being consumed by the Milky Way right now, 25,000 light years away. The closest galaxy outside of the Milky Way is the Sagittarius Dwarf elliptical galaxy, 70,000 light years from Earth

© NASA

1,000 light years
Milky Way
The edge of the Milky Way is about 1,000 light years away from Earth. Keep in mind that our solar system is already on the outer edges of the Milky Way itself, about 28,000 light years from its centre

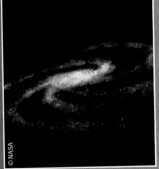
© NASA

... miles
4 trillion miles
10 light years
1,000 light years
100,000 light years
10 million light years
1 billion light years
11-15 billion light years

Galaxy on the move

The spinning galaxy rotates differentially (the closer objects are to the centre, the less time they take to complete an orbit). The Sun travels around the galactic centre at 800,000k/ph (500,000mph), taking 225 million years to make one orbit.

The galaxy rotates differentially, which means that objects closer to its core orbit the core faster than the stars in the arms of the galaxy. The Milky Way rotates at about 170km per second. Our solar system, located around 30,000 light years away from the galactic core, completes an orbit once every 225 million years. The Milky Way is also moving through space at about 630km per second, relative to the cosmic background radiation – the Big Bang's remnants. It moves in the direction of a gravitational anomaly in the universe, known as the Great Attractor.

When galaxies collide

Astronomers are predicting that in about 3 to 5 billion years, the Andromeda galaxy may collide with the Milky Way. The violent crash will result in a blob-like elliptical galaxy, dubbed 'Milkomeda'. Currently Andromeda is about 2.5 million light years from the Milky Way, but it is moving towards our galaxy at 120km per second. The possibility of stars and planets within the galaxies actually colliding is highly unlikely, but the different gravitational fields will jostle them out of their current locations. Our solar system could even be ejected during the collision, but that probably wouldn't affect the planets much. By the time of the proposed collision, Earth will probably already be devoid of life due to the Sun's increasing heat.

Galaxy collisions can be less dramatic than they sound

© NASA

> "If the Milky Way collided with the nearby Andromeda galaxy, we woul⸢d⸣ barely notice a thing on Earth"

NASA's Hubble Space Telescope took this image of the Antennae galaxies, which began colliding a few hundred million years ago

SA / NASA

Galaxy collisions
What happens when two galaxies collide?

When two galaxies cross paths, the chance of any stars colliding is almost zero. In fact, if the Milky Way collided with the nearby Andromeda galaxy, we would barely notice a thing on Earth. Instead, the multitude of dust and gas in each galaxy interacts and creates the characteristic spectacle. As the material inside the stars interacts gravitationally, newly formed gas clouds give birth to stars. Friction between the gases can cause numerous

become instrumental in the formation of new stars.

Colliding galaxies usually take millions or even billions of years to merge. As they collide, tidal gravitational forces will rip the smaller of the two galaxies apart, scattering dust and stars. The inner core of the collision will heat up and radiate strongly, creating one of the brightest infrared objects in space. In this instance the larger galaxy will swallow the smaller one, but on some occasions the galaxies may pass through each other and

Joining forces
What happens when two galaxies collide?

1. First contact
The first signs of a galaxy collision will be a bridge of matter between the two, caused by gravitational forces

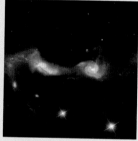

2. Tidal tails
Long streams of gas and dust known as tidal tails spiral out of the collision as the material is thrown out

3. Ripped apart
Gravitational forces pull the matter in all directions, creating shock waves throughout the cloud of gas

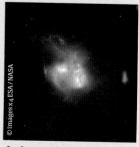

© Images x 4 ESA / NASA

4. A star is born
The core of the collision is subjected to intense frictional and gravitational forces, resulting in the formation of massive stars

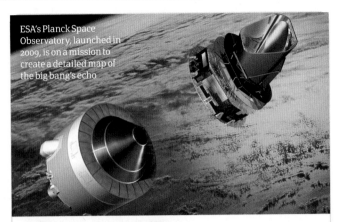

ESA's Planck Space Observatory, launched in 2009, is on a mission to create a detailed map of the big bang's echo

Cosmic Microwave Background Radiation

The most conclusive piece of evidence for the big bang that was discovered by accident

Immediately after the big bang, the universe was incredibly hot and dense, and subsequently cooled to about three degrees kelvin. One remnant of this process is the Cosmic Microwave Background Radiation (CMBR) present throughout the universe. It is constant at almost every point in the cosmos, which is known as isotropy. The opposite of this, anisotropy (not constant), is present to an extent in the CMBR, and supports the observation that matter in the universe is not quite uniformly distributed.

CMBR is a form of thermal radiation detectable in the microwave spectrum with a temp of approx 2.7 kelvins, cooled since its formation 600 million years after the big bang (about 15 billion years ago) by the expansion of the universe. Initially, the universe was a white-hot fog of plasma and thermal radiation. Once it cooled and stable atoms formed, the photons within continued to travel through the expanding universe, a relic of its early life and the CMBR we can now observe. ✿

A small percentage of the static seen on television screens is the result of background microwaves

Why do planets have moons?

How did these rocks get into a planet's orbit?

Planets have moons because early in their formation they were introduced to other space-faring rocks that either crashed into the planet and threw off debris, or were trapped in the planet's gravitational pull. Over billions of years the orbits of these rocks, now under the influence of the planet's gravity, were squashed into a spherical shape that kept them encircling their host planet.

To visualise how a moon becomes ensnared, imagine the earth is a ball placed on a floating sheet of frictionless paper (to represent gravity). The ball depresses the paper and if you roll a coin (to represent a moon) around this depressed area at a fast enough speed, it will circle the ball indefinitely.

So, why don't moons have their own moons? The answer is that the planet they are orbiting has a much stronger gravitational pull, so over time it would selfishly take other objects in as another moon for itself. ✿

A scanning electron microscope zooms in on interplanetary dust

1 μm

What is cosmic dust?

Spring-cleaning is tough for the universe

Although once considered a nuisance when attempting to observe other bodies in the universe, cosmic dust has since been hailed as incredibly fascinating. When a star expels atoms, some will become ions by gaining or losing too many electrons and becoming negatively or positively charged respectively. These oppositely charged ions form an ionic bond and stick together in tiny crystals just a few thousand nanometres across, known as star dust (or, more generally, cosmic dust). The accumulation of a large amount of cosmic dust over time leads to the formation of planets such as the Earth.

Other forms of cosmic dust include circumplanetary dust, which can form in rings around a planet (such as those surrounding Saturn). ✿

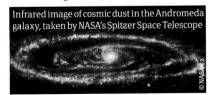

Infrared image of cosmic dust in the Andromeda galaxy, taken by NASA's Spitzer Space Telescope

"The first recorded supernova [SN 185] was spotted by Chinese astronomers in 185 AD"

SUPERNOVAS

With more energy than a billion suns, a size greater than our solar system and the potential to destroy entire planets millions of miles away, some stars certainly know how to go out with a bang. Here we take a look at supernovas, some of the most powerful explosions in the universe

When we delve into certain realms of astronomy, the scale of events and objects are often impossibly large to imagine. If we think of planets like Earth and Mars we can at least get some sort of grasp as to their size, as we can consider them relative to other bodies. As we get to bigger objects, like Jupiter and the Sun, our understanding gets somewhat muddled, but we can still comprehend how enormous they are by using Earth as a starting point (for example, the Sun is over 100 times the size of Earth). It's when we get to the larger celestial occurrences, like supergiant stars and black holes,

however, that things really start to become unfathomable. In this article we'll be taking a look at one of these mammoth celestial events – supernovas – and we'll try to get our heads around just how large, powerful and crucial they are.

Supernovas have fascinated astronomers for millennia, appearing out of nowhere in the night sky and outshining other stars with consummate ease. The first recorded supernova, known today as SN 185, was spotted by Chinese astronomers in 185 AD and was apparently visible for almost a year. While this is the first recorded sighting, there have doubtless been many supernovas in preceding

years that confounded Earth dwellers who were unable to explain the sudden appearance of a bright new star in the sky.

One of the most notable supernova events likely occurred about 340,000 years ago when a star known as Geminga went supernova. Although it was unrecorded, astronomers have been able to discern the manner of its demise from the remnant neutron star it left behind. Geminga is the closest known supernova to have exploded near Earth, as little as 290 light years away. Its proximity to Earth meant that it might have lit up the night sky for many months, casting its own shadows and

CLOSEST **1. Betelgeuse**
Expected to explode within a million years, this star, which is 18 times the mass of the Sun, is just 640 light years from Earth.

SOONEST **2. Eta Carinae**
This giant star – which is 100 times the mass of our Sun and over 8,000 light years away – could go supernova in just 10,000 years time.

BIGGEST **3. SN 2006gy**
In 2006 this giant supernova from a star 150 times the mass of our Sun was discovered 238 million light years away.

DID YOU KNOW? *Supernova is derived from the Latin term nova, meaning new, to denote the next phase in a star's life*

Countdown to a supernova
What events lead up to the explosion of the two known types of supernova?

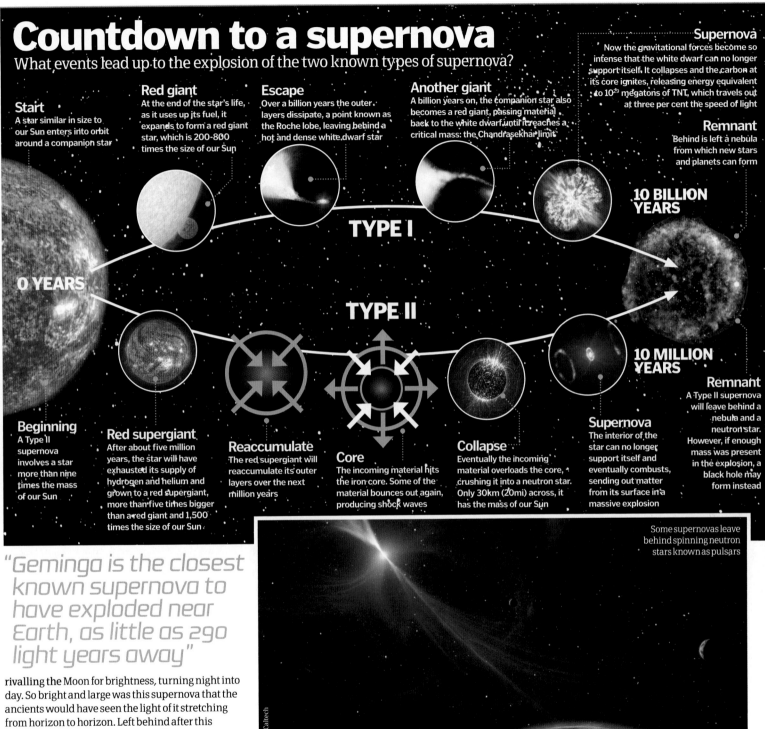

Start
A star similar in size to our Sun enters into orbit around a companion star

Red giant
At the end of the star's life, as it uses up its fuel, it expands to form a red giant star, which is 200-800 times the size of our Sun

Escape
Over a billion years the outer layers dissipate, a point known as the Roche lobe, leaving behind a hot and dense white dwarf star

Another giant
A billion years on, the companion star also becomes a red giant, passing material back to the white dwarf until it reaches a critical mass: the Chandrasekhar limit

Supernova
Now the gravitational forces become so intense that the white dwarf can no longer support itself. It collapses and the carbon at its core ignites, releasing energy equivalent to 10^{25} megatons of TNT, which travels out at three per cent the speed of light

Remnant
Behind is left a nebula from which new stars and planets can form

TYPE I

TYPE II

0 YEARS

10 BILLION YEARS

10 MILLION YEARS

Beginning
A Type II supernova involves a star more than nine times the mass of our Sun

Red supergiant
After about five million years, the star will have exhausted its supply of hydrogen and helium and grown to a red supergiant, more than five times bigger than a red giant and 1,500 times the size of our Sun

Reaccumulate
The red supergiant will reaccumulate its outer layers over the next million years

Core
The incoming material hits the iron core. Some of the material bounces out again, producing shock waves

Collapse
Eventually the incoming material overloads the core, crushing it into a neutron star. Only 30km (20mi) across, it has the mass of our Sun

Supernova
The interior of the star can no longer support itself and eventually combusts, sending out matter from its surface in a massive explosion

Remnant
A Type II supernova will leave behind a nebula and a neutron star. However, if enough mass was present in the explosion, a black hole may form instead

Images © ESO/L Calcada/JPL-Caltech/ESA/HST

Some supernovas leave behind spinning neutron stars known as pulsars

© NASA/JPL-Caltech

"Geminga is the closest known supernova to have exploded near Earth, as little as 290 light years away"

rivalling the Moon for brightness, turning night into day. So bright and large was this supernova that the ancients would have seen the light of it stretching from horizon to horizon. Left behind after this supernova was a neutron star rapidly rotating at about four times a second, the nearest neutron star to Earth and the third largest source of gamma rays to us in our observations of the cosmos. Other notable stellar explosions include Supernova 1987A, a star located in the Large Magellanic Cloud that went supernova in 1987. This originated from a supergiant star known as Sanduleak -69°202. It almost outshone the North Star (Polaris) as a result of its brightness, which was comparable to 250 million times that of the Sun.

It is a testament to the scale of these explosions that even ancient civilisations with limited to no astronomical equipment were able to observe them. Supernovas are bright not only visually but in all forms of electromagnetic radiation. They throw out x-rays, cosmic rays, radio waves and, on occasion, may be responsible for causing giant gamma-ray bursts, the largest known explosions in the universe. It is by measuring these forms of electromagnetic radiation that astronomers are able to glean such a clear picture of the formation and demise of supernovas. In fact, it is estimated that 99 per cent of the energy that a supernova exerts is in various forms of electromagnetic radiation other than visible light, making the study of this invisible (to the naked eye at least) radiation incredibly important, and something to which many observatories worldwide are tuned. Another type of stellar explosion you may have heard of is a nova. This is similar in its formation to a supernova, but there is one key difference post explosion: a supernova obliterates the original star, whereas a nova leaves behind an intact star somewhat similar to the original progenitor of the explosion.

Our understanding of the universe so far suggests that pretty much everything runs in cycles. For

"As destructive as they may be, supernovas are integral to the formation of the universe"

Only a Type II supernova can become a black hole

© NASA/JPL-Caltech

Could a superno

The universe is a dangerous place. Black holes, gamma-ray bursts and pulsars could all seriously damage or even destroy our planet if they were close enough, but the fact of the matter is that there is nothing in our vicinity that poses an immediate threat – at least for the next few billion years. The nearest star that could go supernova is Betelgeuse, 640 light years away. In fact this star could be about to go supernova in a minute, a year or a thousand years; all astronomers know is that it has reached its Chandrasekhar limit and it could blow at any second, at which point it will appear as one of the brightest stars (other than the Sun) in the sky. But just how close would a star have to be to cause irreparable damage to Earth?

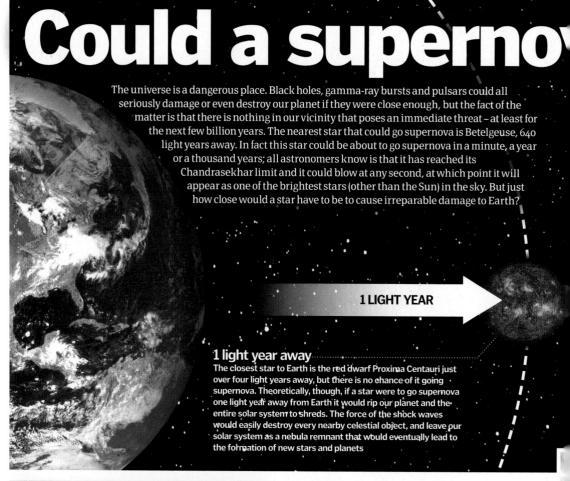

1 LIGHT YEAR

1 light year away
The closest star to Earth is the red dwarf Proxima Centauri just over four light years away, but there is no chance of it going supernova. Theoretically, though, if a star were to go supernova one light year away from Earth it would rip our planet and the entire solar system to shreds. The force of the shock waves would easily destroy every nearby celestial object, and leave our solar system as a nebula remnant that would eventually lead to the formation of new stars and planets

example, a star is born from a cloud of dust and gas, it undergoes nuclear fusion for billions of years, and then destroys itself in a fantastic explosion, creating the very same dust and gas that will lead to the formation of another star. It is thanks to this cyclic nature of the universe that we are able to observe events that would otherwise be extremely rare or nonexistent. If stars were not constantly reforming, there would be none left from the birth of the universe 13.7 billion years ago.

As destructive as they may be, supernovas are integral to the structure and formation of the universe. It is thought that the solar system itself formed from a giant nebula left behind from a supernova while, as mentioned earlier, supernovas are very important in the life cycle of stars and lead to the creation of new stars as the old ones die out. This is because a star contains many of the elements necessary for planetary and stellar formation including large amounts of helium, hydrogen, oxygen and iron, all key components in the structure of celestial bodies. On top of these, many other elements are thought to form during the actual explosion itself.

There's no doubt that supernovas are one of the most destructive forces of the universe, but at the same time they're one of the most essential to the life cycle of solar systems. As we develop more powerful telescopes over the coming years we will be able to observe and study supernovas in more detail, and possibly discover some that do not fall into our current classification of Type I or Type II. The study of supernovas alone can unlock countless secrets of the universe, and as we further our understanding of these colossal stellar explosions we'll be able to learn more about the cosmos as a whole.

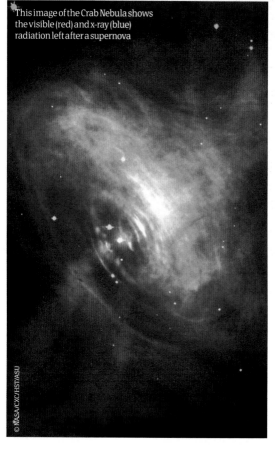

This image of the Crab Nebula shows the visible (red) and x-ray (blue) radiation left after a supernova

© NASA/CXC/HST/ASU

All that remains...
What is left behind once a star goes supernova?

Inside a massive star, before it goes supernova, the nuclei of light elements like hydrogen and helium combine to form the basic constituents of other celestial bodies and even life (such as carbon and oxygen). Stars release these vital elements when they go supernova, providing the material for new stellar and planetary formation.

To date there are roughly 300 known supernova remnants in the universe. Depending on the type and mass of a supernova (see the diagram on the previous page), the remnants left behind can be one of several things. In the vast majority of cases some form of nebula will be left behind. Inside this nebula will often be a spinning neutron star. The rate of spin of this neutron star, also known as a pulsar, depends on the original mass of the exploded star, with some pulsars rotating upwards of a thousand times per minute!

These highly dense stars contain the mass of the Sun packed into an area no bigger than the city of London. If the supernova remnant exceeds four solar masses (the mass of our Sun), due to an extremely heavy initial star or by more material accumulating around the remnant from nearby objects, then the remnant will collapse to form a black hole instead of continuing to expand.

Superstar

One of the most famous supernova remnants in reasonably close proximity to Earth is the Crab Nebula, the remains of a star that went supernova in 1054, about 6,000 light years away. A spinning neutron star known as the Crab Pulsar is located at its centre.

DID YOU KNOW? *The Chandrasekhar limit is named after Indian astrophysicist Subrahmanyan Chandrasekhar*

destroy Earth?

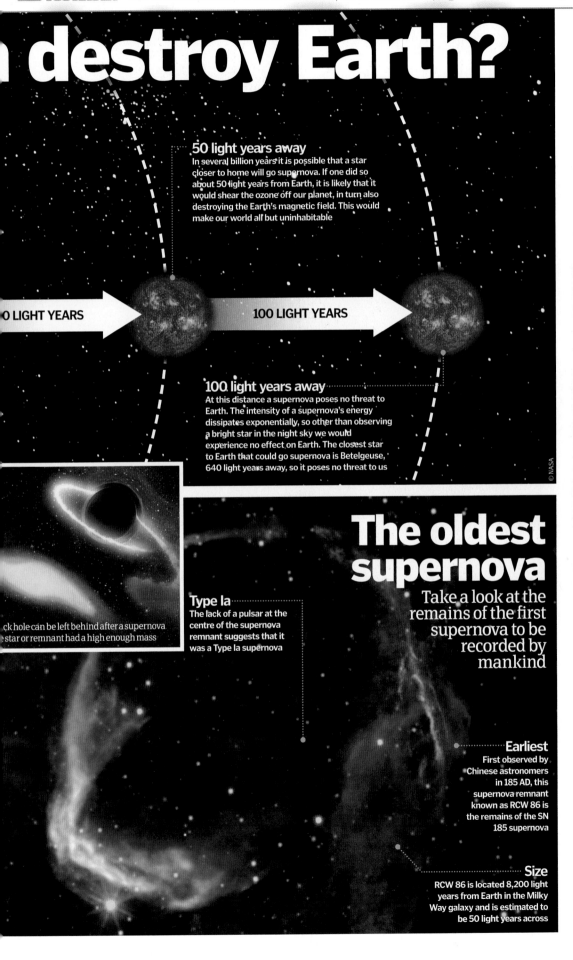

50 light years away

In several billion years it is possible that a star closer to home will go supernova. If one did so about 50 light years from Earth, it is likely that it would shear the ozone off our planet, in turn also destroying the Earth's magnetic field. This would make our world all but uninhabitable

O LIGHT YEARS | **100 LIGHT YEARS**

100 light years away

At this distance a supernova poses no threat to Earth. The intensity of a supernova's energy dissipates exponentially, so other than observing a bright star in the night sky we would experience no effect on Earth. The closest star to Earth that could go supernova is Betelgeuse, 640 light years away, so it poses no threat to us

© NASA

ck hole can be left behind after a supernova
star or remnant had a high enough mass

Type Ia

The lack of a pulsar at the centre of the supernova remnant suggests that it was a Type Ia supernova

The oldest supernova

Take a look at the remains of the first supernova to be recorded by mankind

Earliest

First observed by Chinese astronomers in 185 AD, this supernova remnant known as RCW 86 is the remains of the SN 185 supernova

Size

RCW 86 is located 8,200 light years from Earth in the Milky Way galaxy and is estimated to be 50 light years across

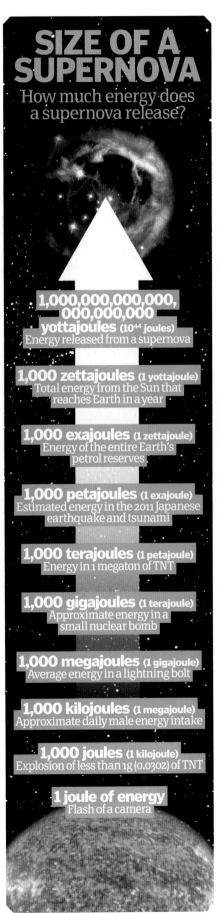

SIZE OF A SUPERNOVA

How much energy does a supernova release?

1,000,000,000,000,000,000,000 yottajoules (10^{44} joules)
Energy released from a supernova

1,000 zettajoules (1 yottajoule)
Total energy from the Sun that reaches Earth in a year

1,000 exajoules (1 zettajoule)
Energy of the entire Earth's petrol reserves

1,000 petajoules (1 exajoule)
Estimated energy in the 2011 Japanese earthquake and tsunami

1,000 terajoules (1 petajoule)
Energy in 1 megaton of TNT

1,000 gigajoules (1 terajoule)
Approximate energy in a small nuclear bomb

1,000 megajoules (1 gigajoule)
Average energy in a lightning bolt

1,000 kilojoules (1 megajoule)
Approximate daily male energy intake

1,000 joules (1 kilojoule)
Explosion of less than 1g (0.03oz) of TNT

1 joule of energy
Flash of a camera

209

Neutron stars

A neutron star sits at the centre of the Crab Nebula

These remnants of supernovae are some of the most massive objects in the universe

A star with a mass of less than 1.5 solar masses (the mass of the Sun) forms a white dwarf at the end of its lifetime, owing to its gravity being too weak to collapse it further. If the mass of a star is greater than five solar masses, the forces will be so intense that the star collapses past the point of a neutron star and becomes a black hole. However, between these two extremes a neutron star will form as the result of a supernova, although only approximately one in a thousand stars will become one.

As a star runs out of fuel it will eventually collapse in upon itself. In the formation of a neutron star, the protons and electrons within every atom are forced together, forming neutrons. Material that is falling to the centre of the star is then crushed by the intense gravitational forces in the star and forms this same neutron material.

Like the Earth, magnetic fields surround neutron stars and are tipped at the axis of rotation, namely the north and south poles. However, the magnetic field of a neutron star is more than a trillion times stronger than that of the Earth's magnetic field.

The gravitational forces in a neutron star are also incredibly strong. The matter is so densely packed together into a radius of 12 miles (20km) that one teaspoon of mass would weigh up to a billion tons, about the same as a mountain. They also spin up to 600 times per second, gradually slowing down as they age.

Oddly enough, as a neutron star gets heavier it also gets smaller. This is because a greater mass means a greater force of gravitational attraction, and therefore the neutrons are squeezed more densely together. In fact, if you were able to drop an object from a height of one metre on the surface of a neutron star, it would hit the ground at about 1,200 miles (2,000km) per second.

Supernovae can leave neutron stars as remnants

© NASA

Magnetar

A neutron star with an extraordinarily large magnetic field is known as a magnetar. Small 'glitches' in the magnetic field of a magnetar can cause giant stellar quakes, one of the largest known explosions in the universe.

© ESO

DID YOU KNOW? The revolution of a neutron star can be so fast that its surface rotates at about 18,640 miles per second

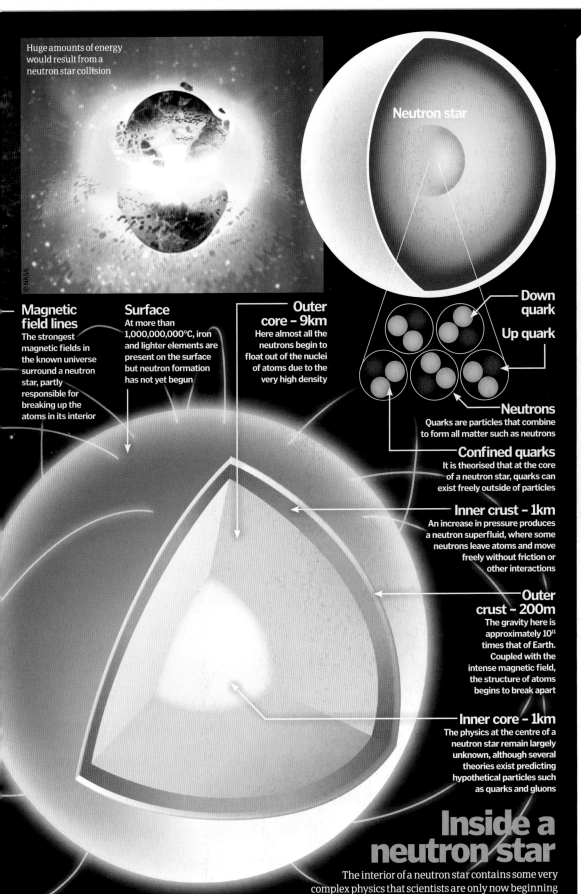

Huge amounts of energy would result from a neutron star collision

© NASA

Neutron star

Down quark

Up quark

Magnetic field lines
The strongest magnetic fields in the known universe surround a neutron star, partly responsible for breaking up the atoms in its interior

Surface
At more than 1,000,000,000°C, iron and lighter elements are present on the surface but neutron formation has not yet begun

Outer core – 9km
Here almost all the neutrons begin to float out of the nuclei of atoms due to the very high density

Neutrons
Quarks are particles that combine to form all matter such as neutrons

Confined quarks
It is theorised that at the core of a neutron star, quarks can exist freely outside of particles

Inner crust – 1km
An increase in pressure produces a neutron superfluid, where some neutrons leave atoms and move freely without friction or other interactions

Outer crust – 200m
The gravity here is approximately 10^{11} times that of Earth. Coupled with the intense magnetic field, the structure of atoms begins to break apart

Inner core – 1km
The physics at the centre of a neutron star remain largely unknown, although several theories exist predicting hypothetical particles such as quarks and gluons

Inside a neutron star

The interior of a neutron star contains some very complex physics that scientists are only now beginning to understand. The conditions are unlike anything found elsewhere in the universe, making neutron stars a unique and fascinating object to examine.

Radiation
Pulsars emit beams of radiation that sweep through our line of sight

Rotating pulsars
Most neutron stars begin life as a rapidly rotating pulsar with strong magnetic fields

© Science Photo Library

Pulses
Pulses of high energy are caused by the rotation and magnetic axis being out of line

Pulsars

A rapidly rotating neutron star that emits jets of particles and a large amount of electromagnetic energy (such as x-rays and light) is known as a pulsar. All neutron stars begin life as a pulsar, but as they age and lose rotational energy they are no longer considered a pulsar. The jets of electromagnetic radiation are fired out from the north and south poles of the pulsar. The gravitational force of a pulsar is so strong that apart from at the poles, matter and even light are not able to escape from its surface.

Pulsars can rotate up to 1,000 times per second, although some spin much faster. Their rate of rotation is so regular that they are the most accurate record of time in the universe; no clock on Earth can replicate their accuracy. We observe pulsars as their emitted radiation sweeps through our line of sight. Their high rotation speeds are due to a misalignment of their rotation and magnetic axis, sending them into an uncontrollable but regular spin.

Stellar quakes

What causes these giant explosions that rock the universe?

At the heart of a stellar quake is a neutron star, which has a highly dense mass of protons and electrons that have been forced together to form neutrons. Neutron stars have up to five times the mass of the Sun but are only about 20 kilometres in diameter. They spin on average at 400 rotations per second, but their strong magnetic fields cause them to slow down over time. The highest observed spin speed of a neutron star is 1,122 rotations per second.

As they rotate, the incredibly strong gravitational force of the star counteracts the spin of the star. The former attempts to draw in the equator, while the centrifugal forces resulting from the spin of the star try to push the equator out. This changes its shape from an oblong to a sphere, cracking the rigid iron crust. Mountains only a few centimetres tall begin to appear across the surface as the tension builds.

Eventually, the tension in the surface reaches such a level that the crust 'snaps' and a huge number of gamma rays and x-rays are released as a stellar quake. As the geometry of the star readjusts, the strong magnetic fields temporarily drop to a lower energy level. Combined with the energy released from inside the star, this creates one of the largest known flashes of x-rays in the universe. ✿

27 December 2004 saw a neutron star flare up so brightly it blinded all the x-ray satellites in space for an instant

© NASA

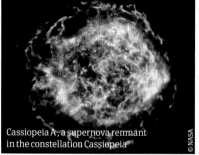

Cassiopeia A, a supernova remnant in the constellation Cassiopeia

© NASA

An image taken by the Chandra Observatory of a giant eruption

© NASA

Magnetars

Recent evidence suggests the primary causes of the largest stellar quakes are magnetars, large neutron stars with an incredibly powerful magnetic field. At twice the size of a regular neutron star, a magnetar can have up to 30 times more mass than the Sun, despite the Sun being 46,000 times larger. A tablespoon of mass from a magnetar would weigh the same as 274 Empire State buildings. The magnetic field of a magnetar is several trillion times stronger than that of Earth while its rigid crust is 10 billion times stronger than steel and 1.5km thick.

© ESO/L. Calçada

1. HOT

The Sun
Our Sun burns hotter and brighter than around 85 per cent of other stars in the Milky Way, at roughly 6,000 Kelvin (5,727°C/10,340°F).

2. HOTTER

Beta Virginis
This white F-type star, aka Zavijava, is found in the constellation Virgo and has a surface temperature of 10,000 Kelvin (9,727°C/17,540°F).

3. HOTTEST

Sigma Orionis
This star is only a few million years old, is bright blue and has a surface temperature of around 30,000 Kelvin (29,727°C/53,540°F).

DID YOU KNOW? *There are approximately 8,000 ultra-blue stars around the centre of the Andromeda galaxy*

Why are some stars blue?

These red giants got blue about being old...

While scanning our spiral neighbour, the Andromeda galaxy, 2.54 million light years away, the Hubble Space Telescope detected a group of bright blue spots near the galactic nucleus. Nothing unusual in that – blue spots are a fairly common sight indicating young, hot supergiant stars. But NASA was surprised to see their ultraviolet light in this region of space and even more surprised to discover that they were dimmer and had a range of surface temperatures that didn't match the profile of infant stars.

In fact, these are rare ultra-blue stars – old red giants past their prime that have ejected most of their surface material to expose hot blue cores. This much ejection is unusual and likely happens because they are richer in chemical elements other than the normal helium and hydrogen, which makes it much easier for the star to slough more layers into space. Another hypothesis is that the proximity to their binary partners makes it easier for them to shed more of their mass.

Towards the end of a star's life, the temperature dramatically rises, transforming it into a red giant

In this area of the Andromeda galaxy, once red giant stars have consumed most of their fuel, the blue inner cores are all that remain

© NASA

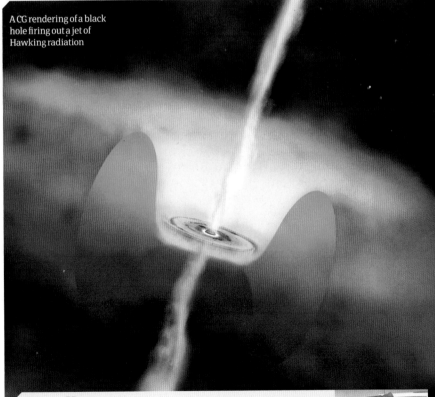

A CG rendering of a black hole firing out a jet of Hawking radiation

Hawking radiation

Find out what can escape from black holes, the universe's ultimate prisons

According to quantum physics, throughout the universe there are endless pairs of subatomic particles that appear from nothingness and almost immediately disappear again. One of these has a negative mass and the other positive, which is why they instantly annihilate each other, but their existence for any determinable length of time is theoretically impossible.

However, Professor Stephen Hawking proposed that around a black hole something rather unusual happens. As in open space these two subatomic particles form, however they do not destroy each other. Instead, the negative mass particle is pulled into the black hole, while the positive one is fired out.

The latter exits in the form of measurable radiation, which is constantly ejected. This was coined 'Hawking radiation', and explains why black holes appear to glow extremely brightly as opposed to being totally dark. Interestingly, the negative-mass particles slowly eat away at the mass inside the black hole. Eventually they consume all of the mass within the entity, causing it to collapse and subsequently explode. While this occurrence has never actually been observed, it's now widely believed to be the eventual fate of almost all black holes.

No dice

Einstein wasn't a fan of quantum physics theories. Believing the universe to be more ordered, he once quipped: "God does not play dice." The discovery of Hawking radiation, however, led Professor Hawking to rebut, "God not only plays dice, but he sometimes throws them where they cannot be seen."

Inside a black hole

Almost incomprehensible in size, black holes are hauntingly beautiful phenomena where the laws of space and time are rewritten. We take a look at the Sagittarius A* black hole at the centre of our galaxy

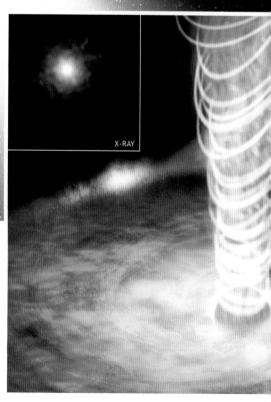

X-RAY

A black hole is a region of space containing, at its centre, matter compressed into a point of infinite density called a singularity (an area where spacetime curvature becomes infinite), which itself is surrounded by a sphere of space where the gravitational pull is so total that not even light can escape its pull – hence its name. The black hole is the result of the deformation and warping of spacetime (a mathematical model where space and time are combined into a single continuum) caused by the total collapse of individual stars or by the coalescence of binary neutron stars.

This collapse occurs at the culmination of a star's life span when, under the pressure of gravity, it is compressed perpetually – unable to resist due to the non-existence of nuclear fusion in its core – until it reaches critical mass. At this point, providing the star is over 1.4 to three solar masses (our Sun equals one solar mass) – a necessity for black hole formation instead of a white dwarf – the star will go into core-collapse supernova, expelling much of its remaining outer layers at one tenth the speed of light and leaving behind either a neutron star or, if the solar mass is high enough, a black hole. ✿

LARGE
1. Stellar-mass black hole
Stellar-mass black holes have masses up to 15-20 solar masses. These mainly form from stars going into core-collapse supernova.

LARGER
2. Intermediate-mass black hole
These type of black holes contain thousands of solar masses. These variants mainly form from collisions of smaller black holes.

LARGEST
3. Supermassive black hole
The biggest black holes by far, supermassive variants can contain hundreds of thousands to billions of solar masses.

DID YOU KNOW? Sagittarius A* is a massive 26,000 light years from Earth

The Milky Way
The position of Sagittarius A* in our galaxy

Sagittarius A* lies at the heart of out galaxy the Milky Way. Unfortunately, from Earth Sagittarius A* is blocked from optical sight and presently scientists can only observe it through the actions of its surrounding stars.

Sagittarius A*

Introducing the Milky Way's very own supermassive black hole

At the heart of almost every galaxy lies a black hole, even our own the Milky Way, which centres on a region of space called Sagittarius A* – at the middle of which lies a supermassive black hole. Black holes like these, however, do not form directly but from the coalescence of multiple smaller stellar-mass and intermediate mass black holes, which then form a supermassive black hole such as Sagittarius A*. Supermassive black holes also often form from the slow accretion of matter from neighbouring stars, the mass collapse of large stellar gas clouds into a relativistic star (a rotating neutron star), or directly from external pressure caused by the Big Bang.

While unimaginable due to its very nature (it absorbs all light), its distance from Earth and the fact that the Sagittarius A* region is removed by 25 magnitudes of extinction from Earth (blocked from optical sight), our own supermassive black hole can only be observed by scientists through the actions of neighbouring cosmic phenomena. Indicating the presence of its existence most notably is the movement of star S2, which has been monitored by scientists following a slow elliptical orbit with a period of 15.2 years and a closest distance of less than 17 light hours from its orbit centre. From the slow motion of S2, scientists have extrapolated that the object which it is orbiting around has a solar mass of 4.1 million, which when taken with its relatively small diameter, strongly affirms that it is a black hole since no other known object can have such a large mass at such a small volume.

Sagittarius A* is a relatively small supermassive black hole when compared with others of its ilk, such as the black hole at the centre of the OJ 287 galaxy, which has a mass of 18 billion solar masses.

An x-ray image of a black hole with accompanying illustration

Composite image of a black hole

Centre
At the heart of the black hole its huge extragalactic jet bursts forth

Ergosphere
The surrounding ergosphere and stellar clouds from which the black hole accretes mass

Event horizon
The event horizon of the black hole, a one-way border in spacetime from which nothing can escape

X-ray

Radio

Optical

All Images © NASA

215

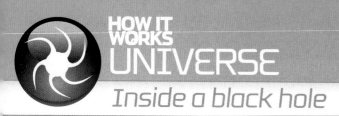
"The simplest black holes have mass but neither charge nor angular momentum"

Inside our black hole

What are its properties and structure?

To understand our Sagittarius A* black hole it is important to understand how black holes in general work. After any black hole stabilises post formation, it has only three possible independent physical properties: charge, mass and angular momentum. Now, when an object is accreted (swallowed) by a black hole its own mass, charge and momentum is equalised with the black hole's own, distributing the matter evenly along its event horizon (a one-way spacetime boundary), which then oscillates like a stretchy membrane. The course that this pattern follows, however, depends on the individual black hole's properties and type.

The simplest black holes have mass but neither charge nor angular momentum, accreting mass to a point-singularity centre, however most types of black hole formed from the core-collapse supernova of a star are thought to retain the nearly neutral charge it once possessed. Other, and theorised by scientists to be far more common, types of black holes – due to the spinning nature of stars – are rotating variants. These form from the collapse of stars or stellar gas with a total non-zero angular momentum and can be both charged and uncharged. These black holes, unlike the totally round, static variants, bulge near their equator under the phenomenal velocity of their spin (the quicker the rotation the more deformed the black hole will be) and instead of accreting matter to a point-singularity do so to a smeared disc singularity. Eventually all black holes, however dependent on their charge or rotation, revert to a non-rotating, uncharged variant.

Unfortunately, from the measurements taken from the stars surrounding our Sagittarius A* black hole, scientists have been left unsure about its physical properties. However, recent research from the University of California, Berkeley, suggests that A* rotates once every 11 minutes or at 30 per cent the speed of light. This information, when combined with the known close proximity of the surrounding stars (a spinning black hole drags space with it, allowing atoms to orbit closer to one that is static), would seem to suggest that not only is the gravitational pull of Sagittarius A* mitigated to a degree by its rotation but also that these measurements are accurate.

Formation of extragalactic jets from black hole accretion disk

Extragalactic jet
Relativistic jets, extremely powerful streams of plasma, carry energy away from the heart of the accretion disk

EXTRAGALACTIC JET

Microlensing magnification region
An illustration depicting swirling clouds of stellar gas pouring into a black hole

Black hole
The singularity at the centre of the black hole. All mass that reaches this point is crushed to infinite density

Accretion disk
The black hole's accretion disk is formed from diffuse material orbiting around its centre

As mass is accreted by a black hole it is heated up under the pressure of gravity

How spacetime is distorted

Away from a black hole, particles can move freely in any direction, only being restricted by the speed of light

EVENT HORIZON

As particles approach the event horizon of the black hole, spacetime starts to deform, restricting the freedom of the paths in which particles can follow

TIME

SPACE

BLACK HOLE

TIME

SPACE

Do the worm

1 Certain theories postulate that rotating black holes could be avoided by entities and actually used as a wormhole shortcut through space and time.

Weakling

2 Despite their colossal size and perpetual accretion of matter, black holes can only suck in matter from a very small surrounding region as gravity is incredibly weak.

Primordial

3 In the current epoch of the universe only the collapse of stars carry the requisite density to form a black hole, however shortly after the big bang densities were greater.

Micro-management

4 Theoretically it is possible for micro-black holes to form through the high-speed collision of sub-atomic particles, although this is unlikely to ever happen.

Spaghetti

5 Any object that passes an event horizon will be stretched into long thin strands under the strong gravitational field of the black hole.

DID YOU KNOW? *The coinage of the phrase 'black hole' didn't occur until 1967*

Let's do the time warp
The theoretical consequences of time and space distortion

The event horizon (a boundary in spacetime through which matter and light can only pass through inwardly) of a black hole is one of its central characteristics, and one that brings a host of issues for any object that passes through it. As predicted by general relativity (our geometric theory on gravitation) due to the colossal mass of the black hole – which by these rules is infinite at the heart of the black hole – spacetime is deformed, as mass has a direct bearing on it. Indeed, when the event horizon is passed, the mass's distortion becomes so great that particle paths are bent inwardly towards the singularity (centre) of the black hole, unable to alter their course. At this point both time and space begin to be warped.

The consequences of this, while theoretical, are mind blowing. For example, general theory states that if a hypothetical astronaut were about to cross the event horizon of a black hole, then apart from being stretched physically (spaghettification), they'd also be stretched in time. So, while the astronaut would pass the event horizon at a finite point in his own time, to a hypothetical distant observer, he'd appear to slow down, taking an infinite time to reach it. Further, if the astronaut were wearing a watch, it would tick more slowly as he approached the event horizon than a watch worn by the observer, an effect known as gravitational time dilation. Finally, when the astronaut reached the singularity, he'd be crushed to infinite density and over an infinite time (to the observer) before having his mass added to that of the black hole.

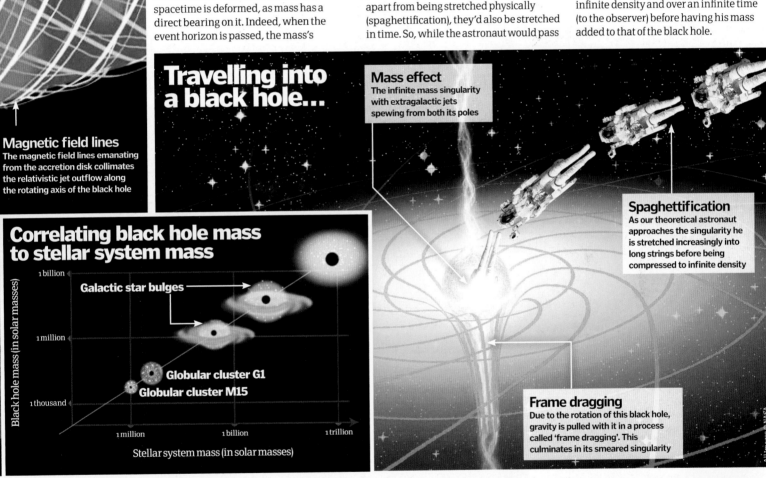

Travelling into a black hole...

Magnetic field lines
The magnetic field lines emanating from the accretion disk collimates the relativistic jet outflow along the rotating axis of the black hole

Mass effect
The infinite mass singularity with extragalactic jets spewing from both its poles

Spaghettification
As our theoretical astronaut approaches the singularity he is stretched increasingly into long strings before being compressed to infinite density

Frame dragging
Due to the rotation of this black hole, gravity is pulled with it in a process called 'frame dragging'. This culminates in its smeared singularity

Correlating black hole mass to stellar system mass

Black hole mass (in solar masses):
- 1 billion
- 1 million
- 1 thousand

Galactic star bulges

Globular cluster G1
Globular cluster M15

Stellar system mass (in solar masses):
- 1 million
- 1 billion
- 1 trillion

All images © NASA

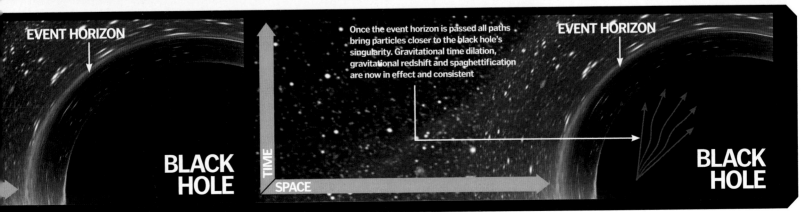

EVENT HORIZON

BLACK HOLE

Once the event horizon is passed all paths bring particles closer to the black hole's singularity. Gravitational time dilation, gravitational redshift and spaghettification are now in effect and consistent

EVENT HORIZON

BLACK HOLE

TIME

SPACE

"Quasars accrete matter from a supermassive black hole from their centre"

Quasars

The supermassive black holes that are trillions of times brighter than our Sun

Quasars (quasi-stellar radar sources) are the size of our solar system but contain the mass of over a million stars. This statistic initially baffled scientists as quasars outshone galaxies containing billions of stars, significantly larger bodies in the universe, by 100 times.

The answer is that quasars accrete matter from a supermassive black hole at their centre, 'supermassive' being defined as up to a few billion times the mass of our Sun. Quasars are found at the centre of galaxies and are known as active galactic nuclei, taking in several solar masses of

matter every year. One of the most powerful objects in the universe, quasars are present in about 5-10% of all galactic centres.

The mass of swirling gas surrounding a quasar is responsible for its incredible luminosity, being heavily heated by the intense gravitational forces in action. They are so dense that some will only emit this high level of electromagnetic radiation for a few hours, and may halve or double their output in as little as a week. Quasars are live for a few billion years and are usually only present in galaxies at the start of their lifetime in the universe.

Gravitational waves

The near undetectable fluctuations of space-time that bend the cosmos

Gravitational waves are fluctuations in the fabric of space-time caused by the motion of matter. Violent events in the universe, such as two black holes colliding, produce these ripples that propagate through space at, or near, the speed of light. They travel much like a wave, stretching and shrinking distances but becoming weaker as they move further from their source. While the movement of any matter produces gravitational waves, it is only large-scale events that will produce any detectable readings. Gravitational waves, predicted by Einstein's theory of general relativity, have so far been almost impossible to detect, and the main proof to date of their existence was the discovery of a binary system containing two neutron stars in 1974. Measuring the oscillation of space-time due to gravitational waves is equivalent to measuring the change in the size of an atom within the distance from the Sun to the Earth. Today the search for a detectable gravitational wave goes on at observatories in the USA, firing light down two long tubes measuring 2.5 miles (4km) at right angles to each other and detecting differences in the reflected light.

The Laser Interferometer Gravitational-Wave Observatory (LIGO) in Livingston USA, is used to search for gravitational waves

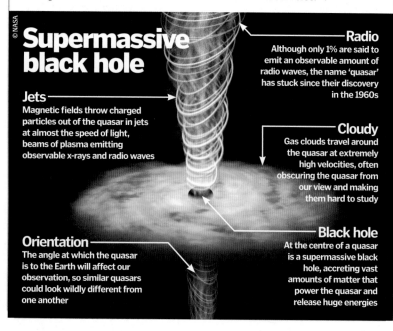

Supermassive black hole

Jets
Magnetic fields throw charged particles out of the quasar in jets at almost the speed of light, beams of plasma emitting observable x-rays and radio waves

Radio
Although only 1% are said to emit an observable amount of radio waves, the name 'quasar' has stuck since their discovery in the 1960s

Cloudy
Gas clouds travel around the quasar at extremely high velocities, often obscuring the quasar from our view and making them hard to study

Orientation
The angle at which the quasar is to the Earth will affect our observation, so similar quasars could look wildly different from one another

Black hole
At the centre of a quasar is a supermassive black hole, accreting vast amounts of matter that power the quasar and release huge energies

This NASA visualisation of two merging black holes applies Einstein's theory of general relativity to illustrate gravitational waves

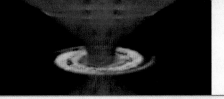

DID YOU KNOW? *The Cygnus X-1 supergiant's ominous companion used to be a star around ten times the mass of our Sun*

Exploring event horizons

What makes these a black hole's point of no return?

There are three basic elements to a black hole explained by general relativity. There's the singularity itself, at the heart of a black hole and made of stellar matter compressed to an infinite density. Outside the singularity is the black hole's interior space, a region that's hard for even the most learned astronomers to imagine, where the rules of physics as we know them get bent and broken, and where space and time are stretched and compressed like putty.

If you've been zooming about interstellar space in your impossibly fast spacecraft, stumbled upon a black hole and entered its interior space, then it's already too late for you because you're past the third component of a black hole: its event horizon.

Also known as the Schwarzschild radius (after German physicist Karl Schwarzschild), it's the part that lets us know where black holes are by outlining them in black. It marks the point of no return for anything falling beyond it, as to re-cross it would require travelling faster than the speed of light, which – as far as we know – is impossible.

Event horizons aren't solely attributed to black holes – they're just a noteworthy phenomenon that possesses them. According to some theories governing the expansion of the cosmos, there are areas that won't ever be observable because light will never reach us from them. So the boundary limit at which we can observe the universe is also referred to as an event horizon. ✿

What did Karl Schwarzschild do?

Physicist Karl Schwarzschild solved part of Einstein's theory that calculated the size of a black hole's event horizon, or Schwarzschild radius. It states that any mass can become a black hole as long as it can collapse down to its Schwarzschild radius, although in the case of massive stellar objects two to three times the size of our Sun, this is inevitable. Typically, a supermassive star like this will consume all its fuel before gravity leads it to collapse past electron/neutron degeneracy and it passes its own event horizon to become a singularity.

CG artwork of a black hole in the spiral galaxy MCG-6-30-15, which was found to emit vast amounts of energy by ESA's XMM-Newton orbiting observatory

Accretion discs explained

Black holes are usually only detected when near another celestial body, such as Cygnus X-1 in the constellation Cygnus. Here, what used to be a pair of stars actually turns out to be a hot blue supergiant and the remnants of its former companion, which has devoured all its nuclear fuel and collapsed to become a singularity. The black hole is stripping the blue star of material, 'sucking' gas into it, which forms an accretion disc around the event horizon. This gas emits radiation on multiple wavelengths, including visible light and X-rays – 90 per cent of which is absorbed by the black hole. However, ten per cent is radiated away from the event horizon, enabling us to observe the accretion disc and estimate where the black hole is located.

Below-left: Image of Cygnus X-1, highlighted in red
Below-right: An artist's concept of Cygnus X-1, with an accretion disc marking its event horizon

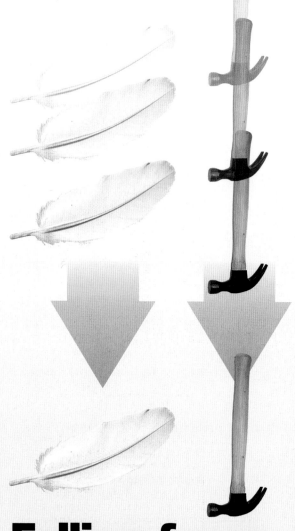

Falling force

Legend has it that Galileo famously disproved Aristotle by dropping two cannonballs of different mass from the top of the Tower of Pisa and showing that they land simultaneously. In 1971, astronaut Dave Scott dropped a feather and a hammer on the moon, proving that all objects fall at the same rate in a vacuum.

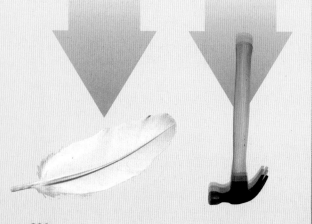

What is

Surprisingly weak yet mysteriously powerful, gravity is the super glue of the universe

 Everything in the universe is made of matter – the cosmic 'stuff' of creation. Mass is a measurement of the amount of matter contained in any object, from planets to protons. The Earth, for example, has a mass of 5.9742×10^{24} kilograms, while the mass of a single proton is $1.67262158 \times 10{-27}$ kilograms.

When we think of gravity, we usually think of the gravitational force exerted by massive (literally) celestial bodies like the Earth, the Moon or the Sun. But the truth is that any object of any mass – even a sub-atomic particle – exerts a gravitational pull on nearby objects.

Sir Isaac Newton proved that objects of greater mass exert a stronger gravitational force. That's why we typically talk about gravity in reference to planets and not protons. But the shocking truth about gravity is that even a colossal hunk of rock like the Earth exerts an exceptionally puny pull. An infant, in fact, can defeat the combined gravitational pull of every single atom on the planet by lifting a wooden block off the floor.

That's what makes Newton's discoveries so amazing, even today. Gravity – this wimp of a force – is somehow powerful enough to pull the moon into orbit and keep the Earth cruising in a perfect elliptical path around the Sun. Without the constant tug of gravity, planets would crumble into dust and stars would collapse.

Gravity is also responsible for giving objects weight. But don't confuse weight with mass. While mass is a measurement of the amount of matter in an object, weight is the downward force exerted by all of that matter in a gravitational field. In the zero-gravity vacuum of space, objects are weightless, but they still have mass.

On the surface of the Earth, where the force of gravity is essentially constant, we consider mass and weight to be equal. But that same object – with the same mass – will weigh 17 per cent less on the Moon, where the gravitational pull is weaker. On Jupiter – not the best place to start a diet – that same object will weigh 213 per cent more. ✿

Issac Newton

Sir Isaac Newton was born in 1642, the same year that Galileo died. While Galileo proved that objects of different masses fell at the same rate, it wasn't until Newton published his revolutionary *Principia Mathematica* – the most influential physics text of all time – that this mysterious force was finally given a name: gravity.

Newton's Universal Law of Gravitation was the first to explain gravity in clear, mathematical terms. It was also the first truly 'unified' theory, explaining both earthly and heavenly mechanics. To readers of his day, it would have been completely inconceivable to imagine that the same force that pulls apples from trees could also coax the Moon into orbit.

Over 300 years after their publication, Newton's elegant formulas still played a vital role in putting humans on the Moon for the first time.

5 TOP FACTS
GRAVITY

Black hole
1 A black hole's gravitational pull is so strong that even light can't escape from what's known as its 'event horizon', an invisible boundary around it.

Mighty moon
2 The Moon's low gravity means objects weigh one sixth of their Earth weight. A strong man could lift a small car on the Moon!

Escape velocity
3 Deimos, a moon of Mars, has such low gravity that if you jumped, you'd easily achieve escape velocity and send yourself into space.

Gravity and fitness
4 Prolonged exposure to zero gravity poses health risk for astronauts, including bone loss, muscle atrophy and even immune problems.

Pulling power
5 Size and mass effect gravity: Uranus has 14.5 times the mass of Earth but because of its size, it only has around 90 per cent of Earth's gravity.

DID YOU KNOW? Albert Einstein won the Nobel Prize for Physics in 1921

gravity?

Albert Einstein

While Newton was able to mathematically prove the existence of gravity, he had no idea where it came from or how it actually worked. In the Newtonian world view, gravity was a constant, independent force that acted instantaneously. If the Sun were to disappear, Newton argued, then the planets would immediately spin off into the void.

In 1905, a young and unknown Albert Einstein postulated that light travelled at a discrete speed limit through the vacuum of space. Since nothing can travel faster than light, the force of gravity cannot act instantaneously. If the Sun disappeared, it would take over eight minutes for the loss of gravity to be felt by Earth.

But Einstein's most mind-boggling gravitational insight came in 1916 with the General Theory of Relativity. In his radical view of the universe, the three dimensions of space are merged with a fourth dimension of time and represented as a flexible, two-dimensional 'space-time' fabric.

According to Einstein, objects of great mass act like bowling balls on a trampoline, bending and warping the space-time fabric. If a smaller object rolls too close one of these bowling balls, it will be drawn toward it. Gravity is not some mysterious independent force, but the result of the collective wrinkles in the fabric of the universe.

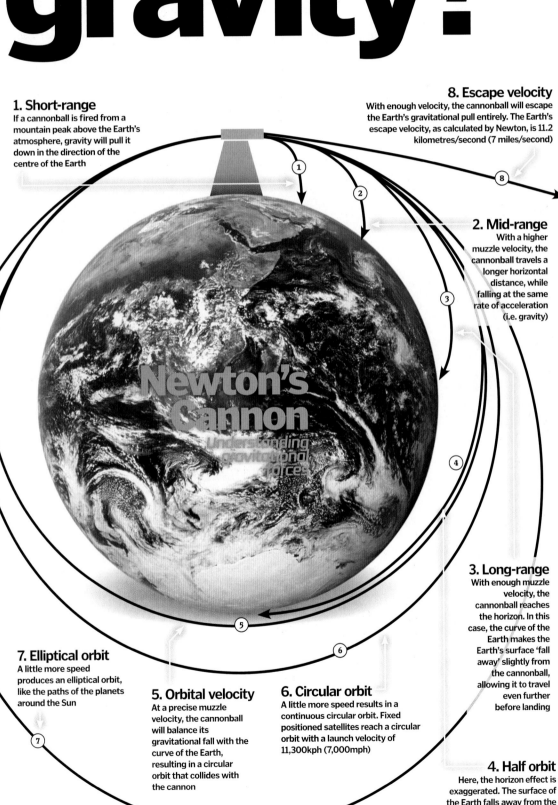

Newton's Cannon
Understanding gravitational forces

1. Short-range
If a cannonball is fired from a mountain peak above the Earth's atmosphere, gravity will pull it down in the direction of the centre of the Earth

8. Escape velocity
With enough velocity, the cannonball will escape the Earth's gravitational pull entirely. The Earth's escape velocity, as calculated by Newton, is 11.2 kilometres/second (7 miles/second)

2. Mid-range
With a higher muzzle velocity, the cannonball travels a longer horizontal distance, while falling at the same rate of acceleration (i.e. gravity)

3. Long-range
With enough muzzle velocity, the cannonball reaches the horizon. In this case, the curve of the Earth makes the Earth's surface 'fall away' slightly from the cannonball, allowing it to travel even further before landing

7. Elliptical orbit
A little more speed produces an elliptical orbit, like the paths of the planets around the Sun

5. Orbital velocity
At a precise muzzle velocity, the cannonball will balance its gravitational fall with the curve of the Earth, resulting in a circular orbit that collides with the cannon

6. Circular orbit
A little more speed results in a continuous circular orbit. Fixed positioned satellites reach a circular orbit with a launch velocity of 11,300kph (7,000mph)

4. Half orbit
Here, the horizon effect is exaggerated. The surface of the Earth falls away from the cannonball nearly equal to gravity's rate of acceleration

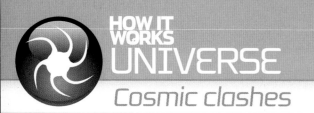

"Only one direct collision between two asteroids has ever been observed"

Asteroid colli

What happens when one asteroid impacts another?

This image of asteroid P/2010 A2 was snapped by the Hubble Space Telescope in January 2010 – the first asteroid collision to be directly observed

© NASA, ESA, and D. Jewitt (University of California, Los Angeles)

Throughout the solar system, there are potentially millions of asteroids – rocks left over from the formation of the solar system some 4.5 billion years ago – just waiting to be discovered. Some will have been ejected from a planet following a collision, such as the Pluto-sized object believed to have crashed into Mars early in its formation. Others are the remnants of failed planetary formation, often unsuccessful due to the effects of a nearby body. One culprit, Jupiter, prevented the formation of another planet between itself and Mars, leaving the asteroid belt.

With millions of asteroids travelling through the solar system – many of these confined to the Kuiper belt beyond Neptune and the aforementioned asteroid belt – it is often thought that collisions between them are frequent. Indeed, many works of fiction portray asteroid belts as dense areas of rock that are difficult for a spacecraft to traverse. However, this is anything but the case. Asteroid collisions are very, very rare. The chance of two colliding is roughly equivalent to winning the lottery every day for a week. Only one direct collision between two asteroids has ever been observed, with thanks going to the Hubble Space Telescope in January 2010. It will most likely be many years before another is seen, but that doesn't make the study of these collisions any less important. On the contrary, by having an advanced knowledge of what to expect if we see two asteroids collide, or seeing the aftermath of a collision we may have missed, we'll be able to glean more information about their composition, origin and importance in the solar system the next time we witness a collision. ✿

TYPES OF COLLISION

There are many more small asteroids in the solar system than large ones, so it is extremely unlikely that two large asteroids of comparable size will ever hit one another. Instead, the collision of a small asteroid with one more than 50,000 times bigger is more common. For every million asteroids that are 0.1 kilometres (0.06 miles) wide, there are only 1,000 wider than one kilometres (0.6 miles), and just one bigger than ten kilometres (six miles). For this reason, as seen in our diagrams, cratering is much more common than fracturing, which happens more regularly than shattering.

CRATERING

1. Approach
Cratering occurs when the incoming asteroid is less than 1/50,000th the size of the larger body

2. Impact
A crater ten times the size of the impactor forms on the surface

3. Debris
Ejected debris falls into the same orbit around the Sun as the asteroid, and thus can hit it again

1. Approach
If the incoming asteroid is exactly 1/50,000th the size of the larger asteroid, it will cause a fracturing collision

2. Impact
Most of the energy in the collision is used up in breaking the larger asteroid into pieces, forming cracks across the surface

COLLISION

1. Shoemaker-Levy
In July 1994, Comet Shoemaker-Levy 9 collided with Jupiter, providing the first observation of such a collision in our solar system.
© SEDS D. Seal

FATALITY

2. Nakhla
In 1911, a meteor landed in Nakhla, Egypt, apparently killing a dog. If this myth is true, it is the only recorded meteor fatality.
© NASA

MAN-MADE

3. Tempel 1
NASA sent an impactor probe crashing into the comet Tempel 1 in 2005. This was the first mission to artificially eject material from a comet.
© NASA/JPL

DID YOU KNOW? At least one new asteroid has been discovered every year since 1847

sions

Asteroids vs comets

What's the difference between asteroids and comets?

Asteroids and comets are both remnants of the early formation of the solar system 4.5 billion years ago. As of August 2011, there were less than 4,500 known comets in the solar system, compared to over 550,000 known asteroids (although there are thought to be many millions more).

Asteroids are composed of rocky material and metals, while comets are made of ice. As a result, asteroids formed nearer the Sun than comets, because ice could not remain solid at a close distance. Comets that formed further out and later approached the Sun lose material with each orbit because the ice melts, forming a tail behind the body. Asteroids, on the other hand, do not lose material, and thus do not have a tail.

Comets are often found in large elongated orbits extending outwards up to 50,000 times the distance from the Earth to the Sun. By comparison, Neptune – the furthest planet of the solar system – is just 30 times further from the Sun than the Earth. Concurrently, asteroids are usually found following a circular orbit around the Sun and they tend to group together in belts, such as the asteroid belt found between Jupiter and Mars, which was formed when the gravitational pull of Jupiter prevented the asteroids from forming into another planet.

© NASA

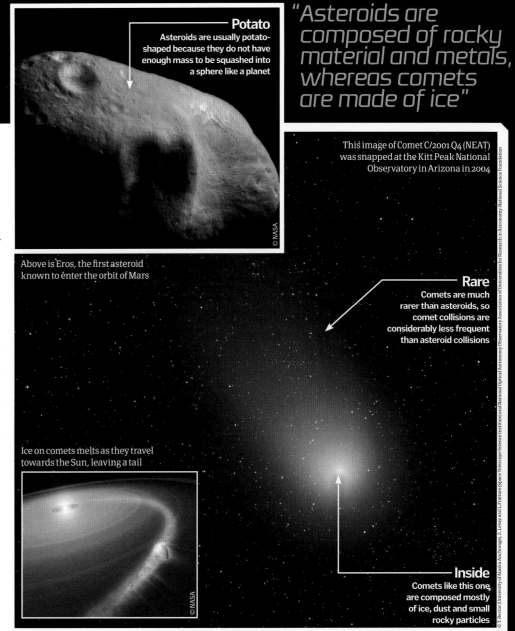

Potato
Asteroids are usually potato-shaped because they do not have enough mass to be squashed into a sphere like a planet

"Asteroids are composed of rocky material and metals, whereas comets are made of ice"

This image of Comet C/2001 Q4 (NEAT) was snapped at the Kitt Peak National Observatory in Arizona in 2004

Above is Eros, the first asteroid known to enter the orbit of Mars

Rare
Comets are much rarer than asteroids, so comet collisions are considerably less frequent than asteroid collisions

Ice on comets melts as they travel towards the Sun, leaving a tail

© NASA

Inside
Comets like this one are composed mostly of ice, dust and small rocky particles

© T. Rector (University of Alaska Anchorage), Z. Levey and L.Frattare (Space Telescope Science Institute) and National Optical Astronomy Observatory/Association of Universities for Research in Astronomy-National Science Foundation

---

...TURING

SHATTERING

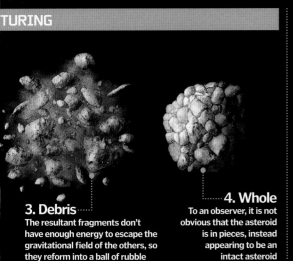

3. Debris
The resultant fragments don't have enough energy to escape the gravitational field of the others, so they reform into a ball of rubble

4. Whole
To an observer, it is not obvious that the asteroid is in pieces, instead appearing to be an intact asteroid

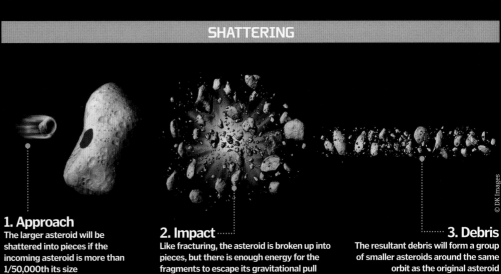

1. Approach
The larger asteroid will be shattered into pieces if the incoming asteroid is more than 1/50,000th its size

2. Impact
Like fracturing, the asteroid is broken up into pieces, but there is enough energy for the fragments to escape its gravitational pull

3. Debris
The resultant debris will form a group of smaller asteroids around the same orbit as the original asteroid

© DK Images

The ESA and NASA's Ulysses spacecraft unexpectedly stumbled across a comet tail

The blue ion tail and the dust tail of Hale-Bopp are both clearly visible here

This photograph of Halley's comet was taken in 1910

Comet tails

What's trailing behind and in front of these rocks as they hurtle through space?

Comets are small, icy bodies in orbit around the Sun surrounded by a gaseous coma that consists of water, carbon dioxide and other gases. The most noticeable features of a comet are its tails, with most having two: a dust and ion tail. Both tails point away from the Sun at varying angles due to the solar wind, regardless of the comet's directions.

The dust tail of a comet appears whitish-yellow, because its microscopic dust particles reflect sunlight. It is anywhere from 600,000 to 6 million miles (1 to 10 million km) in length, pushed out from the comet by the solar wind and curving slightly because of the comet's orbit around the Sun. The other tail, known as the plasma or ion tail, is composed of charged gases (ions) such as carbon monoxide, and stretches as far as 100 million miles (160 million km) from the comet. The solar wind also pushes this tail away, but it is largely unaffected by the comet's orbit. This means that when the comet approaches the Sun the tail runs behind it, but when the comet moves away from the Sun, the ion tail leads in front of the comet.

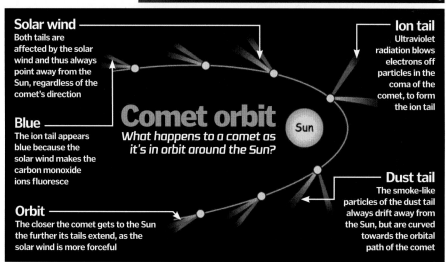

Solar wind
Both tails are affected by the solar wind and thus always point away from the Sun, regardless of the comet's direction

Blue
The ion tail appears blue because the solar wind makes the carbon monoxide ions fluoresce

Orbit
The closer the comet gets to the Sun the further its tails extend, as the solar wind is more forceful

Comet orbit
What happens to a comet as it's in orbit around the Sun?

Sun

Ion tail
Ultraviolet radiation blows electrons off particles in the coma of the comet, to form the ion tail

Dust tail
The smoke-like particles of the dust tail always drift away from the Sun, but are curved towards the orbital path of the comet

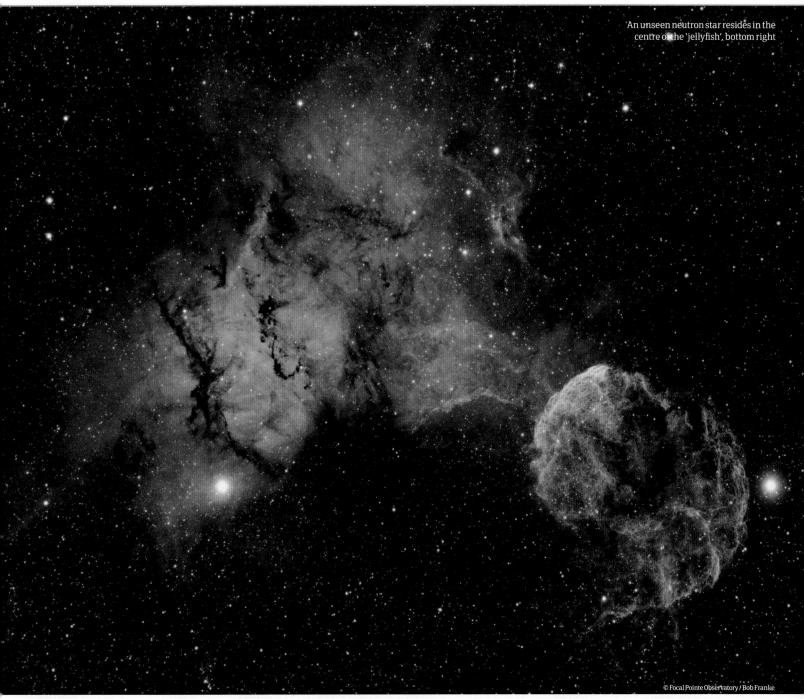

'An unseen neutron star resides in the centre of the 'jellyfish', bottom right

© Focal Pointe Observatory / Bob Franke

The jellyfish nebula

We take a look at this oddly shaped supernova remnant

The jellyfish nebula is so named for the odd-shaped object at the bottom-right of this image. In the image the emission of oxygen, hydrogen and sulphur are shown in blue, green and red respectively. The 'jellyfish' is a supernova remnant, formed when a star went supernova over 30,000 years ago. This event sent out shockwaves through space that swept up and heated interstellar dust and gas, creating the spectacle we can now see. The northern part of the 'jellyfish' was created by a fast shockwave moving at about 360,010km/h (223,700mph), while the southern part was the result of a slower shockwave that travelled at 108,000km/h (67,100mph). At the centre of the remnant is a dense neutron star, left when the initial star exploded.

The jellyfish nebula is roughly 5,000 light years away and about 300 light years across. Either side of the 'jellyfish' you can see two bright stars: Mu Geminorum and Eta Geminorum. The former (on the left of the image) is a red giant 68 light years closer to Earth than the nebula, while the latter (on the right of the image) is also a red giant but 50 light years further away than the nebula. In the main, central part of the image is an emission nebula known as 'sharpless 249', formed from the emission of hot, ionised gases from a nearby hot star. ⚙

225

Searching for alien messages

1. Vast potential
The Milky Way galaxy contains 500 million stars, which have exoplanets in the habitable zone that are capable of supporting intelligent life forms

2. Signal
If aliens create technology like ours they might strive to contact other alien civilisations, using radio signals in the electromagnetic spectrum

3. Distance
Star systems with known exoplanets are from 20 to 75,000 light years away. Any message will already be as old as the time it takes to get here

4. Reception
Radio telescopes have to filter out interference from man-made and natural radio emissions, and target areas of the galaxy and wavelengths that are most likely to be sending out signals

5. Message
What kind of message can we expect? Will we be able to decode it if it contains complex information? Should we answer it?

The search for extraterrestrial life

Our galaxy could be the home to millions of different alien life forms, but how do we find them?

5 TOP FACTS
FALSE ALARMS

Martian canals
1 At the beginning of the 20th Century, American astronomer Percival Lowell popularised the idea that long dark lines on Mars were canals built by intellectual Martians.

Signals from Mars
2 Nikola Tesla received signals that repeated the numbers 1, 2, 3 and 4. He claimed they came from Mars, but research suggests they were radio emanations from Jupiter.

CTA 102
3 Gennady Sholomitskii believed a powerful variable radio emission represented a signal from a super civilisation. It was later identified as a quasar, designated CTA 102.

Little green men
4 Jocelyn Bell and Antony Hewish discovered a 1.3373-sec signal via radio telescope. They named it 'little green men' (LGM-1), but it was the first pulsar (CP1919).

GCRTJ1745-3009
5 The Very Large Array telescope at Socorro, New Mexico recorded five highly energetic low-frequency radio emissions in 2002. They might be caused by a pulsar or neutron star.

DID YOU KNOW? *Carl Friedrich Gauss suggested cutting a giant Pythagoras triangle in the Siberian forest to signal to ETs*

Virtually every part of our planet is teeming with life, and it would be extraordinary that life – even on the lowest microbial level – does not exist on planets beyond our solar system. On a statistical level, our Milky Way spiral galaxy has a diameter of 100,000 light years and contains between 200 and 400 billion stars, a quarter of which have planets orbiting them. Of them, there could be 500 million planets that move in the habitable zone that can sustain life like our own.

If an alien civilisation were to reach our level of technological ability, it seems only logical that they would beam out messages in search of other life forms. The main restriction is that energy, matter, or information cannot travel faster than the speed of light – which is 300,000 kilometres (186,411 miles) per second. A far-flung alien message might take some 75,000 light years to reach Earth. Indeed, at best the nearest habitable zone planet, called Gliese 581g, is around 20 light years away.

When Enrico Fermi looked at the odds of intelligent life evolving to our level of technology, he was surprised that we had not been contacted already. The Fermi paradox is that despite the probability of extraterrestrial life, we have no evidence of its presence. There are several answers to the Fermi paradox; it might simply be that we are alone and that our creation was a very rare series of events that has not been duplicated elsewhere. Intelligent life forms might have a tendency to die out through natural disaster or warfare, or they could have transcended our technology and use more sophisticated forms of communication that are currently beyond our means of detection.

Radio telescopes have mainly been used to listen for any regular 'alien' signals in a narrow radio bandwidth. Another possibility is that aliens might signal to us in the optical wavelengths using powerful laser beams. In 2006 the Planetary Society began searching for an extraterrestrial laser signal using a 1.8-metre (72-inch) reflecting telescope. Although it processes as much data in one second as all books in print, it has only detected a few pulses of light as it searches the northern hemisphere, and all of them have been ruled out as extra terrestrial signals.

Astrobiologists consider the possibilities of detecting alien microbial life through their biosignature. Extremophile Earth microorganisms have been found to survive and reproduce, which at least offers some hope to finding this type of microbial life elsewhere in the solar system. Astrobiologists are also working on mass spectrometers and high-energy

Habitable zones...
...and where we are looking

1. Venus
Outside the inner boundary of the HZ – too hot (460°C) to sustain life

2. Earth
Earth orbits in the centre of the habitable zone that surrounds the Sun

3. Mars
Mars is on the outer boundary of the HZ; further exploration will determine if it is or was in the HZ

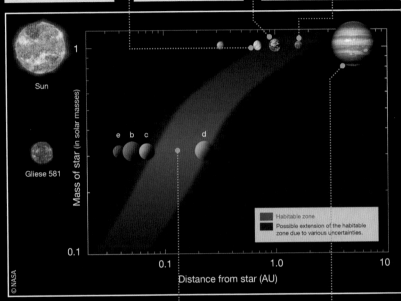

5. Extrasolar planets
Extrasolar planets, like Gliese 581d and g, are in an HZ that is closer to its smaller parent star

4. Jupiter
Although Jupiter and Saturn are outside the HZ, some of their moons might have primitive organisms living on them

The habitable zone (HZ) is a belt of space around a star that is either too hot or too cold for life to exist on any planet orbiting in this zone. The habitable zone is often called the Goldilocks zone after the children's story, referring to finding conditions for life that are "just right". The HZ varies according to the size, mass, luminosity and life-cycle of the parent star. Stars with a low mass and luminosity will have an HZ closer to them than a larger, brighter star. Unstable or short-lived stars are less likely to nurture life.

Primitive life might live outside the HZ, but it is very likely to be microbial or extremely different to 'life' as we know it. It is also postulated that life only occurs in star systems in the galactic habitable zone (GHZ), that are close enough to the galactic centre to form Earth-like planets but far enough away from fatal levels of radioactivity. The GHZ of our galaxy is about 6,000 light years wide and 25,000 light years from the centre.

SETI research concentrates its efforts on the newly discovered extrasolar planets in their respective habitable zone, and radio telescopes concentrate on

listening to transmissions between 1,420 MHz (21cm) emissions from neutral hydrogen and 1,666 MHz (18cm) emissions from hydroxyl. This quiet range of the electromagnetic spectrum, nicknamed the water hole, is a logical place for water-based life to send signals as hydrogen and hydroxyl form water.

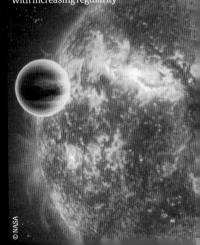

Extrasolar planets are being discovered with increasing regularity

The Drake equation

American astronomer Frank Drake formulated the Drake equation in 1961, to estimate the number of possible intelligent extraterrestrial civilisations that might exist in our Milky Way galaxy

N
The number of alien civilisations capable of transmitting signals into space, based on estimates in the rest of the equation

ne
The number of planets that might potentially support living organisms

fi
The fraction of planets that develop can intelligent life

L
The length of time alien civilisations might exist and send out communications

$$N = R^* \, f_p \, n_e \, f_l \, f_i \, f_c \, L$$

R*
This estimates the yearly rate of star formations in the Milky Way galaxy

fp
The fraction of star formations that support planetary systems

fl
The proportion of planets that actually develop and nurture living organisms

fc
The number of alien civilisations that can create a technology to broadcast signals into space

Is there anybody out there?

The Berkeley Open Infrastructure for Network Computing version of SETI@ home harnesses your computer's unused power to analyse signal patterns

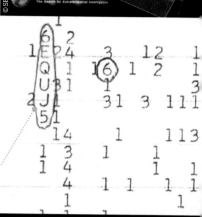

x-rays to detect life that does not consist of RNA, DNA or proteins.

Meteorites have been closely examined to see if they contain evidence of alien life forms. The Allan Hills 84001 (ALH84001) meteorite, which is thought to have come from Mars 13,000 years ago, was declared by David McKay to contain minute traces of fossilised bacteria. This hit the headlines in 1996, but terrestrial contamination and non-biological processes have been given as alternative explanations. Microfossils in carbonaceous meteorites were also discovered by astrobiologist Richard B Hoover in March 2011.

SETI (Search for Extraterrestrial Intelligence) research has also had several false alarms, the most famous being the so-called 'Wow' signal received in 1977 by the Big Ear radio telescope at the Ohio State University. Dr Jerry Ehman was so impressed by the 72-second long signal originating from the constellation Sagittarius, he wrote "Wow!" next to the alphanumeric code 6EQUJ5 on the printout.

It has never been detected again and might have been created by a terrestrial signal.

Until recently, we were not sure that star systems hosted Earth-like planets. Since October 1995 when a Hot Jupiter extrasolar planet was found in the Pegasus constellation, 50 light years away, hundreds of extrasolar planets have been discovered. NASA's Kepler spacecraft was launched in 2009 to search for Earth-sized planets in the habitable zone of star systems up to 3,000 light years away, which are on the same galactic plane as Earth. So far, it's discovered 54 planets orbiting in the habitable zone of its parent planet. Now these planets have been identified, work is being carried out to find oxygen and other chemical signatures that might indicate that they actually harbour life on them.

When, or if, we find primitive life or contact intelligent ET life depends on whether there is life to find. Throughout our search, we need to take into account exotic or advanced ET life forms that might be unrecognisable to us. ✿

For more information about SETI@ home, visit the website http:// setiathome.berkeley.edu

The wow factor
The note Dr Jerry Ehman scribbled to indicate his amazement of the 72-sec long signal via radio telescope

What is SETI?

SETI (Search for Extraterrestrial Intelligence) is conducted by several organisations to detect extraterrestrial life. SETI@home is unique because instead of using a huge supercomputer purpose-built to analyse the data collected by a specific radio telescope, it uses internet-connected computers to create a virtual supercomputer.

SETI@home software works as a screensaver, which borrows your computer when you're not using it. It collects the data in small chunks from the internet, analyses it and then sends the results back to SETI@home. The digital data is taken piggyback from the Arecibo telescope. The network is linked to 456,922 active computers worldwide and is run

by the Space Sciences Laboratory at the University of California. Despite the equivalent of 2 million years of computing time, it has yet to come across an unambiguous ET signal. A weak signal was observed from SHGb02+14a between the Pisces and Aries constellations at the 1420MHz frequency. There is no star system observable at this location and could have been produced by a technical glitch.

The SETI Institute is a non-profit organisation that covers virtually every aspect of SETI research. In the Nineties, it ran Project Phoenix using the Parkes radio telescope in Australia and a radio telescope in West Virginia, to study 800 stars within a 200 light year range of Earth. No ET signals were found.

The Arecibo message

The Arecibo radio telescope in Puerto Rico sent the first message to be deliberately beamed into space on 16 November 1974. The 1,679 binary-digit message was sent over a three-minute long period on the 2,380MHz radio frequency. Data such as DNA was aimed at the Messier 13 star cluster in the Hercules constellation, and will take 25,000 years to reach it.

The Golden Record

The Voyager 1 and 2 spacecraft were launched in 1977 to explore the outer planets of the solar system and beyond. Both deep space probes are expected to be in interstellar space by 2014. Like a message in a bottle, they carry a 30cm (12in) diameter gold-plated copper disc. The disc contains greetings from Earth in 55 different languages and a range of Earth-related pictures, sounds and music chosen by a committee headed by the late astronomer Carl Sagan.

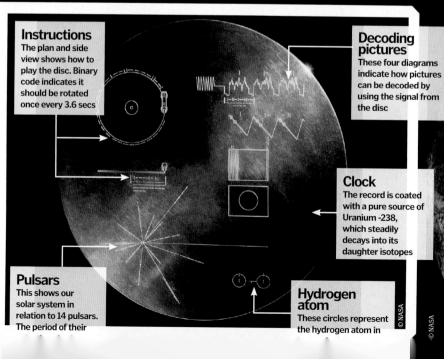

Instructions
The plan and side view shows how to play the disc. Binary code indicates it should be rotated once every 3.6 secs

Decoding pictures
These four diagrams indicate how pictures can be decoded by using the signal from the disc

Clock
The record is coated with a pure source of Uranium -238, which steadily decays into its daughter isotopes

Pulsars
This shows our solar system in relation to 14 pulsars. The period of their

Hydrogen atom
These circles represent the hydrogen atom in

Pale blue dot

The Earth is a mere 0.12 pixel-sized speck as viewed by the Voyager 1 spacecraft at a distance of 6.1 billion kilometres (3.7 billion miles). Astronomer Carl Sagan called this a "pale blue dot" that is "the only home we've ever known."

2x © NASA

Life on Mars

Mars was regarded as the home of human-like life until the Sixties, when the Mariner space probes showed it was a cratered planet with an atmosphere consisting of carbon dioxide (CO2). The 1972 Mariner 9 mission did, however, show evidence of running water on the surface of the planet in the past.

In 1976, the Viking 1 and 2 spacecraft landed on Mars to put soil samples in a nutrient labelled with radioactive carbon-14. If any organism were present, it would digest the nutrient and give off recognisable gasses. However, results gave no clear sign of life.

Since their arrival on the Red Planet in 2004, the two Mars Exploration rover craft Spirit and Opportunity have all but confirmed that liquid water did flow on the surface of Mars several hundred million years ago. This indicates that life could have existed on Mars and might still be hidden beneath its surface.

NASA's Mars Science Laboratory, which consists of the Curiosity rover, will analyse samples of Martian soil in great detail to find out for certain whether microbial life is present or can live in this environment when it lands in mid-2012 as planned.

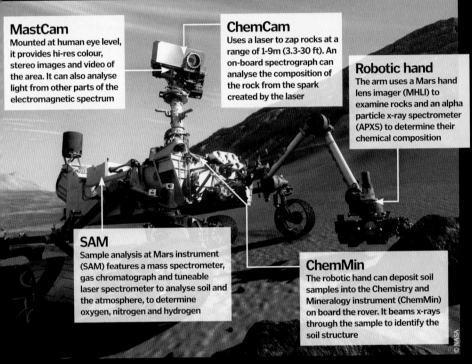

MastCam
Mounted at human eye level, it provides hi-res colour, stereo images and video of the area. It can also analyse light from other parts of the electromagnetic spectrum

ChemCam
Uses a laser to zap rocks at a range of 1-9m (3.3-30 ft). An on-board spectrograph can analyse the composition of the rock from the spark created by the laser

Robotic hand
The arm uses a Mars hand lens imager (MHLI) to examine rocks and an alpha particle x-ray spectrometer (APXS) to determine their chemical composition

SAM
Sample analysis at Mars instrument (SAM) features a mass spectrometer, gas chromatograph and tuneable laser spectrometer to analyse soil and the atmosphere, to determine oxygen, nitrogen and hydrogen

ChemMin
The robotic hand can deposit soil samples into the Chemistry and Mineralogy instrument (ChemMin) on board the rover. It beams x-rays through the sample to identify the soil structure

© NASA

Life in the solar system

Several surprising places might harbour life beyond Mars. Hopes that the brew of methane, ammonia, hydrogen and water stirred by lightning in Jupiter's atmosphere would create life have been considered and dismissed. Now, as a result of two Voyager probes passing Jupiter in 1979, Europa, one of Jupiter's moons, is discovered to have an icy surface with a liquid water ocean underneath it. If heat is being vented at the bottom of the ocean, it could well promote the existence of microbial life.

Two moons of Saturn are also regarded as having oceans of water beneath their surface. NASA's Cassini spacecraft found that the 505km (313mi) diameter Enceladus has potential for life, due to water indicated by geysers of ice particles that jet from its surface. The 5,150km (3,200mi) diameter Titan has a smoggy atmosphere and ethane/methane lakes that may contain primitive organisms and indicate similar conditions to those on Earth millions of years ago. NASA is planning to send a Titan Mare Explorer (TiME) in 2015

Titan, whose Earth-like conditions could harbour primitive life

© NASA

INTERVIEW
Philip Plait

Dr Philip Plait is an astronomer, author and blogger who covers all things universe-related in the Bad Astronomy blog

Q: Have you personally taken part in any search for alien life projects?
Philip Plait: No, but some years ago, when I was working on Hubble, I tried to get pictures of extrasolar planets – which, unfortunately, didn't work out. However, I've written numerous times on astrobiology topics, and it was the subject of an episode of a TV show I filmed.

Q: What are our chances of finding aliens?
PP: I know Seth Shostak of SETI has said that if aliens are out there and broadcasting using radio, we'll detect them in the next 25 years or so. There are a lot of assumptions in there, but it's an interesting calculation. I can't say for sure when it will happen, of course, but I'd sure like to be around if and when it does. One way or the other, though, I doubt it'll be via spaceships. It's far more likely that it'll be through some sort of light-speed communication method, like radio.

Q: Where do you think we should be looking?
PP: Everywhere! It might make sense to look at stars like the Sun to start with, since we know they can have planets and live long lives, enough time for intelligent life to develop. But one thing we know about nature is that it's more clever than we are, so I wouldn't limit the search at all.

Q: Do you think there's intelligent life out there, or is it likely to be microbial?
PP: Given what we know now – there are billions of Sun-like stars out there, and a good fraction of them have planets – I suspect there's lots of life in the Milky Way. But out of the 4.5 billion years the Earth's been around, it had basically gloop living on it for more than half that time. So I think if we ever travel to other planets, that's what we'll find mostly. But open this up to the "whole universe", and I'm thinking the answer leans towards yes, there are other civilisations out there. The number of stars is in the quintillions. That's a pretty good number to start with.

Q: What is the current status of ET searching?
PP: SETI's Allen Telescope Array is currently mothballed due to lack of funds, and that's not good. The technology is advancing rapidly, which is why Seth gave that 25-year timeframe. I'm hoping that they'll get the ATA running again soon.

Q: What current or future mission most excites you about the search for ET?
PP: Right now, Kepler is the best thing going: it may very well detect planets the mass and size of Earth orbiting their stars at the right distance to have liquid water on their surface. That's not finding life, but it would be a major step in that direction. I don't think any astronomer would bet against it, but knowing there's another possible Earth out there would be motivating.

Q: Do you think aliens may have visited/communicated with us in the past?
PP: In recent history, I doubt it – the evidence simply isn't there. But time is very long and deep; any civilisation may well have come here a long time ago...

ASTRONOMY

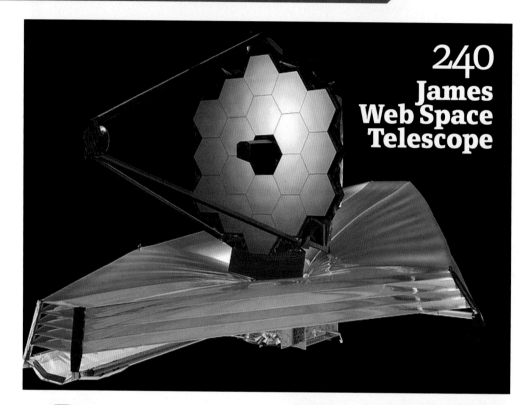

240
James Web Space Telescope

232
Telescopes

243
Measuring stars

**234
Seeing
stars**

**238
Sombrero
galaxy**

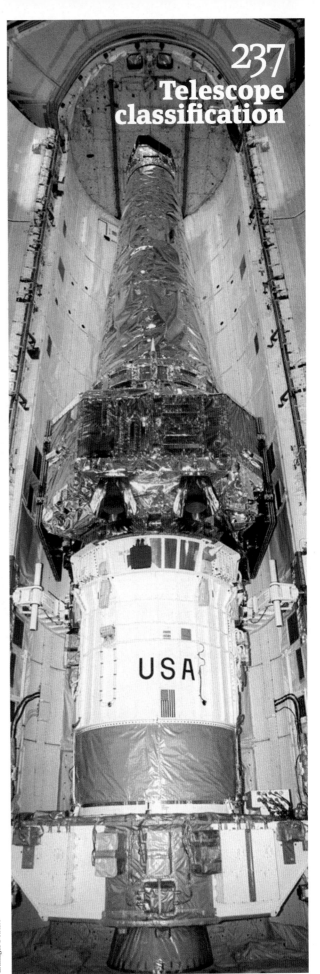

**237
Telescope
classification**

Telescopes

The telescope was the first step in really opening up the universe for scrutiny...

Telescopes are all designed to do the same thing: collect and magnify light so that we can examine it. Practically speaking, we most often use them to observe the cosmos. There are three main types of scope: refractive, reflective and compound. Hans Lippershey is credited with inventing the first working telescope in 1608, which was a refracting type using lenses. Lippershey's invention was known as a Dutch perspective glass and probably consisted of a convex lens at the end and a concave lens as an eyepiece. Numerous other astronomers worked to improve upon this initial design, including Galileo Galilei and Johannes Kepler; Galileo's version of the refracting telescope was the first to be called a 'telescope', with Greek poet Giovanni Demisiani coining the name.

All refracting telescopes had one flaw, however: the lenses created chromatic aberration, resulting in a blurry image. To combat this, astronomers made telescopes with longer and longer tubes, among other designs, but these were hard to manoeuvre.

In 1668, Isaac Newton created the first reflecting telescope, which used mirrors to focus the light and avoided chromatic aberration. After Newton, Laurent Cassegrain improved on the reflecting telescope by adding a secondary mirror to reflect light through an opening in the primary mirror. The refracting telescope still held pull though

because it was simply better at observing deep-sky objects as well as distant terrestrial objects. Since the lens was the issue, British inventor Chester Moor Hall came up with the achromatic lens in 1773.

The Herschelian telescope (made by William Herschel), a reflector built in 1778, did away with the secondary mirror by tilting the primary mirror slightly. Astronomers tried making more reflective mirrors to better optimise light. Advancements such as coating mirrors with silver and, later on, aluminium, allowed for reflective telescopes with ever-larger diameters to be built.

In 1930, German optician Bernhard Schmidt sought to create a hybrid telescope that took the best features of both refractive and reflective. The first compound, or catadioptric, telescope, had a primary mirror in the back of the telescope and a lens at the front. Later, a secondary mirror was added to create the Schmidt-Cassegrain model, and many variations followed. The compound telescope is the most popular design today.

Through the 20th century telescopes began to be developed for other types of electromagnetic wavelengths, such as radio, gamma ray, X-ray and ultraviolet. ☼

The ESO's Very Large Telescope (VLT) actually comprises four main telescopes called Antu, Yepun, Melipal and Kueyen

---

1608
Dutch perspective glass
He may not have been the first to build one, but German-born spectacle maker Hans Lippershey is credited with designing the first telescope, a refracting one with 3x magnification; it was called the Dutch perspective glass.

1668
Newtonian telescope
The first reflecting telescope was honed by Isaac Newton, who created it to help prove his theory that white light actually consists of a spectrum of colours. His telescope used a concave primary mirror and a flat, diagonal secondary mirror.

▷ 1600s

▷ 17

Telescope timeline
We reveal how this visual amplification device has evolved century by century

1610
Galilean telescope
Galileo Galilei perfected Lippershey's design, creating a telescope with a 33x magnification. He used it to make some significant discoveries, like the phases of Venus and some of Jupiter's moons.

1672
Cassegrain telescope
Priest Laurent Cassegrain came up with a new design for reflecting telescopes, using a concave primary mirror and a convex secondary mirror. This enabled light to bounce through a hole in the primary mirror onto an eyepiece.

Maks-Cass telescope up close

The Meade ETX 125 combines quality and portability to make it one of the most popular Maksutov-Cassegrain telescopes around

Jargon buster
Summing up the basic telescope types

Refractive
Your classic tube telescope, these use a large curved lens at one end, which bends the light that passes through and focuses it at the smaller lens, or eyepiece.

Reflective
These use a concave mirror to send light to a flat mirror. Light is reflected out one side to an eyepiece that magnifies and focuses to create an image.

Compound
Also called catadioptric, these use both lenses and mirrors. They are an all-round telescope for viewing both the planets and deep space.

Solar
These are designed solely to be used during the day to observe the Sun, and often employ a cooling mechanism as the heat can cause turbulence in the telescope.

Astronomical observatory
Land-based ones may contain numerous telescopes, and there are also observatories off our planet, including the Hubble Space Telescope.

Lens
The Maksutov-Cassegrain is mainly a reflecting telescope, but has a lens through which light passes before it reaches the mirror to help counteract any aberrations. This corrector lens is a negative meniscus, which has a concave surface on one side and a convex surface on the other

Tube
Maks-Cass scopes have a short tube length relative to the distance that the light actually travels. That's because the mirror setup 'folds' light. Light reflects off the primary mirror at the back of the telescope, which is concave, back to the front. The secondary mirror, which is smaller and convex, reflects the light back through a tiny hole in the primary mirror

Computer controls
Many telescopes can be computer-controlled, which further simplifies locating celestial bodies. You plug in the controller, and you can use it to slew (move) the telescope in any direction. You can also put in your location, and the device will move and locate objects in the sky for quick and easy stargazing

Viewfinder
It can be difficult to locate an object in a telescope, so most come with a viewfinder – a small, wide-field scope that has crosshairs and helps you to centre the telescope on a specific object. This model includes a dew shield

Eyepiece
Light ultimately reaches the back of the telescope, where the eyepiece is located. This telescope uses a Plössl, or symmetrical, eyepiece, which comprises two lenses: one concave and one convex. It makes for a large apparent field of view (the circle of light seen by your eyes)

Setting circles
The declination (on the side) and right ascension (on the bottom) setting circles are used to locate stars and other celestial bodies based on equatorial co-ordinates often found in sky maps. Many telescopes have digital setting circles, which provide the viewer with a database of objects and make it simple to point your telescope in the right direction

1840
First lunar photo
John William Draper was the first to capture the Moon in 1840. Using the daguerreotype process and a 13cm (5in) reflecting telescope, Draper took a 20-minute long exposure and helped found the field of astrophotography.

1967
First automated telescope
Arthur Code and other researchers used one of the first minicomputers to control a 20cm (8in) telescope. It measured a fixed sequence of stars using a punched paper tape.

1993
Keck telescopes
The Keck telescopes are two 10m (33ft)-diameter reflecting telescopes that saw first light in May 1993. They are located at the WM Keck Observatory on Mauna Kea in Hawaii. Each large mirror is actually composed of smaller segments, which are adjusted and controlled via computers.

> 1800s   > 1900s   > 2000s >

1917
Hooker 100-inch telescope
With a 2.5m (8.2ft) reflecting mirror, Hooker's telescope in Los Angeles, CA, was the largest in the world until 1948. Interestingly, in 1924 Edwin Hubble used it to observe galaxies outside the Milky Way, ultimately concluding that our universe is expanding.

1990
Hubble Space Telescope
NASA's Discovery shuttle placed the Hubble Space Telescope into low Earth orbit in April 1990. It is a reflecting telescope that contains five different scientific instruments for space observations, including spectrographs and photometers.

2005
Large Binocular Telescope
Located in Arizona, the Large Binocular Telescope is one of the most advanced optical telescopes in the world. Built in 2005, it has two 8.4m (28ft) aperture mirrors. The first image observed was of the spiral galaxy NGC 2770, 88 million light years away.

1. Light shade
Like a camera lens hood, designed to block out unwanted light sources

3. Finderscope
A smaller telescope with a wider field of view, designed to allow quicker spotting of the chosen target

The Coronet Cluster as observed by the Chandra X-ray Observatory

© NASA

5. Eyepiece
The 'optical out' for the chosen target's light source, designed to the scale of the human eye

6. Focuser knobs
Similar to an adjustable camera lens, good for making incremental adjustments to provide better image clarity

4. Finderscope bracket
The often detachable bracket holding the finderscope in place

2. Telescope main body
The main body of the telescope system where light is reflected, refracted or both to a focus point

Telescopes are a wide-ranging form of technology used by scientists, astronomers and civilians alike, to observe remote objects by the collection of electromagnetic radiation

How do telescopes see stars?

9. Latitude adjustment T-bolts
Twin bolts used to stabilise latitude

From their origins as simple hand-held instruments formed from a crude coupling of convex objective lens and concave eyepiece used to observe distant objects, to their utilisation in collecting and monitoring electromagnetic radiation emanating from distant space phenomena, telescopes are one of the human race's most groundbreaking inventions. Indeed, now there are telescopes which can monitor, record and image almost all wavelengths of the electromagnetic spectrum, including those with no visible light and their usage is widening our understanding of the world around us and the far-flung reaches of space. Here, we take a look at some of the forms of telescope in use today, exploring how they work and what they are discovering. ❋

7. Counterweight
A simple counterweight to aid stability

Head to Head
OPTICAL TELESCOPES

SINGLE MIRROR

1. GTC
Found in an observatory in the Canary Islands, the Gran Telescopio Canarias is the world's biggest single-aperture optical telescope.

TWO MIRRORS

2. LBT
The Large Binocular Telescope in the mountains of southeast Arizona is the world's largest optical telescope on a single mount.

MIRROR ARRAY

3. SALT
The Southern African Large Telescope is a large optical telescope capable of recording stars a billion times too faint to see with the naked eye.

DID YOU KNOW? The original patents for the optical telescope were filed in 1608 and it was first unveiled in the Netherlands

Messier 82 is about 12 million light-years away but the Hubble telescope still captured this amazing image

© NASA

NGC 281 is visible in amateur telescopes from dark sky locations

© NASA

The 84" telescope in Kitt Peak Observatory, Arizona

TYPES OF... OPTICAL TELESCOPES

Learn all about the types of optical telescope used by amateur and professional astronomers alike

1 Reflecting
One of the most common types of optical telescope, a reflector utilises one curved mirror and one flat mirror to directly reflect light throughout its main body and form an image. The reflecting telescope was created in the 17th Century as an alternative to the refracting telescope, which at the time suffered from severe chromatic aberration (a failure to focus all colours at the same point).

2 Refracting
The first type of telescope to be invented in 1608 was a refractor. Utilising a partnership of a convex objective lens and a concave eyepiece lens to form its image, refractors are still used today. However, there are numerous technical considerations including lens sagging, chromatic aberration and spherical aberration that have demeaned their effectiveness in recent years.

3 Catadioptric
The most advanced and stable of all optical telescopes are catadioptrics, which employ a mixture of mirrors and lenses to form an image, as well as a number of correctors to maintain accuracy. The first catadioptric telescope was made by the optician Bernhard Schmidt who, with his patented Schmidt telescope, corrected the optical errors of spherical aberration, coma, and astigmatism.

The optical telescope

Since its creation in 1608, the optical telescope has made the close viewing of far away things a piece of cake. But how do they work?

The standard optical telescope works by reflecting or refracting large quantities of light from the visible part of the electromagnetic spectrum to a focus point observable through an eyepiece. In essence, the large objective lens or primary mirror of the telescope collects large quantities of light from whatever it is targeted at, then by focusing that light on a small eyepiece lens, the image formed is magnified across the user's retina, making it appear closer and considerably larger than it actually is. Therefore, the power of any given telescope is directly relative to the diameter or aperture of the objective lens or primary mirror, with the larger the lens/mirror, the further and larger the image produced.

8. Azimuth adjustment knob
A crucial mechanism used to adjust the telescope to the direction of the celestial target

235

Radio telescopes

Characterised usually by their large dishes, radio telescopes allow us to receive signals from the depths of space

The radio telescope works by receiving and then amplifying radio signals produced from the naturally occurring emissions of distant stars, galaxies and quasars. The two basic components of a radio telescope are a large radio antenna and a sensitive radiometer, which between them reflect, direct and amplify incoming radio signals typically between wavelengths of ten metres and one millimetre to produce comprehensible information at an optical wavelength. Due to the weak power of these cosmic radio signals, as well as the range in wavelength that they operate in, radio telescopes need to be large in construction, as the efficiency of the antenna is crucial and can easily be distorted by terrestrial radio interference.

The most common radio telescope seen is the radio reflector; this consists of a parabolic

antenna – the large visible dish – and operates in a similar manner to a television satellite dish, focusing incoming radiation onto a receiver for decoding. In this type of radio telescope, often the radio receiver/solid-state amplifiers are cryogenically cooled to reduce noise and interference, as well as having the parabolic surface of the telescope equatorially mounted, with one axis parallel to the rotation axis of Earth. This equatorial mounting allows the telescope to follow a fixed position in the sky as the Earth rotates, therefore allowing elongated periods of static, pinpoint observation.

The largest filled-aperture telescope is the Arecibo radio telescope located in Puerto Rico, which boasts a 305-metre dish. Contrary to other radio telescopes with movable dishes however, the Arecibo's dish is fixed, instead relying on a movable antenna beam to alter its focus.

The Mount Pleasant radio telescope in Australia

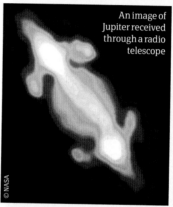
An image of Jupiter received through a radio telescope

A supernova remnant imaged from signals received by a radio telescope

1. Radio wave Incoming radio waves are diverted toward the secondary reflector

2. First focal room An observation capsule located at the primary focus point

3. Parabolic reflector Dishes need to be large as radio waves are weak and sporadic

4. Receiver Receivers need to be hyper-sensitive in order to capture signals

6. Support structure Radio telescopes tend to be made from light materials

5. Secondary reflector The secondary reflector diverts radio waves down to the receiver

5 TOP FACTS
TELESCOPES

Famous Hubble
1 One of the most famous telescopes is the Hubble Space Telescope. Orbiting 600km above the Earth, it can look deep into space as it's above the atmosphere.

Types of light
2 Using different types of light can reveal new discoveries about the universe. When scientists first used x-rays to study the sky they discovered black holes.

Long story
3 Before reflecting telescopes were developed in the 17th Century as an alternative, some refracting telescopes were as much as 600 feet long.

First radio telescope
4 The first radio antenna used to identify an astronomical radio source was one built by Karl Guthe Jansky, an engineer with Bell Telephone Laboratories, in 1931.

Do it yourself
5 Buying and using even a low power telescope will reveal some amazing sights including the same observations made by Galileo all those centuries ago.

DID YOU KNOW? The world's largest filled-aperture radio telescope based in Arecibo, Puerto Rico has a 305-metre dish

Telescope classification
Which telescopes are able to see what in the universe

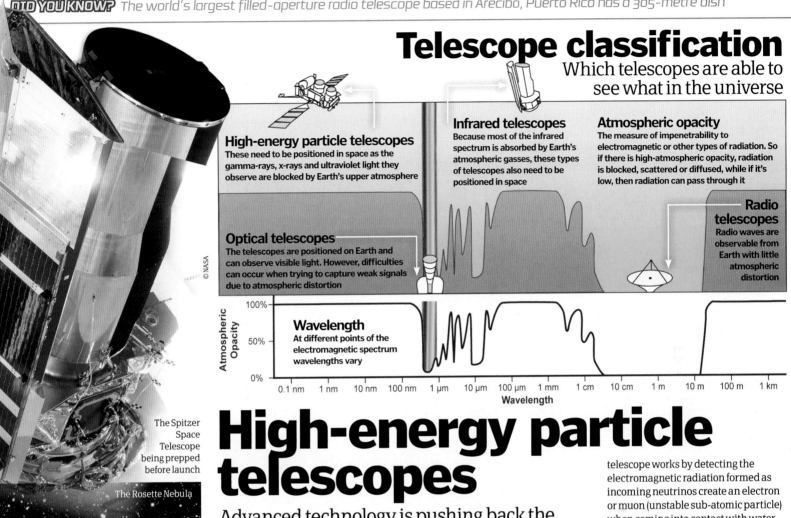

High-energy particle telescopes
These need to be positioned in space as the gamma-rays, x-rays and ultraviolet light they observe are blocked by Earth's upper atmosphere

Infrared telescopes
Because most of the infrared spectrum is absorbed by Earth's atmospheric gasses, these types of telescopes also need to be positioned in space

Atmospheric opacity
The measure of impenetrability to electromagnetic or other types of radiation. So if there is high-atmospheric opacity, radiation is blocked, scattered or diffused, while if it's low, then radiation can pass through it

Optical telescopes
The telescopes are positioned on Earth and can observe visible light. However, difficulties can occur when trying to capture weak signals due to atmospheric distortion

Radio telescopes
Radio waves are observable from Earth with little atmospheric distortion

Wavelength
At different points of the electromagnetic spectrum wavelengths vary

Atmospheric Opacity — 100%, 50%, 0%

Wavelength: 0.1 nm, 1 nm, 10 nm, 100 nm, 1 µm, 10 µm, 100 µm, 1 mm, 1 cm, 10 cm, 1 m, 10 m, 100 m, 1 km

© NASA

The Spitzer Space Telescope being prepped before launch

The Rosette Nebula

High-energy particle telescopes

Advanced technology is pushing back the boundaries of high-energy astronomy

The limits of radio and optical telescopes have led scientists in exciting new directions in order to capture and decode natural signals from distant galaxies.

One of the most notable is the x-ray telescope, which differs in its construction thanks to the inability of mirrors to reflect x-ray radiation, a fundamental necessity in all reflection-based optical and radio telescopes. In order to capture x-ray radiation, instead of being directly reflected into a hyper-sensitive receiver for amplification and decoding, it is acutely reflected a number of times, changing the course of the ray incrementally each time. To do this the x-ray telescope must be built from several nested cylinders with a parabolic or hyperbolic profile, guiding incoming rays into the receiver.

Crucially, however, all x-ray telescopes must be operated outside of the Earth's atmosphere as it is opaque to x-rays, meaning they must be mounted to high-altitude rockets or artificial satellites. Good examples of orbiting x-ray telescopes can be seen on the Chandra X-ray Observatory and the Spitzer Space Telescope.

Other high-energy particle telescopes include gamma-ray telescopes, which study the cosmos through the gamma-rays emitted by stellar processes, and neutrino telescopes, a form of astronomy still very much in its infancy. A neutrino telescope works by detecting the electromagnetic radiation formed as incoming neutrinos create an electron or muon (unstable sub-atomic particle) when coming into contact with water.

Because of this, neutrino telescopes tend to consist of submerged phototubes (a gas-filled tube especially sensitive to ultraviolet and electromagnetic light) in large underground chambers to reduce interference from cosmic rays. The phototubes act as a recording mechanism, storing any Cherenkov light (a type of electromagnetic radiation) emitted from the interaction of the neutrino with the electrons or nuclei of water. Then, using a mixture of timing and charge information from each of the phototubes, the interaction vertex, ring detection and type of neutrino can be detected.

© NASA

The Chandra X-ray Observatory

USA

© NASA

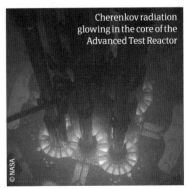

Cherenkov radiation glowing in the core of the Advanced Test Reactor

© NASA

"The black hole at the centre of the Sombrero Galaxy is a billion times the mass of our Sun"

The Sombrero Galaxy

Named for its hat-like shape, what makes this galaxy so special?

Technically known as M104, the Sombrero Galaxy gets its odd appearance from an unusually large central bulge of stars that feature in a prominent dust lane also containing many globular clusters.

The Sombrero Galaxy was originally discovered by Pierre Méchain in 1781, and rediscovered independently by William Herschel in 1784. It later helped 20th Century astronomers deduce that the universe was expanding in all directions. Initially believed to be a young star surrounded by luminous gas, astronomer VM Slipher discovered in 1912 that M104 was actually a large galaxy moving away from Earth at 700 miles per second.

In the centre of this 50,000 light-years-wide galaxy resides a huge black hole that X-ray evidence suggests is a billion times the mass of our Sun. The large, glowing bulge around the centre of the galaxy is the result of the light from billions of old stars found throughout, while about 2,000 globular clusters between 10 and 13 billion years old surround the galaxy – ten times more than in our own Milky Way. Inside the dust lanes and rings surrounding the central bulge are younger, brighter stars.

The Sombrero Galaxy, about 29 million light years from Earth, lies southwards of the Virgo Cluster in the night sky. It is tilted edge-on to Earth at an inclination of about six degrees, is easily seen through small telescopes, and is almost visible with the naked eye. ✿

The image was taken by NASA's
Hubble Space Telescope

James Webb Space Telescope

The successor to Hubble will change the way that we see the universe

The James Webb Space Telescope (JWST), originally known as the Next Generation Space Telescope, employs engineering techniques never used on a space telescope before and will produce unparalleled views of the universe. The JWST is scheduled for launch in 2018 in a joint venture between the ESA, NASA and Arianespace, the world's first company to offer commercial rocket launches. Primarily, the JWST will observe infrared light from distant objects.

To gather light on the telescope the primary mirror on the JWST is made of 18 hexagonal beryllium segments, which are much lighter than traditional glass and also very strong. To roughly point the telescope in the direction of its observations a star tracker is used, and a Fine Guidance Sensor (FGS) is employed to fine-tune the viewings.

The secondary mirror on the JWST, which reflects the light from the primary mirror into the instruments on board, can be moved to focus the telescope on an object. Each of the 18 hexagonal segments can also be individually adjusted and aligned to produce the perfect picture. While Hubble's primary mirror is just 2.4 metres in diameter, the mirror on JWST is almost three times as big at 6.5 metres in diameter, allowing for much more distant and accurate observations.

A box called the Integrated Science Instrument Module (ISIM) sits behind the primary mirror to collect the light incident on the telescope. The ISIM is attached to a backplane, which also holds the telescope's mirrors and keeps them stable. A sunshield, composed of five layers of Kapton with aluminium and special silicon coatings to reflect sunlight, protects the incredibly sensitive instruments. ✿

A full-scale model of the JWST has been travelling the world since 2005

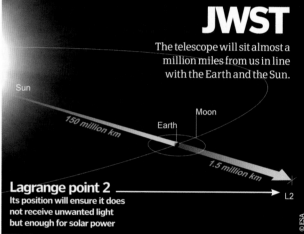

JWST

The telescope will sit almost a million miles from us in line with the Earth and the Sun.

Sun

150 million km

Earth

Moon

1.5 million km

L2

Lagrange point 2
Its position will ensure it does not receive unwanted light but enough for solar power

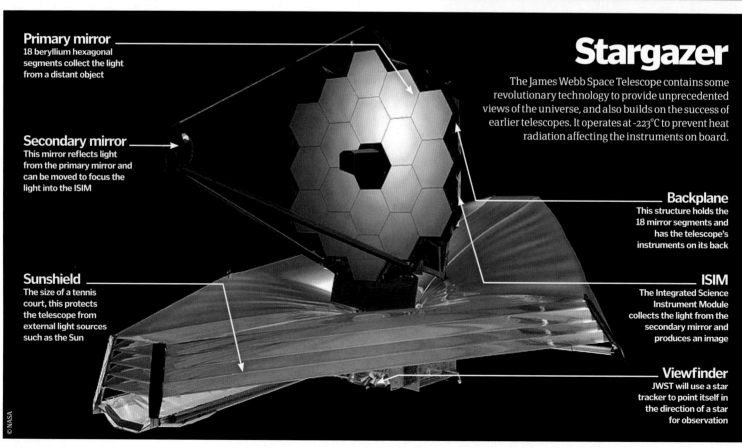

Primary mirror
18 beryllium hexagonal segments collect the light from a distant object

Secondary mirror
This mirror reflects light from the primary mirror and can be moved to focus the light into the ISIM

Sunshield
The size of a tennis court, this protects the telescope from external light sources such as the Sun

Stargazer

The James Webb Space Telescope contains some revolutionary technology to provide unprecedented views of the universe, and also builds on the success of earlier telescopes. It operates at -223°C to prevent heat radiation affecting the instruments on board.

Backplane
This structure holds the 18 mirror segments and has the telescope's instruments on its back

ISIM
The Integrated Science Instrument Module collects the light from the secondary mirror and produces an image

Viewfinder
JWST will use a star tracker to point itself in the direction of a star for observation

European Extremely Large Telescope

How will this record-breaking observatory hunt for Earth-like planets?

Since its invention over 400 years ago the humble telescope has come on leaps and bounds. In the early-20th century astronomers relied on old single or twin-mirror methods to produce images of distant galaxies and stars, but as the size of telescopes increased the quality of imagery reduced. It wasn't until the arrival of the Keck Observatories in Hawaii in the Eighties and Nineties, using 36 smaller mirror segments stitched together like a honeycomb, that telescopes were really able to view distant corners of the universe in stunning detail. This segmented design provides the basis for how the next generation of super-powerful telescopes will work, such as the European Extremely Large Telescope (E-ELT), which is being built by the European Southern Observatory.

What makes the E-ELT stand out from the crowd is its sheer size. Currently, the largest telescope in operation on Earth is the Large Binocular Telescope in Arizona, USA, sporting an aperture that measures a 'measly' 11.9 metres (39 feet) in diameter. The aperture of the E-ELT comes in at a mammoth 39.3 metres (129 feet), about half the size of a football pitch.

The telescope, expected to be finished within a decade, will be built on Cerro Armazones, a 3,000-metre (9,800-foot) mountain located in Chile's Atacama Desert where many other telescopes, including the recently activated Atacama Large Millimeter/submillimeter Array (ALMA), reside. The benefit of this location is obviously its altitude, allowing the cosmos to be viewed with less atmospheric interference than would be experienced at sea level, although some will still be present.

To overcome remaining atmospheric interference, the E-ELT will use a technology known as adaptive optics. Disturbances in the atmosphere can be accounted for by measuring the air within the telescope's view. Tiny magnets move its 800 segmented mirrors about 2,000 times a second to adjust the view to avoid any turbulence.

The primary goal of the E-ELT is to observe Earth-like planets in greater detail than ever before, but it will also be able to see much fainter objects – possibly even the primordial stars that formed soon after the Big Bang. Apart from the E-ELT there are two other extremely large telescopes under construction: the 24.5-metre (80-foot) Giant Magellan Telescope and the Thirty Meter Telescope (which will be 98 feet); both are also expected to be completed within a decade.

Lasers
Powerful lasers at the corners of the primary mirror will allow distant stars to be used as 'guide stars' to help the E-ELT focus on celestial objects

Aperture
The aperture of the E-ELT is 39.3m (129ft) across, enabling it to collect an unprecedented amount of light from distant objects

Light
The E-ELT will be able to gather 100,000,000 times more light than the human eye, or more than all of the 10m (33ft) telescopes on Earth combined

Image
Optical and infrared light is reflected between the mirrors of the telescope before being collected by astronomical cameras

Primary mirror
The principal mirror of the E-ELT is made up of 800 smaller hexagonal mirrors, each 1.4m (4.6ft) across

On reflection
The mirror of the E-ELT will be larger than the combined reflective area of all major research telescopes currently in use, allowing the mammoth structure to detect light from the early universe

Of course, it won't actually be built in central London, but here you can see how it stacks up to Big Ben

ALMA telescope

How this array will give us our best view of the universe from Earth

ALMA will be used to study stars and galaxies that are billions of years old

High in the Chilean Andes on the Chajnantor plain, 5,000m (16,400ft) above sea level, an array of radio telescopes known as the Atacama Large Millimeter Array (ALMA) is under construction, which will provide us with one of the clearest views of the universe yet. Once completed there will be 66 antennas trained at the sky, working in tandem with one another to observe the cosmos, the largest and most expensive ground-based telescope in history.

The truly remarkable aspect of this $1.3bn telescope group – a partnership between scientific teams across the world – is that a giant vehicle known as the ALMA Transporter can individually move each 12-metre wide antenna. This means the spread of the telescopes can range from just 150m to more than 11 miles (18km), providing varying levels of resolution to observe different parts of the universe. Once completed in 2013, ALMA will be ten times more powerful than the Hubble Space Telescope. Normally, ground-based telescopes cannot compare to space telescopes, the latter of which do not have their view obstructed by the Earth's atmosphere. However, the huge scale of the ALMA array, coupled with its height above sea level where the atmosphere is thinner, will allow ground-based telescopes to match their space-faring brothers. ⚙

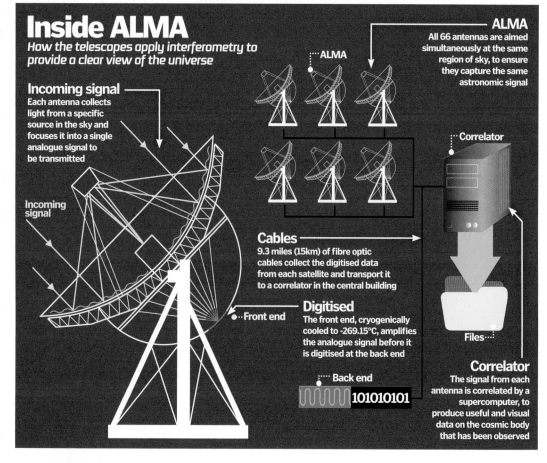

Inside ALMA
How the telescopes apply interferometry to provide a clear view of the universe

ALMA
All 66 antennas are aimed simultaneously at the same region of sky, to ensure they capture the same astronomic signal

Incoming signal
Each antenna collects light from a specific source in the sky and focuses it into a single analogue signal to be transmitted

Incoming signal

Correlator

Cables
9.3 miles (15km) of fibre optic cables collect the digitised data from each satellite and transport it to a correlator in the central building

Front end

Digitised
The front end, cryogenically cooled to -269.15°C, amplifies the analogue signal before it is digitised at the back end

Files

Back end
101010101

Correlator
The signal from each antenna is correlated by a supercomputer, to produce useful and visual data on the cosmic body that has been observed

What's the biggest star?

The largest star in the universe that we know of is VY Canis Majoris, a red hypergiant star 5,000 light years from Earth. It is 2,100 times the size of our Sun and, if it were placed at the centre of our solar system, its surface would extend beyond the orbit of Saturn.

3x © NASA

The secret of star-gauging

2. Interferometry

Once a star's distance is known, its diameter can be accurately ascertained using a technique called stellar interferometry, which measures electromagnetic waves

ves

ing
d
res

ne

asuring stars

ronomers establish how big a star is?

e the size of a star,
rs need to initially
veral other factors.
ghtness at Earth must
by a measure of its
e planet (which is also
xt, its surface
scertained; this
ier by stars of similar

properties possessing near-identical compositions and temperatures.

Stars behave like 'black bodies', objects in the universe that glow at a particular wavelength or colour, depending on their temperature. Thus, once a star's temperature and brightness have been gauged, its surface area and diameter can be deduced based on previously confirmed data. ✿

© NASA, JPL, Caltech, R Hurt

Star clusters

What causes these stellar parties?

A star cluster is a group of stars brought together over millions or billions of years that have grown gravitationally bound to one another. The two known types are globular and open clusters. One of the most fascinating things about them is that all of the stars in such a group are centred around the same gravitational point, despite also being inside a galaxy.

Open clusters are much smaller than their globular brothers, the former containing just a dozen to a few hundred stars, and the latter potentially encompassing hundreds of thousands. Globular clusters tend to be more uniform too, with the stars forming a sphere around a common central point, while in an open cluster stars are more scattered owing to the weaker gravity. Globular clusters typically have older stars that have been bound for millions of years, whereas open clusters are composed of newer stars that may come and go over time. ✿

© NASA, ESA

"A spectrometer is an instrument that is used to analyse electromagnetic spectrums"

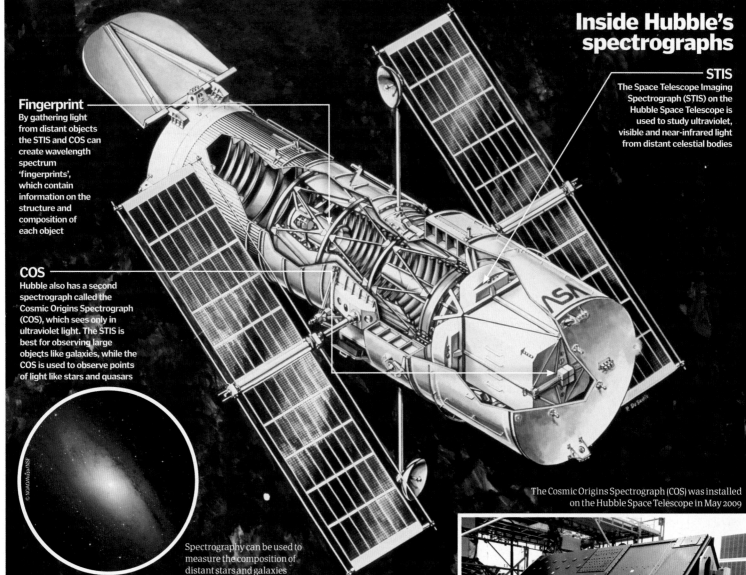

Fingerprint
By gathering light from distant objects the STIS and COS can create wavelength spectrum 'fingerprints', which contain information on the structure and composition of each object

COS
Hubble also has a second spectrograph called the Cosmic Origins Spectrograph (COS), which sees only in ultraviolet light. The STIS is best for observing large objects like galaxies, while the COS is used to observe points of light like stars and quasars

Spectrography can be used to measure the composition of distant stars and galaxies

Inside Hubble's spectrographs

STIS
The Space Telescope Imaging Spectrograph (STIS) on the Hubble Space Telescope is used to study ultraviolet, visible and near-infrared light from distant celestial bodies

The Cosmic Origins Spectrograph (COS) was installed on the Hubble Space Telescope in May 2009

Spectrography

How can we determine the composition of a distant star?

 Spectrography, or spectroscopy, is the study of light from distant objects (such as a black hole or galaxy) to analyse their composition, movements and structure.

It works by measuring the intensity of light present across a range of energies on the electromagnetic spectrum. Every element in the universe has a particular pattern of black lines, known as emission lines, unique to that element on the spectrum. By matching the known emission lines of an element to those observed on a spectrum from an object, the composition can be determined.

A spectrometer is an instrument that is used to analyse these electromagnetic spectrums.

In practice, it does this by observing the light (be it visible, infrared or otherwise) emitted from a source, and deducing the various energies associated with that light. Depending on the elements that are present in a celestial body, the spectrum it produces will be different to that from any other body.

Spectrometers are used on a variety of space telescopes, including the Hubble Space Telescope (see the above diagram), but they can also be used here on Earth to study not only distant space phenomena but objects on our planet too, like plants and minerals. Spectrography is very useful in astronomy, providing us with the answers to how stars form, what they are made of and more. ☼

Hydrogen spectrograph
Discover how the emission of hydrogen from a star appears on the electromagnetic spectrum

Photons
Energy is released by elements as photons, which produce the observable lines on a spectrum

Pattern
By matching the pattern of lines with existing spectrographs, scientists can establish what they are looking at

1. SOHO
Launched in 1995, SOHO is a Europe-led mission designed to study the Sun. Compared to both following missions, the visual fidelity of its findings were limited.

2. STEREO
NASA's next step was to take the study of the Sun into the third dimension. Utilising two spacecraft its mission was to study the nature of CMEs.

3. SDO
The SDO's visual capabilities dwarf both previous missions. Just three seconds of HD video revealed more detail about solar flares than many scientists ever knew.

DID YOU KNOW? *The total mass of the SDO spacecraft at launch was 3,100kg, yet the SDO itself weighs just 290kg*

NASA's Solar Dynamics Observatory

If you think 1080p HD video is impressive, your tech-buds are in for a treat with the SDO...

The Solar Dynamics Observatory (SDO) is the crowning mission of a new NASA scientific endeavour designed to study our Sun. As the cornerstone of the Living With a Star program, the SDO is quite simply the most advanced spacecraft ever devised to help unlock the secrets of our Sun. Using the very latest technology the SDO can gather high quality data, process it with more advanced instruments and beam it back to Earth faster than any other scientific experiment undertaken by man.

And an important mission it is too, since being able to understand and predict the processes of our Sun is becoming ever more important in this digital age. Launched in February 2010, the SDO will hopefully furnish us with the capability to better protect ourselves from 'space weather' side effects like power grid failures, long-haul flight radiation, not to mention satellite, telecommunications and GPS disruptions. ✱

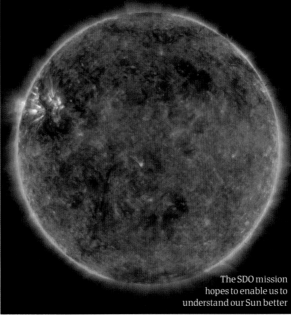

The SDO mission hopes to enable us to understand our Sun better

Road to discovery

The SDO is designed around a five-year mission, though has enough resources to ensure a ten year life span. In that time scientists hope to gain in-depth information about how and why changes in the Sun produce its 11-year solar cycle brought on by changes in its magnetic field. As a major component of the Heliophysics System Observatory (essentially a whole fleet of solar, heliospheric and geospace spacecraft working together) it'll also help unlock the secrets of the complex processes at work in space in general.

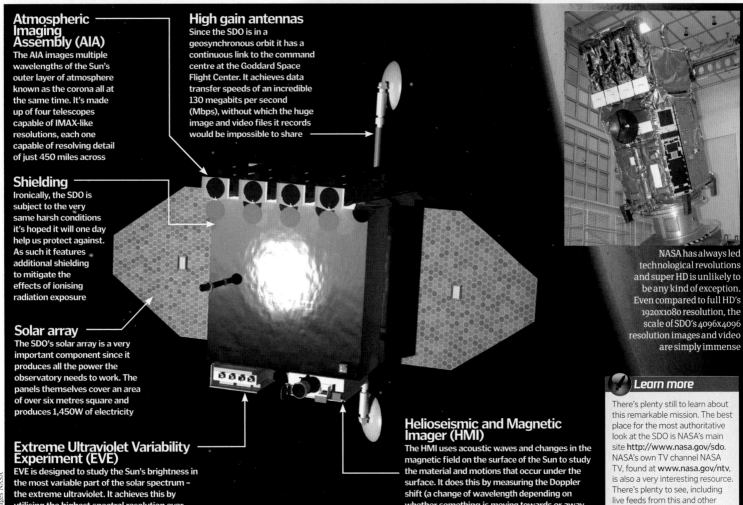

Atmospheric Imaging Assembly (AIA)
The AIA images multiple wavelengths of the Sun's outer layer of atmosphere known as the corona all at the same time. It's made up of four telescopes capable of IMAX-like resolutions, each one capable of resolving detail of just 450 miles across

High gain antennas
Since the SDO is in a geosynchronous orbit it has a continuous link to the command centre at the Goddard Space Flight Center. It achieves data transfer speeds of an incredible 130 megabits per second (Mbps), without which the huge image and video files it records would be impossible to share

Shielding
Ironically, the SDO is subject to the very same harsh conditions it's hoped it will one day help us protect against. As such it features additional shielding to mitigate the effects of ionising radiation exposure

Solar array
The SDO's solar array is a very important component since it produces all the power the observatory needs to work. The panels themselves cover an area of over six metres square and produces 1,450W of electricity

Extreme Ultraviolet Variability Experiment (EVE)
EVE is designed to study the Sun's brightness in the most variable part of the solar spectrum – the extreme ultraviolet. It achieves this by utilising the highest spectral resolution ever achieved by a space observatory

Helioseismic and Magnetic Imager (HMI)
The HMI uses acoustic waves and changes in the magnetic field on the surface of the Sun to study the material and motions that occur under the surface. It does this by measuring the Doppler shift (a change of wavelength depending on whether something is moving towards or away from you) to calculate velocities of movement

NASA has always led technological revolutions and super HD is unlikely to be any kind of exception. Even compared to full HD's 1920x1080 resolution, the scale of SDO's 4096x4096 resolution images and video are simply immense

Learn more
There's plenty still to learn about this remarkable mission. The best place for the most authoritative look at the SDO is NASA's main site http://www.nasa.gov/sdo. NASA's own TV channel NASA TV, found at www.nasa.gov/ntv, is also a very interesting resource. There's plenty to see, including live feeds from this and other missions currently in progress.

"The collision of these galaxies will result in a merger between a young and an old galaxy"

Cosmic exclamation point

The two colliding galaxies that strikingly resemble a punctuation mark

Shown here is galaxy VV 340 North above VV 340 South – collectively known as just VV 340 (or Arp 302) – with the former being imaged side-on, and the latter head-on. The resultant image of the two galaxies, which are approximately 450 million light years from Earth, coincidentally bears some resemblance to an exclamation mark due to the positioning of the two galaxies relative to us.

VV 340 North is classified as a luminous infrared galaxy (LIRG) because of the large amount of infrared light it gives off. In fact, LIRGs emit energy hundreds of times faster than typical galaxies, such as our own Milky Way. It is likely that a surpermassive black hole – a dense singularity with a mass greater than 1 million suns – is the source of energy at the centre of VV 340 North, and indeed other LIRGs as well. Most of the ultraviolet and short-wavelength optical emissions from the galaxy pair come from VV 340 South, suggesting that it contains much more actively forming newborn stars than VV 340 North, which contains much older stars. Therefore, the collision of these two galaxies in a few million years will result in something akin to a merger between a young and an old galaxy, and it is likely that the older galaxy will come out on top due to its greater mass. ✿

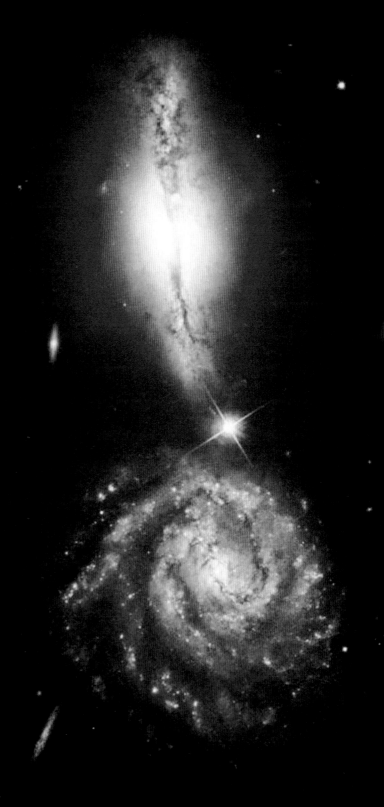

This image is the combination of data from NASA's Chandra X-ray Observatory and the Hubble Space Telescope

The Leonids

While not the most consistent of meteor showers, the Leonids can be one of the most dynamic spectacles in an astronomer's calendar. They're a product of the comet Tempel-Tuttle, which has a radius of around 1.8 kilometres (1.1 miles) and has a 33-year cycle. The comet itself is fairly unremarkable compared to the likes of Halley's or Hale-Bopp, however it leaves behind a dense stream of debris that results in a meteor shower rate that can reach as many as 300 meteors an hour.

© NASA

Meteor showers

Why the most famous of these celestial spectacles are an annual event

Meteors enter the Earth's atmosphere all the time. Spend a little time looking up at the sky at night in the country or a place with similarly low light pollution and there's a good chance you'll see a 'shooting star', the result of air friction burning the meteor up. At certain times of the year astronomers can even forecast an increase in their frequency and luminosity as annual meteor showers hit our planet. So why do these occur regularly and how are scientists able to predict them?

A meteor shower is a group of meteors that originate from the same source. In the common case of one of the most prolific annual meteor shower events in the cosmic calendar, the Perseids, they're material stripped off the comet Swift-Tuttle by solar radiation as it passes the Sun. This debris then trails behind the comet, spreading out along its orbit and, if the Earth's own orbit crosses its path, then a meteor shower ensues. As it happens, both Earth and Swift-Tuttle follow very regular paths, which is why when Earth crosses Swift-Tuttle's orbit a predictable, late-July event occurs that peaks in August at around 75 meteors an hour.

Perhaps the most famous comet of them all, Halley's, has its own regular meteor shower called the Orionids that appear in October, though at a much lower rate than the Perseids.

Is the Swift-Tuttle comet a threat?

Swift-Tuttle has a 130-year orbit of the Sun and its first recorded sighting was by astronomers Lewis Swift and Horace Tuttle 150 years ago in July 1862. Astrophysicist Brian Marsden's calculations for the next perihelion (the name for any satellite's closest approach to the Sun) in 1992 were off by 17 days, which put the comet on a potential collision course with Earth in 2126. It panicked astronomers, as the comet is around 9.7 kilometres (six miles) wide, which is roughly the same size as the Chicxulub asteroid that's generally held to be the major culprit in the extinction of the dinosaurs 65 million years ago. But having traced Swift-Tuttle's orbit back 2,000 years, Marsden was able to refine his calculations to put the comet a comfortable 24 million kilometres (15 million miles) away for its next appearance. However, if the calculations play out, there *will* be a real cosmic near-miss when 3044 rolls around, as Swift-Tuttle will pass within just 1.6 million kilometres (1 million miles) of our planet.

© SPL

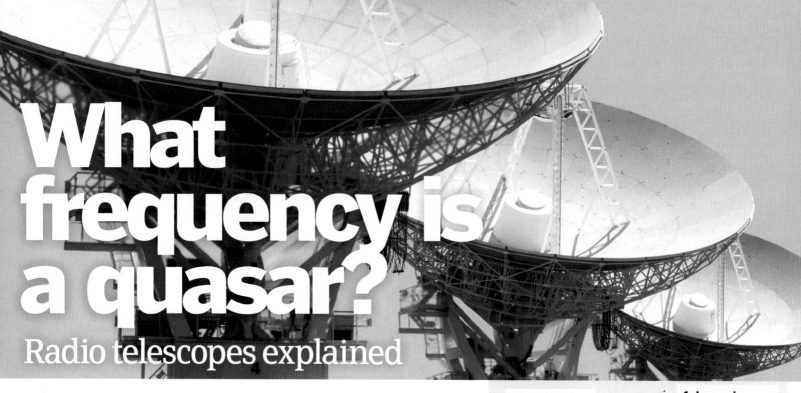

What frequency is a quasar?
Radio telescopes explained

Some objects in space are viewable with the naked eye. Other anomalies such as quasars (the most powerful source of energy in the universe – a kind of star galaxy) and pulsars (spherical neutron stars) require the use of a radio telescope. These telescopes receive and amplify frequencies from deep space using antennas, and measures their intensity.

"By studying the intensity of radio frequencies, astronomers can monitor the conditions of space," says Dr Seth Shostak, a senior astronomer at the SETI Institute. "Radio waves are not hindered by gas and dust between stars, so you can 'look' straight through a galaxy to the other side. Quasars were found because of radio telescopes."

According to Dr Shostak, a radio telescope uses a very low-noise amplifier that collects radio waves, themselves collected using massive antennas. The signal passes through the antenna, spreads through a filtering system, and breaks into thousands of frequency channels – a bit like a Doppler satellite that measures the speed of frequencies. ✷

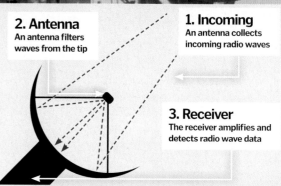

2. Antenna
An antenna filters waves from the tip

1. Incoming
An antenna collects incoming radio waves

3. Receiver
The receiver amplifies and detects radio wave data

Adaptive optics recreate an image
Reassembling a twinkling star

Adaptive optics is a fascinating field – this technology is used in telescopes and can reconstruct an image so that it matches how the object looks in space, without the distortions from the Earth's atmosphere. It's the same technology now being used by optometrists to determine which glasses you might need to wear.

When astronomers study a star, the light is emitted in a spherical shape called a wavefront. As the wavefront passes through the atmosphere, the spheres are distorted in the same way that a distant car is distorted by the heat on a paved road. Some parts of the star are tilted – like the slanted image you might see on a wall when the Sun shines through a window. Other parts are out of focus.

The distorted image is called the input phase, or wavefront phase. Initially, a tilt mirror captures the wavefront, which measures the complex tilt of the image. Next, a deformable mirror is used to adjust the image. This mirror acts like one in a hall of mirrors, except the mirror can be moved a few microns to flatten the image. The image passes through the deformable mirror multiple times, and each time a phase reconstructor – a series of complex algorithms – smooths the image.

In a last step, the adjusted image enters the output phase, which shows the adjusted image without the distortions of tilt and focus. "Adaptive optics cancel out the effects of the atmosphere as well as the imperfections of the telescope," says Stuart Shacklan, a group supervisor of the high contrast imaging group in the optics section at Jet Propulsion Laboratory, a research arm of NASA.

Adaptive optics are used in most astronomical telescopes such as the Palomar Observatory in California and the Keck Observatory in Hawaii. ✷

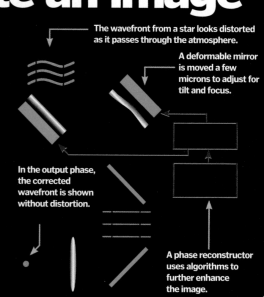

The wavefront from a star looks distorted as it passes through the atmosphere.

A deformable mirror is moved a few microns to adjust for tilt and focus.

In the output phase, the corrected wavefront is shown without distortion.

A phase reconstructor uses algorithms to further enhance the image.

Head to Head SPITZER IMAGES

MOST IMPRESSIVE

1. The Story of Stellar Birth
This image shows young stars in a cosmic cloud in the Cepheus constellation, about 21,000 light years away from Earth.

MOST UNUSUAL

2. Towering Infernos
Stars are born in these 'mountains' of gas and dust, which are found in the Cassiopeia constellation 7,000 light years away.

MOST MYSTERIOUS

3. Mysterious Blob Galaxies Revealed
This red hydrogen blob is 11 billion light years away and contains three galaxies trillions of times brighter than our Sun.

DID YOU KNOW? The Spitzer was formerly known as the Space Infrared Telescope Facility (SITF)

Astronomers use Spitzer's orbit and parallaxing to determine the distance of dark planets and black holes

Spitzer Space Telescope

The last of NASA's four great observatories, the Spitzer Space Telescope was launched in 2003

1. Solar panels
The Spitzer's two solar panels convert solar radiation into 427 watts of electrical energy, which powers the telescope

3. Cryogenic telescope assembly
Inside the assembly are the telescope and three main instruments. It also contains a tank of liquid helium

2. Solar shield
The solar shield is angled away from the rest of the craft and reflects sunlight to minimise heat transfer

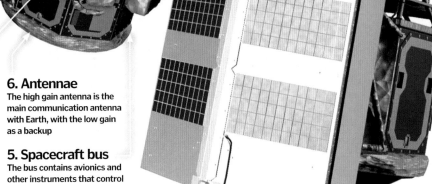

© All images NASA

Objects in space radiate heat in the form of infrared energy, but ground-based telescopes cannot detect it due to the Earth's atmosphere. Because the Spitzer Space Telescope orbits around the Sun, it can record this energy in the form of images. The telescope uses three highly sensitive instruments – a camera, a spectrograph and a photometer – that operate on different wavelengths and detect pixels to form pictures.

Infrared telescopes have to be kept very cold (-268°C) in order to function properly. The Spitzer was launched with a liquid helium supply to keep its instruments cold for a minimum of 2.5 years. It is far enough away from the Earth so that it does not pick up infrared energy from our planet, and was fitted with a solar shield to protect it from the Sun's heat. The liquid helium supply was used up on 15 May 2009, but the camera can still detect some infrared wavelengths. ✦

7. Star trackers and gyroscopes
The star trackers and gyroscopes are mounted on the bus and allow the Spitzer to orientate itself properly in space

6. Antennae
The high gain antenna is the main communication antenna with Earth, with the low gain as a backup

4. Outer shell
The aluminium outer shell is black on one side to radiate heat and shiny on the other side to reflect the Sun's heat

5. Spacecraft bus
The bus contains avionics and other instruments that control the telescope, store data and communicate with NASA

> "A distant star is tracked and used as a reference point to keep the telescope pointing in the same direction"

The SOFIA telescope

Flying eye in the sky probes the secrets of the universe

The Stratospheric Observatory for Infrared Astronomy (SOFIA) project consists of a Boeing 747SP aircraft modified to carry a telescope. Its infrared 2.5 metre reflecting telescope detects energy emitted by astronomical objects that are invisible to the human eye.

Pan American World Airways originally operated the Boeing 'jumbo jet' 747SP used in the project. The SP (special performance) designation means that it has a shorter body and can travel further than the original 747 aircraft. NASA bought it in 1997. A section of another 747SP was used to mock-up the telescope design and structure, before it was fitted to the SOFIA aircraft. The modified aircraft began test flying in 2007, and in December 2009 its telescope system began flight tests. It now operates from NASA's Dryden Aircraft Operations Facility (DAOF) in Palmdale, California and is preparing for its first scientific missions.

Travelling at a height of 12km at a speed of 500mph, the aircraft is subject to considerable shaking and turbulence. To counter these effects the telescope is mounted on a spherical pressurised oil bearing, and is stabilised by three gyroscopes that cope with sudden movements. A deflector fence on the rim of the telescope, and the specially shaped side of the aircraft, help deflect wind away from the telescope aperture. In addition, a distant star is tracked and used as a reference point to keep the telescope pointing in the same direction.

The advantage of SOFIA is that it can fly in the stratosphere, which is typically nine to 12km above the Earth. At this altitude it can detect cosmic infrared radiation that is normally absorbed by water vapour in the lower atmosphere. This makes it far more effective than ground-based infrared observatories, and puts it in the same league as satellite-based telescopes.

NASA's SOFIA observatory (front) with its predecessor the now-retired Kuiper Airborne Observatory (behind) at NASA's Ames Research Center

Full capability for the observatory is expected by 2014

All images © NASA

PIONEERING

1. Convair 990
In 1966, Dr Gerard Kuiper used a NASA-funded Convair 990 jet aircraft with a 30.5cm telescope to make spectroscopic studies of the Sun and solar system.

FIRST

2. KAO
Inspired by Dr Kuiper, NASA converted a Lockheed C-141A military transport aircraft to carry a 91.5cm infrared telescope. It operated from 1975 to 1995.

BIGGEST

3. SOFIA
SOFIA's 17-ton airborne telescope is the largest ever fitted inside an aircraft. It is regarded as medium-sized compared to similar ground-based telescopes.

DID YOU KNOW? The Boeing aircraft used for the project first flew in April 1977, and was christened the Clipper Lindbergh

SOFIA's telescope

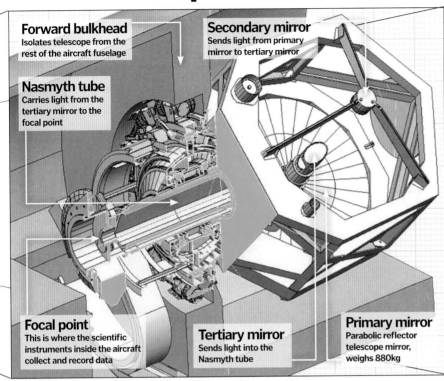

Forward bulkhead
Isolates telescope from the rest of the aircraft fuselage

Secondary mirror
Sends light from primary mirror to tertiary mirror

Nasmyth tube
Carries light from the tertiary mirror to the focal point

Focal point
This is where the scientific instruments inside the aircraft collect and record data

Tertiary mirror
Sends light into the Nasmyth tube

Primary mirror
Parabolic reflector telescope mirror, weighs 880kg

The telescope mirror is made from a glass ceramic material called Zerodur. The internal lightweight honeycomb structure is revealed before it receives its reflective coating

SOFIA's optical system

2. Secondary mirror
The light reflected from the primary mirror is reflected up to the 0.4-metre secondary mirror

4. Focal point
The tertiary mirror reflects the light along a tube inside the fuselage of the aircraft. At the focal point, the light is recorded and analysed by instruments inside the aircraft

3. Tertiary mirror
Positioned a metre above the primary mirror, the tertiary mirror receives the reflected light from the secondary mirror

1. Primary mirror
Light travels inside the telescope to the concave primary mirror

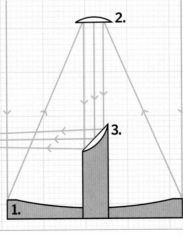

SOFIA versus Hubble

The Hubble and SOFIA telescope projects have several similarities, along with some stark differences. They are both long-term projects that are intended to have a life of at least 15 to 20 years.

In the case of the Hubble telescope, it operates 600km above the Earth and is equipped to record optical and ultraviolet light. SOFIA, flying at an altitude of 12km, concentrates on detecting infrared light and is able to study planetary details and the formation of galaxies.

The beauty of SOFIA is that new instruments and set-ups can be easily fitted and tested, whereas Hubble can only be accessed every two or three years. More importantly, SOFIA costs a tenth of the Hubble telescope project.

Visible light image

Visible light image detail

Besides Jupiter, SOFIA has also recorded infrared images of the M82 galaxy. It shows the formation of stars normally hidden by visible wavelength images.

SOFIA infrared image

SOFIA made its first observations on 26 May 2010. The eight hour flight recorded this composite infrared picture of Jupiter, which can be compared to a visible image of the planet

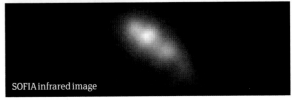

Visible light image

SOFIA infrared image

The Hubble telescope

After a false start and 19 years of faithful service it's a wonder the Hubble space telescope works at all...

Lyman Spitzer Jr was one of the 20th Century's leading scientists. He was also the first person to consider the idea of putting a giant telescope in space and not only lived to see the launch of the Hubble Space Telescope (HST) in 1990, but witness seven years of its incredible contribution to modern science.

Buy why space? Compared to many of the world's most powerful Earth-bound telescopes the Hubble Space Telescope's optics are actually quite small. Bar obvious payload limitations, in space the required optics of a telescope are smaller since the 'seeing' is always perfect. Looking through Earth's atmosphere is not unlike trying to watch television through a desert mirage – the viewing is hindered by a constant shimmer produced by the atmosphere. In space, the Hubble Space Telescope's resolution is so great that it's the equivalent of us being able to distinguish a car's two separate headlights from 6,000 miles away.

Hubble didn't have the smoothest of starts however, and for the first three years of its life was partially sighted due to an error in the manufacture of its 2.4-metre primary mirror. Thankfully, upon its first servicing mission in 1993 its optics were corrected.

It's most recent scheduled servicing mission took place in May 2009, allowing Hubble to remain operational until about 2018 when it's successor - the James Webb Space Telescope - is due to launch.

Instrument housing
The rear of Hubble is where the real magic happens. Fine guidance sensors, cameras and spectrograph work together to give us the remarkable view of the universe some of us take for granted today

Communication antennae
Astronomers and technicians use these antennae to send Hubble orders. Data is bounced off tracking and data relay satellites, then to ground stations and then to the Goddard Space Flight Centre before reaching its destination

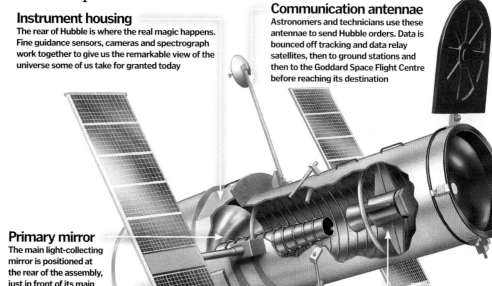

© DK Images

Primary mirror
The main light-collecting mirror is positioned at the rear of the assembly, just in front of its main systems and scientific instruments. The original flaw in the design of this mirror was just two microns off – a fiftieth of a human hair

Secondary mirror
Light is bounced off the primary mirror onto this smaller, secondary mirror before it passes through a small hole in the centre of the larger mirror on its way towards Hubble's various scientific instruments

Solar panels
Hubble requires some 2,800 watts of electricity to remain operational. It uses its large solar cells to produce all of its power and surplus energy is stored in on-board batteries so it can operate from inside the Earth's shadow (around a third of its complete orbit time)

Hubble's control system

To accurately point this bus-sized piece of technology properly requires gyroscopes. They sense its motion and help it to find its target by acting as a reference point. Next come the reaction wheels which steer it towards its next target. Finally come the fine guidance sensors of which there are three. They pinpoint the aim by using star trackers to lock onto bright guide stars.

Hubble's Pointing Control System

The Statistics
Hubble telescope

Service: 22 years (and counting!)
Mass: 11,110kg
Orbital velocity: 7,500 metres per second
Orbit period: 97 minutes
Diameter: 2.4 metres
Telescope focal length: 57.6 metres
Due to be de-orbited: >2021

All images © NASA

Hubble service record
The Hubble telescope was designed to be serviced by astronauts, here's its service history

DEC 1993 The most important part of the first servicing mission (SM1) was to correct the lens abortion. New systems were also installed including the Wide Field Planetary Camera 2.

FEB 1997 Besides important maintenance routines, Hubble's abilities were again upgraded with a new spectrograph, which is able to collect 30 times more data than its predecessor was.

DEC 1999 After the forth of six gyroscopes failed in 1999 Hubble was effectively put offline. Luckily, what was planned as a simple servicing mission turned into a successful rescue.

MAR 2002 Much of the work planned for 1999 was carried out in this mission. A new solar panel array was fitted, and despite being 1/3 of the size of the original provided 30 per cent more power.

MAY 2009 The fifth and final servicing mission. Two new scientific instruments were installed and two previously failed instruments were fixed. Hubble is in the best shape it's ever been in.

5 TOP FACTS PLANETARY NEBULAE

Formation
1 Small-to-medium sized stars, such as our Sun, form these stunning nebulae at the end of their stellar lifetime when they have exhausted their nuclear fuel.

Life and size
2 These nebulae survive for 25,000 to 100,000 years, a short life by astronomical standards, and expand at approximately 16 kilometres per second.

Red giant
3 The dying stars that eject planetary nebulae – red giants – are not massive enough to become supernovae as they have previously shed some of their mass.

The Sun
4 It is estimated that in 5 billion years our Sun will also become a planetary nebula, following a rapid expansion which will eventually consume the Earth.

Not so planetary
5 William Herschel incorrectly described these nebulae as planetary in 1764 when he mistook the star at the centre for a planet, later realising his error but keeping the name.

DID YOU KNOW? The Cat's Eye Nebula was discovered by William Herschel on 15 February 1786

The Cat's Eye Nebula

A dying star's last breath has produced unprecedented insight into nebula formation

Throwing off glowing gas in concentric shells, the Cat's Eye Nebula is one of the most complex and interesting known planetary phase nebulae and is located about three thousand light years from Earth in the Draco constellation. This image, captured by the Hubble Space Telescope in 2004, has led scientists to believe the complicated and intricate structures on display may be the cause of a binary star system in the centre of the nebula because of the unique shell formation.

In astronomical terms the nebula is very young at only about a thousand years old, forming after a sudden change in mass of the central star (or stars). The reason for this change in mass is still unknown, but the lighter rings of gas around the edges are known to have been produced in bursts in the latter stages of stellar evolution before the inner nebula formed. Observations over the past 20 years indicate the nebula is still expanding. ⚙

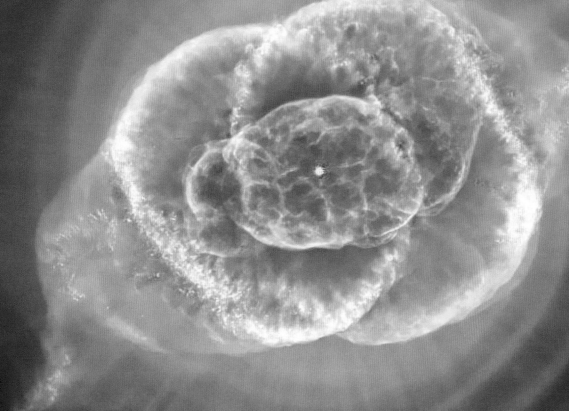

The bright central star is surrounded by a multi-million-degree gas cloud

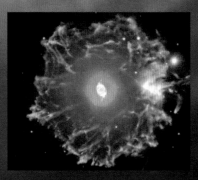

This processed image reveals the concentric rings surrounding the inner core

All Images © NASA

253

"It will be able to capture light instantaneously from a mammoth area of the night sky"

Earth's largest digital camera explained

What makes the Large Synoptic Survey Telescope such an astronomical marvel?

At an altitude of 2,660 metres (8,730 feet) on the El Peñón peak in northern Chile, construction is underway of one of the most remarkable telescopes ever to be devised. The Large Synoptic Survey Telescope (LSST) is unprecedented in size, and with an aperture of 8.4 metres (27.4 feet) it will be able to capture light instantaneously from a mammoth area of 320 square metres (3,440 square feet) in the night sky with its staggering 3.2-billion-pixel digital camera (the biggest on the planet).

The four parts of its name are representative of the major features of the telescope. 'Large' refers to the enormous primary mirror that will provide astronomers with an unrivalled view of the night sky. 'Synoptic' is the movie-like window on the universe the LSST will unveil by taking over 400,000 16-megapixel images every night, allowing astronomers to see videos of celestial objects that change or move rapidly. 'Survey' is the immediate release of data to the public, allowing numerous studies to be made by anyone including mapping the mass of dark matter in the cosmos and tracking the closest asteroids to Earth. 'Telescope', somewhat predictably, refers to the entire structure that will house all of this incredible technology.

Unusually for such a huge telescope, the LSST project is the work of a non-profit private organisation known as the LSST Corporation, which has raised funding through both private pledges and national grants. Construction of the telescope in its high-altitude position – perfect for clear views unhindered by the atmosphere – began back in November 2007, and as of July 2012 the LSST has entered its final design phase. It is set to be completed in 2014 and initially is expected to run until 2024. ✿

Mount
The telescope's mount is a compact and still structure that will reduce image motion and blur

Mirrors
The primary and tertiary mirrors are found inside the telescope, where the light is first reflected

Platform
The LSST's camera will be accessible by a platform running along the side

© Todd Mason

The LSST will be housed at the end of the building on the left in this concept image

Find dark matter
1 The Large Synoptic Survey Telescope will detect signatures of dark energy and dark matter by measuring weak gravitational lensing present in deep space.

Track asteroids
2 In under a minute the LSST will be able to find objects that are merely 140 metres (460 feet) wide in the Asteroid Belt, helping us to chart potentially dangerous near-Earth objects.

Record movies
3 The rapid image-capturing and processing power of the telescope will enable it to watch superfast events in the universe unfold, such as novas and supernovas.

Map the Milky Way
4 The ability of this massive telescope to capture the entire night sky in just three days will be crucial in our continued attempts to map out our galaxy.

Make new discoveries
5 The incredible imaging power of this telescope and its wide field of view mean that it is highly expected to make numerous unprecedented cosmic discoveries.

DID YOU KNOW? Software ~~billionaire~~ billionaire Bill Gates kick-started funding for the LSST by pledging $10m to the project in 2008

Support
At the front is a top-end assembly support structure to hold the mirrors and camera in place

Secondary
The secondary mirror is found near the top of the telescope, where the camera is also mounted

Weight
The entire structure will weigh close to 300 tons and will be movable in a horizontal and vertical plane with a drive power of 336kW (450hp)

Capturing an image

How will the LSST camera snap 3,200-megapixel shots?

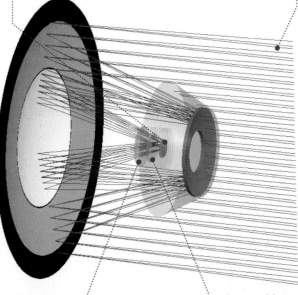

Sensors
21 grids of sensors, known as rafts, collect the light and make up the 3.2-billion-pixel focal plane

Spectrum
The telescope is sensitive to wavelengths from 350 nanometres (ultraviolet) through to 1,040 nanometres (infrared)

First lens
Incoming light is captured by the first lens at the front of the camera

Second lens
The light also passes through a second lens before hitting the detector

The camera

You might be impressed when you see a professional photographer with a camera the size of your arm, but imagine one that was the size of a car...

The largest digital camera ever constructed, the LSST's camera will measure about 1.6 x 3 metres (5.2 x 9.8 feet) and weigh in at around 2,800 kilograms (6,200 pounds). Inside, a variety of 16-megapixel silicon detectors will combine to produce a whopping image resolution of 3.2 gigapixels, or 3.2 billion of your regular pixels, across a 320-square-metre (3,440-square-foot) field of view.

The camera will sit in the middle of the telescope and will operate at approximately -100 degrees Celsius (-148 degrees Fahrenheit) to get the optimal performance out of its detectors.

The data

There's lots of revolutionary tech inside the LSST, but one of the most important bits is the imaging sensors it will use. Capable of capturing light from ultraviolet to infrared, these sensors will produce 30 terabytes of data every night. After a decade of observations it will have produced over 100 petabytes (100 million gigabytes) of data, which will require 250 teraflops of power to process – about 100,000 home PCs!

The telescope

Unlike most other giant telescopes, the LSST will use three mirrors rather than two to capture images. Light is first collected onto an 8.4-metre (27.6-foot) primary mirror, before being reflected onto a 3.4-metre (11.2-foot) secondary mirror. It is then reflected again onto a five-metre (16.4-foot) tertiary mirror in the centre of the primary mirror. Both the secondary and tertiary mirrors are spherical, which allows the light to be intensely focused. The arrangement of this trio gives the LSST an exceptionally wide field of view, enabling it to survey the entire southern sky in just three days performing two observations a night.

Everything you need to know

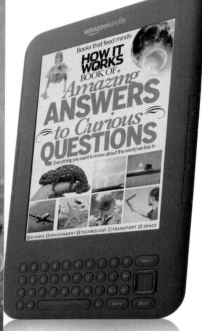

HOW IT WORKS